History of Rocketry and Astronautics

AAS History Series, Volume 9

International Academy of Astronautics
History Symposia

Front Cover Illustration:

Robert Esnault-Pelterie (1881-1957), French aeronautical and astronautical pioneer; early designer and builder of aircraft such as the all-metal monoplane (1906-1907) and inventor of the "joy stick" (ca. 1907); writer of L'Astronautique (1930) and co-founder of the REP-Hirsch Prize (1929).

History of
Rocketry and Astronautics

**Proceedings of the Ninth, Tenth and Eleventh History Symposia of
The International Academy of Astronautics**

Lisbon, Portugal, 1975

Anaheim, California, U.S.A., 1976

Prague, Czechoslovakia, 1977

Frederick I. Ordway, III, Volume Editor

R. Cargill Hall, Series Editor

AAS History Series, Volume 9

A Supplement to Advances in the Astronautical Sciences

IAA History Symposia, Volume 4

Affiliated with the American Association for the Advancement of Science
Member of the International Astronautical Federation

First Printing 1989

ISSN 0730-3564

ISBN 0-87703-309-9 (Hard Cover)
ISBN 0-87703-310-2 (Soft Cover)

Published for the American Astronautical Society
by Univelt, Inc., P.O. Box 28130, San Diego, California 92128

Printed and Bound in the U.S.A.

FOREWORD

Some thirty years ago Lloyd Berkner observed, "of all men on this earth who have reached full maturity since the dawn of civilization, one seventh of them are alive today." Though Berkner alluded to the dramatic increase in the world's population, the analogy likewise obtains for the subject matter of this volume. The history of rocketry and astronautics, at least in terms of its scientific and technical applications, is almost entirely contemporary history, history that has transpired within living memory. Assigned a Berkner fraction, I would guess eight-tenths of this history has unfolded since the turn of the twentieth century. All of us now on earth have witnessed much of this history and the profound effects it has had on contemporary military, political, social and economic events.

The papers in this volume address different elements of the worldwide history of rocketry and astronautics, among them, an accounting of initial efforts to perfect liquid hydrogen-oxygen propulsion systems in the USA, development of the first space rocket engines in the USSR, and early French research of the upper atmosphere using rockets. Although each of these papers focuses on one significant aspect, period, or person, all of them as Harold Zahl once said of history in general, allow us a "look backward toward tomorrow." Collectively, they offer insight into the technical and scientific evolution of astronautics, improve our understanding of the discipline today, and, one would hope ultimately, permit us to extrapolate more intelligently about the future.

> **R. Cargill Hall**
> **Series Editor**
> **USAF Historical Research Center**

PREFACE

This, the ninth volume in the American Astronautical Society's (AAS) History Series, is at the same time the fourth in the AAS series of history symposia sponsored by the International Academy of Astronautics (IAA). Both organizations -- the AAS and the IAA -- have long been involved in preserving the historical record in the fields of rocketry and astronautics, and it is encouraging to know that they are successfully collaborating in this important effort.

The roots of IAA history activities extend to 1961 when the Committee on the History of the Development of Rockets and Astronautics (later to become the History of Astronautics Committee) was established. Its first meeting took place under the chairmanship of Charles Dollfus at UNESCO in Paris on 27 September 1963 during the 14th International Astronautical Congress. What was termed the first International History of Astronautics Symposium was held in late September 1967 at the 18th Congress in Belgrade, Yoguslavia, under Dollfus' chairmanship. Since then, symposia have been held annually in cities in many parts of the world under the leadership of the late Eugene E. Emme, R. Cargill Hall, Frederick C. Durant, III, Viktor N. Sokolsky and others.

During the 36th International Astronautical Congress in Stockholm in 1985, the History of Astronautics Committee celebrated the 25th anniversary of the founding of the International Academy of Astronautics by organizing a retrospective session at the Royal Academy of Sciences. During the same Congress, the committee separately sponsored IAA's own 19th history symposium.

This volume includes papers delivered at the ninth, tenth and eleventh History of Astronautics Symposia held at Lisbon (1975); Anaheim, California (1976); and Prague (1977). The 22 papers are organized topically and chronologically into five parts dealing, respectively, with early solid propellant rocketry; rocketry and astronautics: concepts, theories and analyses after 1880; development of liquid- and solid-propellant rockets from 1880 to 1945; rocketry and astronautics after 1945; and pioneers of rocketry and astronautics.

The distribution of the 22 papers by country of presentation is U.S.A., eight; USSR, seven; and one each from Czechoslovakia, France, Hungary, Poland, Sweden, Switzerland and the United Kingdom. By symposium, ten papers were presented in 1975 in Lisbon; five in 1976 in Anaheim, California; and seven in 1977 in Prague. By topics, early solid propellant rocketry accounts for two papers; concepts, theories and analyses of rocketry and astronautics after 1880, three; the development of liquid-and-solid-propellant rockets from 1880 to 1945, three; rocketry and astronautics after 1945, ten; and pioneers of rocketry and astronautics, four. The symposium and date of delivery appear as an explanatory note at the beginning of each paper.

The 28 authors who participated in this volume represent a variety of disciplines and, through their contributions, have enriched the historical literature in their fields of interest and accomplishment. Throughout the preparation of this volume, the editor maintained direct contact with all authors except Z. Horsky from Czechoslovakia and those from the Soviet Union. Repeated attempts to locate the former were unsuccessful. Soviet authors were ably represented by Professor Sokolsky of the USSR Academy of Sciences' Committee of the Soviet National Association of Natural Science and Technology Historians. The seven Soviet papers as well as the single paper from France appear in translation; all other papers were made available to the editor in English.

Because of the passage of time, illustrations associated with some of the original presentations could not be located. A number of others were of a quality that would normally displease an editor but were considered marginally acceptable. Such problems are unlikely to be experienced in the future since the series editor is now making his volume assignments shortly after the presentation of the papers at the IAA symposia.

The editor acknowledges the help and encouragement given by the many contributors; by members of the History of Astronautics Committee of the International Academy of Astronautics; by series editor R. Cargill Hall; by Dr. Horace Jacobs, publisher; and by David H. DeVorkin; Frederick C. Durant, III; A. Ingemar Skoog; Viktor N. Sokolsky; and Frank H. Winter.

Frederick I. Ordway, III
Volume Editor
Washington D.C., U.S.A.

CONTENTS

Part I
EARLY SOLID-PROPELLANT ROCKETRY

Chapter 1

ANALYSIS OF ROCKET CONSTRUCTION, DESCRIBED IN MANUSCRIPTS AND PRINTED BOOKS DURING THE 16TH AND 17TH CENTURIES[*]

Mieczyslaw Subotowicz[†]

The earliest authors before the 15th Century who dealt with rockets and rocket techniques are: Marcus Graecus [1], Ibn Albaithan [2], Albertus Magnus [3], Roger Bacon [4], Hassan Alrammah [5], and Muratori [6]. Also mentioned in the literature is the Silesian monk, Severinus [7], who used gun powder to accelerate "pipes", which probably refer to rockets. More detailed descriptions of the military rockets and fireworks appear in European writings of the 15th Century.

The first use of rockets in Europe was probably in 1241 in Legnica (Silesia), during the battle between the Polish prince Henryk Pobozny and the Tartars (Figure 1). At the beginning of the 15th Century Konrad Kyeser von Eichstädt [8] wrote a widely-known manuscript that described rocket and powder production. He wrote about the three types of rockets and produced sketches of typical powder rockets (seen in Figure 2) as well as double-direction rockets.

The Italian engineer, Joannes de Fonana [10], presented prototype projects of an aerial torpedo able to produce a blast and of a reaction airplane -- a kind of rocket with the wings. Also known is a sketch of a double-direction rocket of Regionmontanus [12].

Very important achievements in non-standard rocket construction are contained in a manuscript by Konrad Haas [16] found in the library of the city Sibiu in Rumania [53]. The manuscript consists of three parts, probably written by three different authors living in the years 1380-1569. In the third part, techniques for production and some applications of one- and multi-step rockets are described. The unknown author of the first part may be Hans Haasenwein. The author of the third part, Konrad Haas, was born in Dornbach near Vienna and served as chief of the artillery arsenal of the town Sibiu/Herrmannstadt. A relationship appears to exist between Konrad Kyeser's *Bellifortis* with the manuscripts of the later technicians, including Haas. His manuscript contains some sketches of the two-stage rocket,

* Presented at The Ninth IAA History of Astronautics Symposium, Lisbon, Portugal, September 1975.

† Institute of Physics, M. Curie-Skłodowska University, Lublin, Poland.

seen in Figure 3, a three-stage rocket, a double-direction rocket, a rocket battery, a combined two-step rocket, and delta-shaped stabilizers used in rocket flight. Haas also dealt with primitive ballistics and flight theory.

Figure 1 Fresco in the abbey built on the battle place by Legnica, Silesia, of the Polish army against the Tartars in 1241. The fresco shows the drake fire head that could be propelled by rocket action.

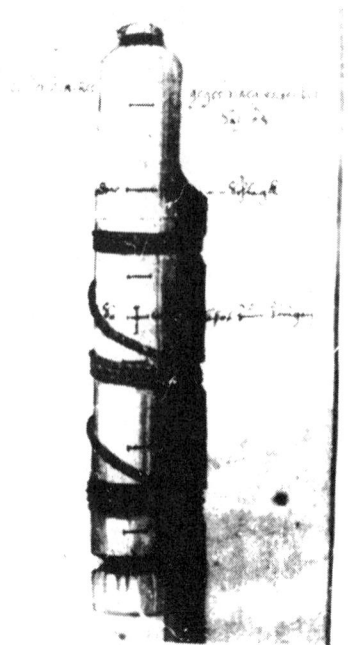

Figure 2 Sketch of rocket from the book of Konrad Kyeser von Eichstädt [8], 1405.

4

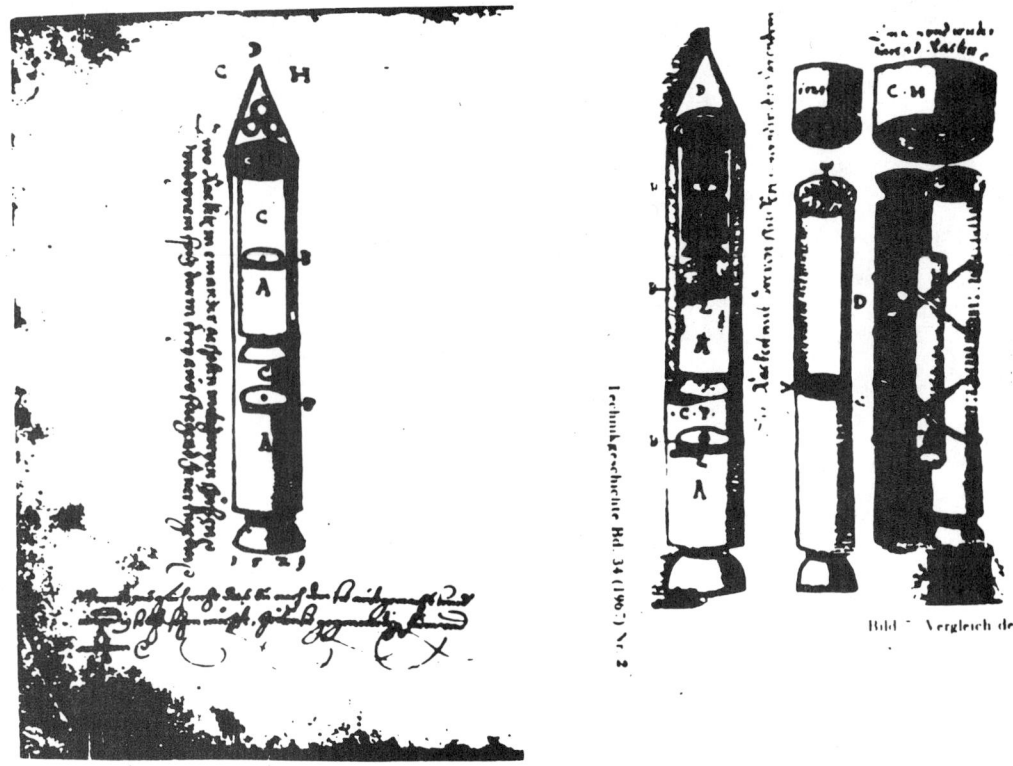

Figure 3 Sketch of two-step rocket from book by K. Haas [16], 1529-1569 (left); and sketch of Haas three-step rocket and double-direction rocket (right) [16]

An author who dealt with non-standard rocket design, Vanuccio Biringuccio [17], described a combined two-stage rocket whose second stage was the rocket battery. Reinhard von Solms [19] wrote on rockets with parachutes. In Leonhard Frönsperger's book [21] are sketches of a two-step rocket and of a double-direction rocket (shown in Figure 4). Frönsperger had probably seen [53] the Haas manuscript [16].

Especially well-known was the book of Johann Schmidlap [24], published in 1561 and republished in 1590, 1591 and 1608. It contains sketches (Figure 5) of two-stage and double-direction rockets. It is highly probable that some parts of the Haas' manuscript were copied by Schmidlap in his book [24, 53].

Details of rocket technology were first published in Poland by Marcin Bielski [25], Figure 6, and by S. Sarnicki [26].

Many technicians and artillery specialists [27-51] dealt with rockets in books or manuscripts. Only non-standard rocket construction is noted in the following paragraphs.

It appears that in the early years of the 17th Century the manuscript of Walenty Sebisch [31], was written. He was the military architect of the town Wroław. The

5

manuscript contains sketches of rockets with the delta-type stabilizers, Figure 7a; rocket batteries, Figure 7b; and something like a two-stage rocket, Figure 7c.

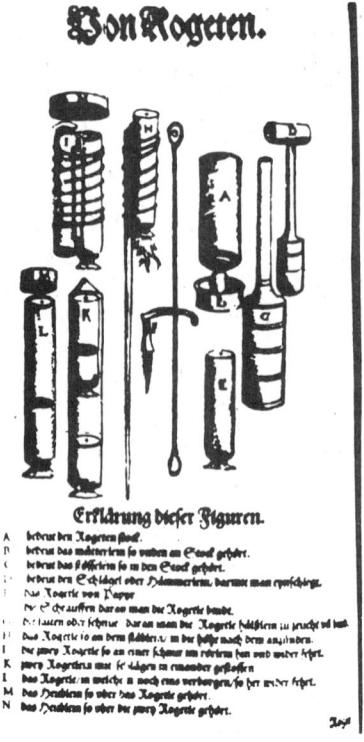

Figure 4   Sketch of two-stage rocket and of double direction rocket from L. Frönsperger [210], 1557.

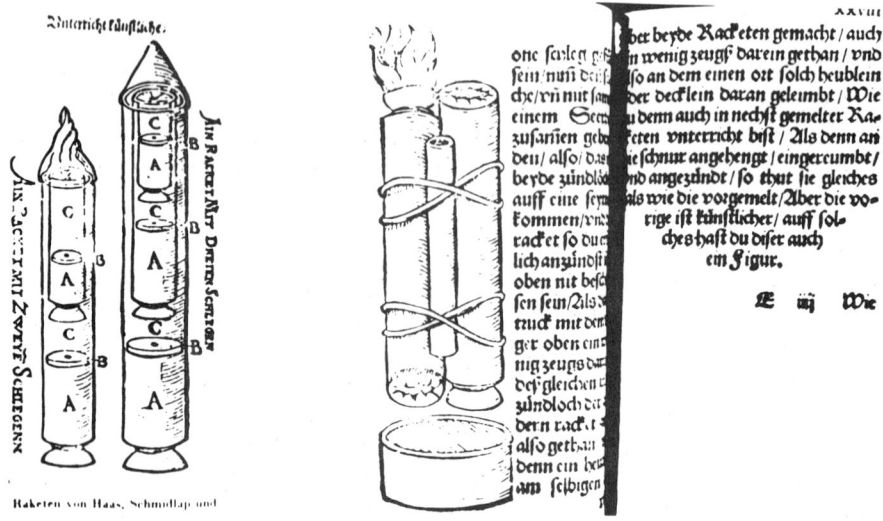

Figure 5   Sketch of the two-stage and three-stage rockets of J. Schmidlap [24], 1561 (left); and sketch of his double-direction rocket (right) [24].

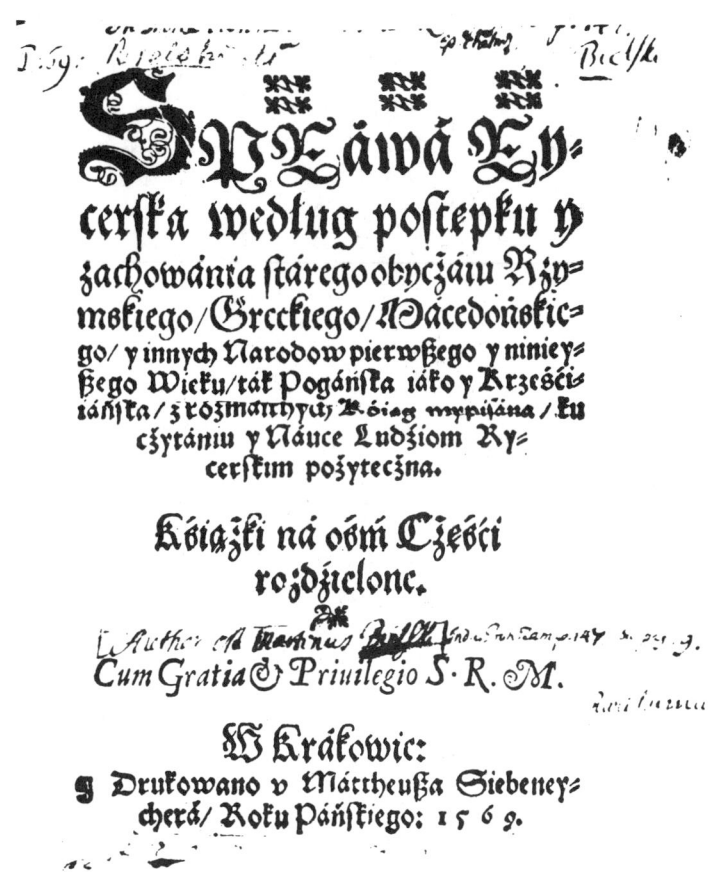

Figure 6   Title page of work by M. Bielski, 1569, written in Polish [25] in which details of rocket production are described.

Another manuscript is that of A. dell Aqua [41], an artillery specialist of Italian origin who served in the armies of Polish kings and princes. His book was written between in 1630 and 1635 and contains a sketch of a two-stage combined rocket (Figure 8). The second stage of the rocket is a rocket battery, which consists of five small rockets.

Kazimierz Siemienowicz [43] occupies a special place among authors of non-standard rocket concepts and designs. Serving as artillery general of the Polish king Władysław IV during the first half of the 17th Century, he wrote an excellent book [43] that was translated into English and other European languages (Figure 9a). Siemienowicz incorporated excellent sketches in his book of various rocket configurations, as noted in Figures 9b and 9c. They included multi-stage rockets, rocket batteries, conical nozzles, delta-type stablizers, double-direction rockets and combined rockets, wherein one or more multi-stage rockets form the rocket battery. Similar rocket concepts appeared in books and manuscripts prepared by many authors during the second half of the 17th Century, and later.

When analyzing non-standard rocket designs by the above-mentioned authors, it is usually not possible to find connections between them. But there are two exceptions, namely, Frönsperger's work [21], and that of Schmidlap [24]. Both are believed to be connected [53] with the Haas' manuscript [16]. When we examine the military and entertainment applications of these rockets, some construction solutions appear quite obvious. Fireworks were in common use for a long period in courts of kings and princes. Therefore, it is highly probable that all the designs and concepts already described were proposed quite independently by different authors, even up to the 20th Century [52].

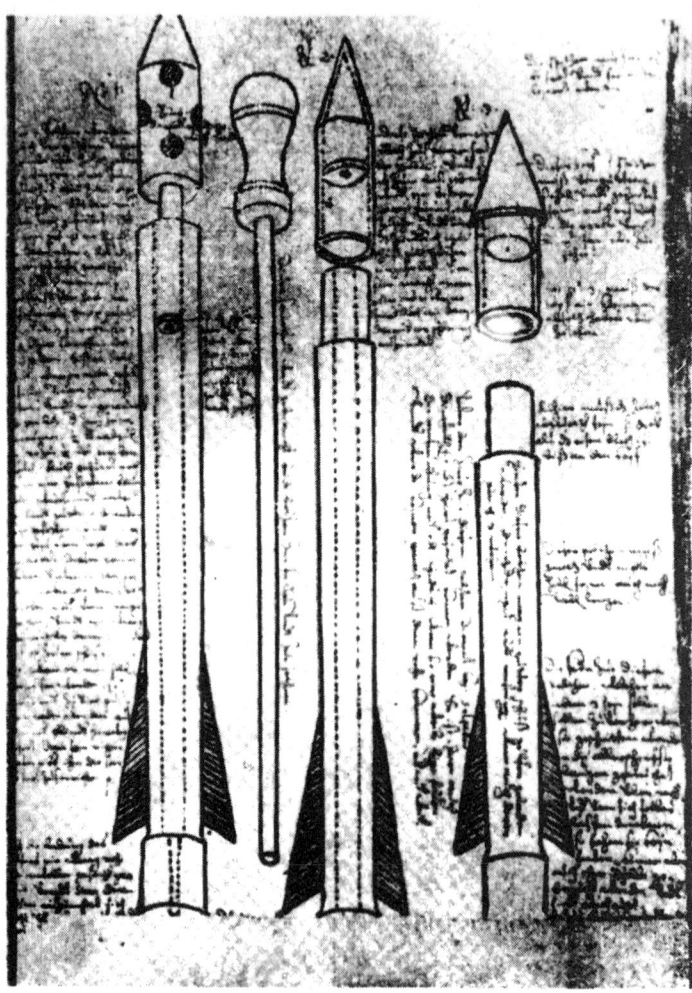

Figure 7a   Delta-type rocket stabilizers by Sebisch [31] about 1600.

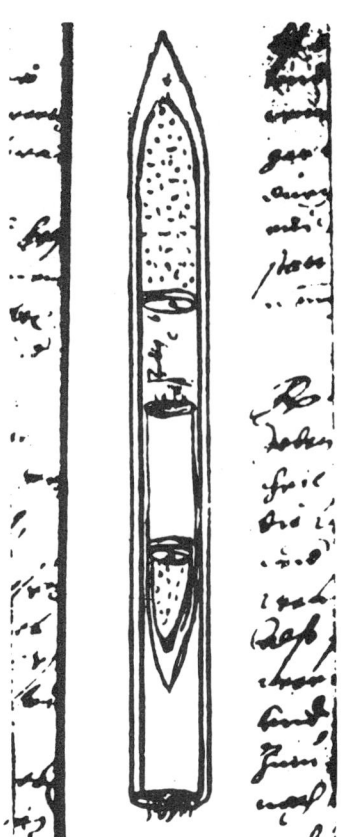 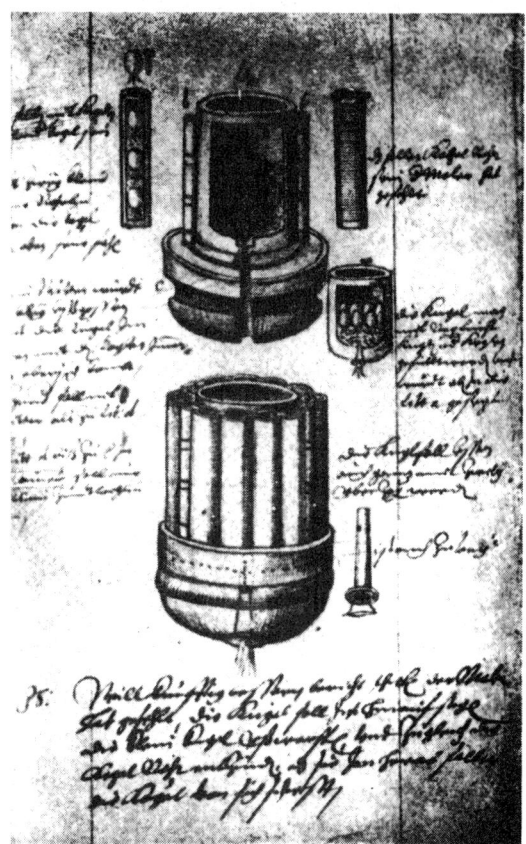

Figure 7b & 7c   Sketch by Sebisch of rocket battery, about 1600 (left); and of his two-stage rocket (right) [31].

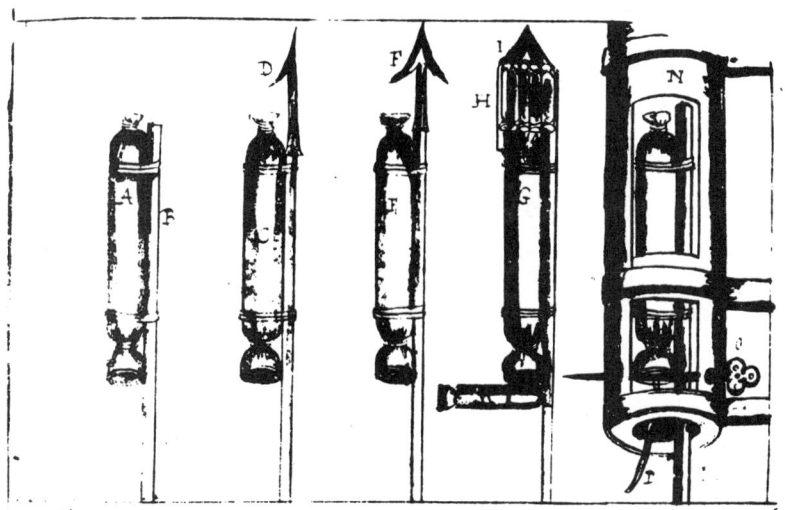

Figure 8   Sketch of two-stage combined rocket by A.dell Aqua [41], 1630-1635.

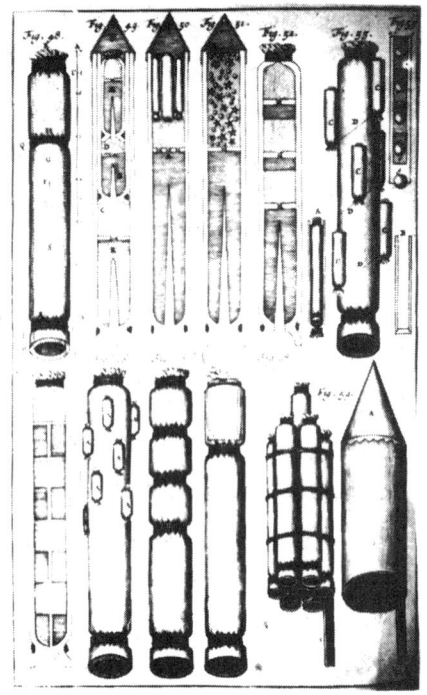

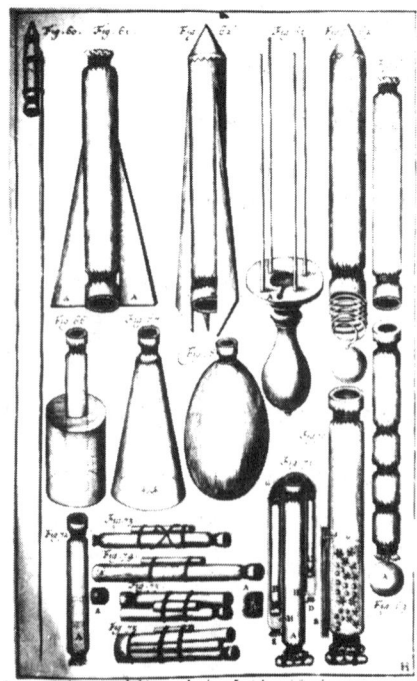

Figure 9   Title page of the English translation, 1729, of the Siemienowicz book [43], 1650 (top left); sketches of his [43] three-stage rocket, two-stage combined rocket and of the rocket battery (top right); of his double-direction rockets and of the delta-type rocket stabilizers, 1650 (bottom).

REFERENCES/BIBLIOGRAPHY

1. Marcos Graecus, *Liber ignium* (Fire-Book), 1230-1250, ed. Paris, 1804

2. Ibn Albaithar (Abú Mohámmad Abdallach ben Ahmad Almaliqi), 1240

3. Albertus Magnus, *De mirabilibus mundi*, between 1250-1280

4. Roger Bacon, *De secretis*, Opus Major, 1268

5. Hassan Alrammah, 1280, "The Book of Fighting on Horseback and with War Engines", manuscript

6. Muratori, 1379. Italian historian, describing the role of rockets in the battle of the Isle of Chiozza

7. Severinus, 1380, Polish monk writing on rockets. He was mentioned in the paper of T. Przypkowski: "Nowe z'ródła historyczne do najdawniejszych zastosowan' rakiet na terenie Polski", Technika Rakietowa, No. 7, 1959, p. 41-47 (in Polish)

8. Konrad Kyeser von Eichstädt, *Bellifortis*, 1405

9. Feuerwerksbuch, before 1430

10. Joannes de Fontana, *Bellicorum Instrumentorum Liber*, 1420

11. Hans Hartlieb, 1437, German writer on powder production

12. Regiomontanus, 1450

13. Franz Helm, *Buch von den probierten Künsten*, 1528-1535

14. Hans Bustetter, 1524-1532

15. Ott von Ochterdingen, 1526-1529

16. Konrad Haas, Sibiu Manuscript, 1529-1569

17. Vanuccio Biringuccio, *De la Pirotechnia*, 1540

18. Gaspar Brunner, 1542]

19. Prince Reinhard von Solms, 1547, manuscript

20. Albert de Prusia, 1551

21. Leonhard Frönsperger, *Von Geschütz und Feuerwerk*, 1557, Frankfurt am Main

22. Hans Camentur, 1560

23. Hans Starck, 1560

24. Johann Schmidlap, Künstliche und rechtschaffene Feuerwerk, Nürnberg, 1561, 1590, 1591, 1608

25. Marcin Bielski, Sprawa Rycerska, Kraków, 1569

26. S. Sarnicki, 1575-77, rekopis: "Ksiegi hetmánskie" manuscript: "Hetman's books", Jagiellonian Library in Cracow, No. 171

27. Franz Brechtel, 1591

28. Luigi Collado, 1592

29. A. Capo Bianco, 1598

30. J. Boillot, 1598

31. Walenty Sebisch 1577-1657, Manuscript in Wrocław about 1600

32. Onisim Michajłow, Ustaw ratnych, puszecznych i drugich dieł, kasajuszczichsia do wojennej nauki, 1607-1621 (in Russian)

33. Ch. Dambach, 1609

34. Prince von Nassau, 1610, manuscript, p. 725

35. A. v. Roomen, 1611

36. Diego Uffano, 1613 Archelia albo artilleria, to iest Naka y Informatia o Strzelbie y Rzeczach do niey nalez'a,cych je,zkiem polskim s'wiez'o napisana, Leszno, 1643; it is Polish translation from the German language by J. Dekan of the Spanish book, "Tratado de la artilleria", Bruxelles, 1613

37. J. Sattler, 1619

38. F. Thybourel, 1620

39. J. Furtenbach, "Architectura navalis" and "Halinitro-Pyrobolia"; 1627, written in German

40. F. de Malthe, 1629

41. A. del Aqua, *Praxis re,czna dziela*, 1630-1635 (ed. PWN Warszawa, 1969)

42. J. Appier de Hanzelet, 1630

43. K. Siemienowciz, *Artis Magnae Artilleriae...*, Amsterdam, 1650

44. Malthus, *Pratique de la guerre contenant l'usage de l'artillerie*, Paris, 1668

45. H. Fabri, 1669

46. Daniel Schwenter, *Delicae physico-mathematicae*, Nürenberg, 1681

47. Valentin Franck von Franckenstein, *Breviculus Pyrotechnicae*, Sibiu, 1697

48. Nicolas François Blondel (1617-1686), *L'art de jeter les bombes*, Haga, 1685

49. Robert Anderson, *The making of rockets*, London, 1696

50. Suvirey de Saint Remy, *Mémoires d'artillerie*, Paris, 1697

51. Noni Ewangelista, *Trattato de Fouchi Artificianti per adenita e ricreazioni*, before 1700, Mariqueni

52. M. Subotowicz, Kwart.Hist. Nauki i Techn., 13, 807-10, 1968

53. D. Todericiu, *Raketentechnik in 16. Jahrhundert ...*, "Technikgeschichte", 34, 97-114, 1967, Düsseldorf

    D. Todericiu, *Preistoria Rachetti Moderne Manuscrisul de la Sibiu* (1400-1569), Bucuresti, 1969

    D. Todericiu, Kwart.Hist. Nauki i Techn., 15, 545, 1970

Part II

ROCKETRY AND ASTRONAUTICS: CONCEPTS, THEORIES, AND ANALYSES AFTER 1880

Chapter 2

ANALYSIS OF EARLY 19TH CENTURY SWEDISH SOLID PROPELLANTS[*]

Jan Hansson[†] and A. Ingemar Skoog[‡]

A number of old solid propellant rockets, originating from the time of the Swedish Royal Rocket Corps (*Kongl. Raket Corpsen,* 1833-1845) or shortly before, have been preserved at the Royal Army Museum (Kungliaga Armemuseum) in Stockholm, still containing the original propellant.

Three rockets of different configuration, a 2-in. Rocket Corps standard-rocket, a rocket with 3 delta-wings (designated 'Vaillant') and a signal rocket, were selected for investigation and for analysis of their propellants at the Swedish National Defence Research Institute.

After thorough determination of outer dimensions and photographic documentation, the internal configuration and propellant condition was determined by means of x-raying. The rockets were disarmed, and chemical and combustion tests were performed in order to determine the performance of the three rockets.

Some notes and reports on the manufacturing of rockets from the time of the Swedish Royal Rocket Corps and the years before its formation have been preserved as well. This enables a certain comparison of the documented characteristics of that time with the ones established by the present analyses.

BRIEF HISTORY OF ANALYSED ROCKETS

After the bombardment of Copenhagen in 1807, a growing interest for war-rockets could be noticed in Sweden among military institutions and scientists. The first contact with Congreve rockets in action came during the Napoleonic war. When Sweden entered the war, The Army of the North was placed under the com-

---

[*] Presented at The Ninth History of Astronautics Symposium, Lisbon, Portugal, September 1975.

[†] Formerly, National Defence Research Institute, Sundbyberg, Sweden; now retired.

[‡] Now employed at Dornier System GmbH, Friedrichshafen, Federal Republic of Germany as head of Manned Space Programmes. Member, International Academy of Astronautics and its History Committee, and of Swedish Society of Aeronautics and Astronautics.

mand of the Swedish Crown Prince Carl Johan, and to it was also attached the British Rocket Brigade (later, The 2nd Rocket Troop). The Rocket Brigade served with gallantry under the Swedish Crown Prince during the Battle of Leipzig in 1813, and Swedish officers saw the results of rockets in a war campaign.

In the years after the Napoleonic war, experiences with rockets were gathered through experiments in Sweden; and, at the same time, rocket manufacturing was studied in several European countries by travelling Swedish officers. This finally led to the formation of the Swedish Royal Rocket Corps (*Kongl. Raket Corpsen*) in 1833 [1].

More than a dozen rockets of various types from the time before and during the existence of the Royal Rocket Corps have been preserved at the Royal Army Museum in Stockholm. Most of these rockets still contain their original propellant. Three different rockets were selected for an investigation of the solid propellant composition and characteristics.

The first to be examined was the Rocket Corps' standard 2-in. rocket (Figure 1), which was manufactured in great numbers from 1833 to 1845. The rocket case is made of sheet iron and joined lengthwise by rivets. The bottom of the case was formed by cutting slots into the cylindrical case and bending the flaps over an inserted metal ring. On top of the rocket-case is attached a spherical, hollow shell containing the explosive fire-composition. The top of the propellant was covered with a layer of pressed clay. A small hole was drilled in the clad layer through which went a fuse for the ignition of the explosive shell. The exhaust outlet, shown in Figure 2, was covered with a piece of canvas glued to the rocket-case and holding the igniter. A small guiding-stick, 2.25 meters long, was attached to the case.

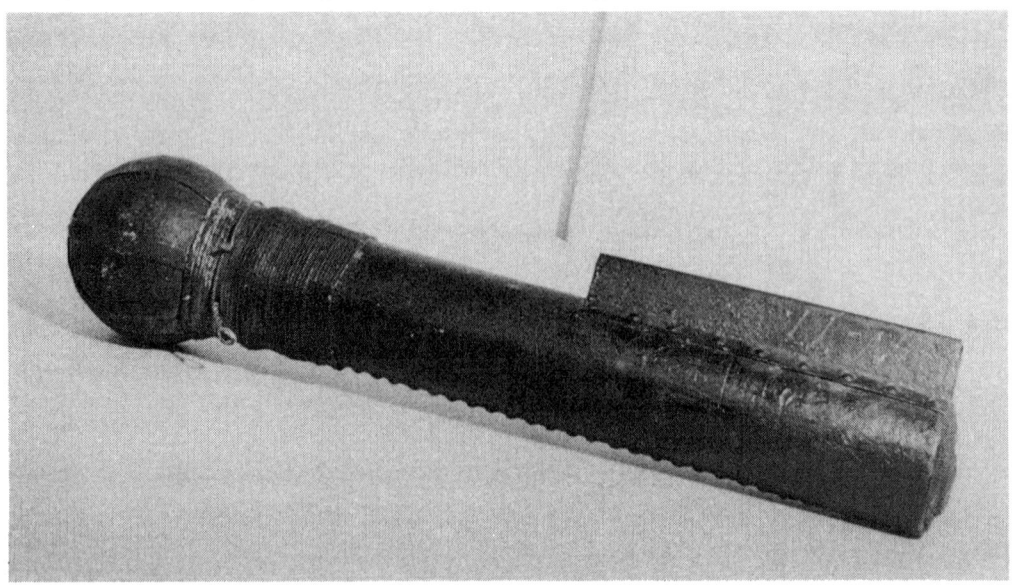

Figure 1   Standard two-inch Rocket (Royal Army Museum, Stockholm, Inventory AM 1216).

Figure 2   Standard two-inch rocket, rear view (Royal Army Museum, Stockholm, inventory AM 1216).

The second rocket, pictured in Figure 3, is one fitted with three delta-wings instead of the guiding-stick. According to the old museum inventory lists (inventory number AM 1212) this rocket is "according to the design of the Frenchman Vaillant, 1821". In Montgéry, *Annales maritimes et coloniales* [2] a Vaillant from Boulogne designed rockets with three delta-wings in the early 1820's.

Figure 3   Vaillant rocket (Royal Army Museum, Stockholm, inventory AM 1212).

No detailed information on this particular Swedish design is known; but, an examination of the rocket itself shows that the three wings are mounted together as a second outer case around what seems to be a normal rocket case from a standard 2-in. rocket. The dimensions and the method of manufacturing identical to the 2-in. standard rocket, and as to the "shirt" at the rear end (Figure 4), it is a part of the inner rocket case, as by the standard rocket, and seems to have been straightened out for an earlier sampling of the propellant. This indicates that this particular type of rocket, although a Vaillant type of design, was probably manufactured in Sweden during the 1830's.

Figure 4   Vaillant rocket, rear view (Royal Army Museum, Stockholm, inventory AM 1212).

The signal-rocket, shown in Figure 5 and Figure 6 and the third rocket to be analysed, has a wrapped paper-case. This rocket (AM 1219) is, according to the inventory lists a design of Colonel Paul Schröderstierna (1769-1838) and dates from the 1830's. However, other sources claim that the work of Colonel Schröderstierna was in general performed before 1825.

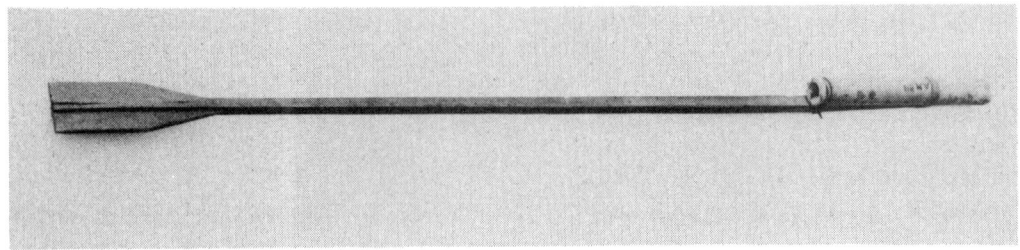

Figure 5   Signal rocket (Royal Army Museum, Stockholm, inventory AM 1219).

Figure 6   Signal rocket, rear view (Royal Army Museum, Stockholm, inventory AM 1219)

SWEDISH 19TH CENTURY PROPELLANTS AND THEIR MANUFACTURE

The propellant composition used by the Royal Rocket Corps was, according to records from 1836, [3], 66.5 percent saltpeter, 22 percent sulphur and 11.5 percent aldercarbon. These three ingredients were ground in separate rotating oak cylinders, passed through a sieve and then mixed in a fourth cylinder for two hours. Later, the composition was moistened with alcohol in order to make it more elastic when pressing it. In small portions, generally about 50 for each standard rocket, the composition was pressed into the case by a screw-press illustrated in Figure 7. The homogeneous rocket body was then placed in a drilling machine in order to bore the burning-surface.

METHODS OF ANALYSIS OF SOME SWEDISH ROCKET PROPELLANTS

Objects of the present study are the three rockets described above. The first rocket (Figure 1 and Figure 2) is the standard 2-in. (56mm)-diameter rocket like the second one (Figures 3 and 4) of the less common type with delta-wings and denoted as a 'Vaillant' rocket. The third is the small signal rocket (Figures 5 and 6) with a paper case. The material of the cases of the first two rockets is riveted sheet iron about 1 mm thick. Weights of the rockets and charges and some measures are given in Table 1.

Table 1

WEIGHTS AND MEASURES OF THREE SWEDISH 19TH CENTURY ROCKETS

Weights and measures	Rocket		
	Standard	Vaillant	Signal
	AM 1216	AM 1212	AM 1219
Weight, g			
total	3433 *	2344 +	189 +
case	408	1142	≈45
warhead	1720	-	-
blackpowder	969	841	65
Measurement, mm			
length	320	350	222
diameter	56	56	28

* Without stick (stick weight∼820 grams).
+ Without warhead or illuminant charge,
(warhead weight for Vaillant type of
rocket ∼ 926 grams).

Before disarming the rockets, both the standard and the delta-wing models were x-rayed to determine the internal configuration and the propellant condition. The standard rocket revealed at least two transversal cracks.

The rockets all had their propellant charges intact[*] when the study was undertaken, but only the standard rocket still possesed its warhead. The signal rocket was easily dismounted by unwrapping the paper. In the two other cases use was made of a kind of flat drill consisting of a 1-inch steel tube on which was fixed a triangular plate acting as boring head. The steel tube was connected to a vacuum cleaner in order to suck away and collect the loose powder. All three propellant charges had an inner hole and a clay wall at the front part separating the charges from the warhead and illuminant composition, respectively. Measurement of cases and charges are presented in Figures 8, 9 and 10.

Though a relatively simple composition, blackpowder can vary considerably with respect to its properties depending on methods of manufacturing and quality of ingredients. There has therefore always been a need for methods to determine the properties of blackpowder. An 18th century eprouvette, an apparatus used to determine the strength of the powder, is pictured in Figure 11. A method of analysis from about the same time consists of burning a thimble of blackpowder poured on a piece of clean paper. A good powder burns without igniting the paper.

---

[*] The shape of the 'Vaillant' rocket indicates that a sample of the propellant might have been taken at an earlier date, which would account for the lower propellant charge weight (Table 1) compared with the standard rocket. (See also p.16).

Black or yellow spots on the paper indicate too much charcoal or sulphur in the powder. White crystals can be potassium nitrate or sodium chloride, the latter salt indicating an impure saltpeter.

Figure 7   Screw-press, 1836, used by the Swedish Royal Rocket Corps (C. Staaf) [3].

Measurements and methods to characterize blackpowder have of course been modernized since that time though much remains to be done. The three old rocket propellants have been studied with the same methods as used for modern blackpowders so far as the size of the samples has permitted. Two of the methods used may require a short description.

The burning velocity was determined with ground propellant in an open aluminum groove, 1 meter long and with a square cross-section 10x10 mm. The groove is fitted with phototransistors at 100 mm interspace along the groove, which indicate the passage of the burning front (Figure 12).

Pressure vs. time when burning in a closed vessel was determined with a steel bomb with 1 volume (Figure 13). Normally, about 20 to 30 grams of propellant is burned in air at normal pressure. Ignition is started with an electrical fuse. The pressure is measured with a transducer and registered with a tape recorder and an oscilloscope.

21

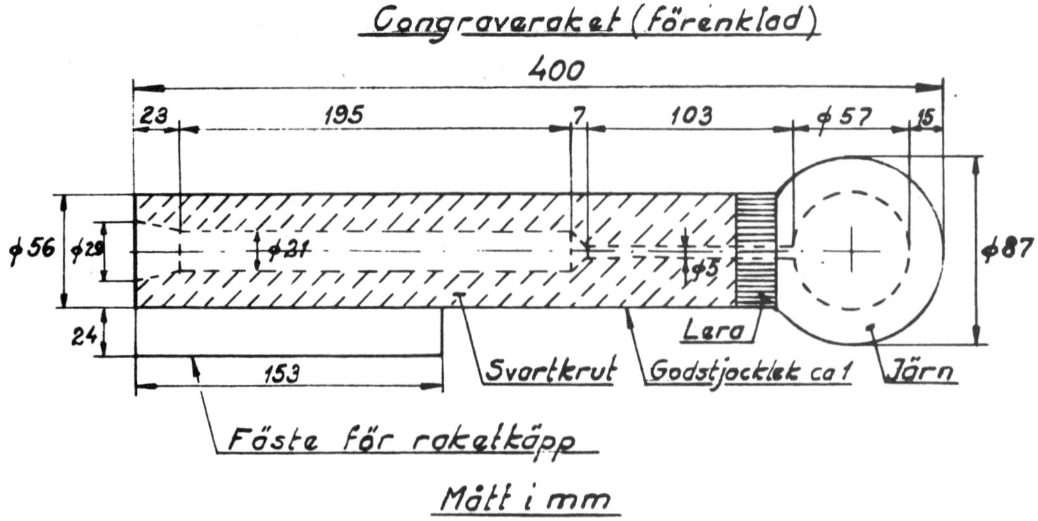

Congravaraket (förenklad)

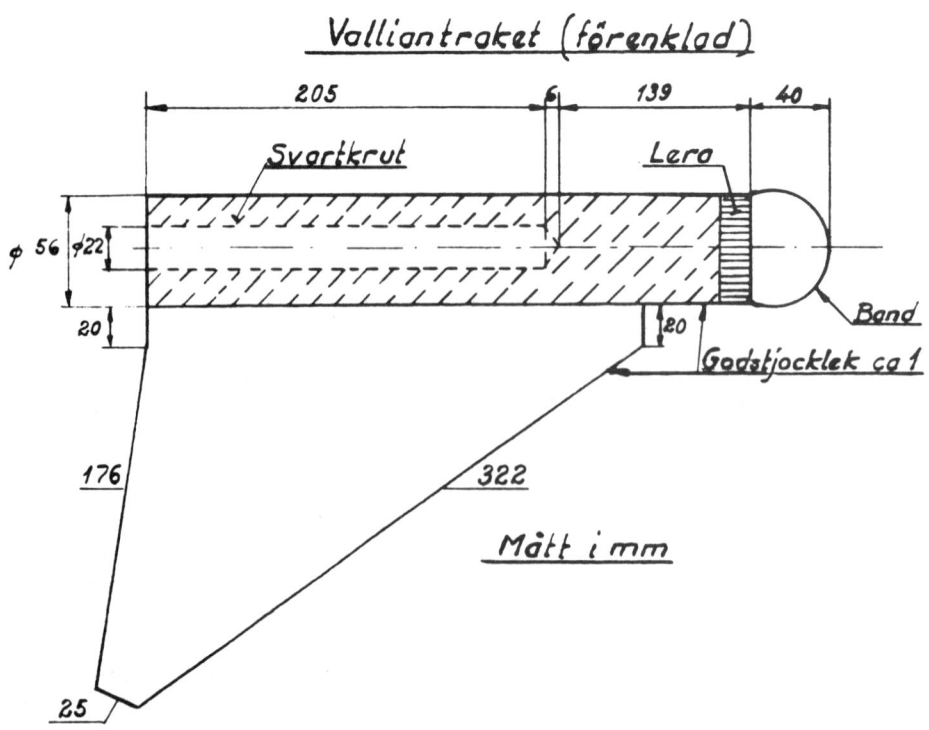

Figure 8   Actual dimensions of standard two-inch rocket (AM 1216) in mm.

Valliantraket (förenklad)

Figure 9   Actual dimensions of Vaillant rocket (AM 1212) in mm.

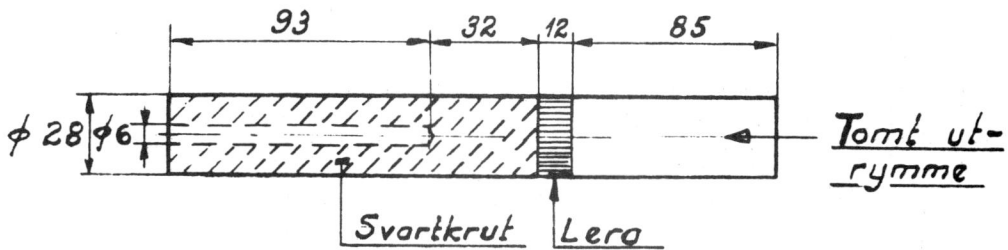

Signalraket (förenklad)

93 32 12 85

⌀28⌀6

Tomt ut-
rymme

Svartkrut Lera

Mått i mm

Figure 10 Actual dimensions of signal rocket (AM 1219) in mm.

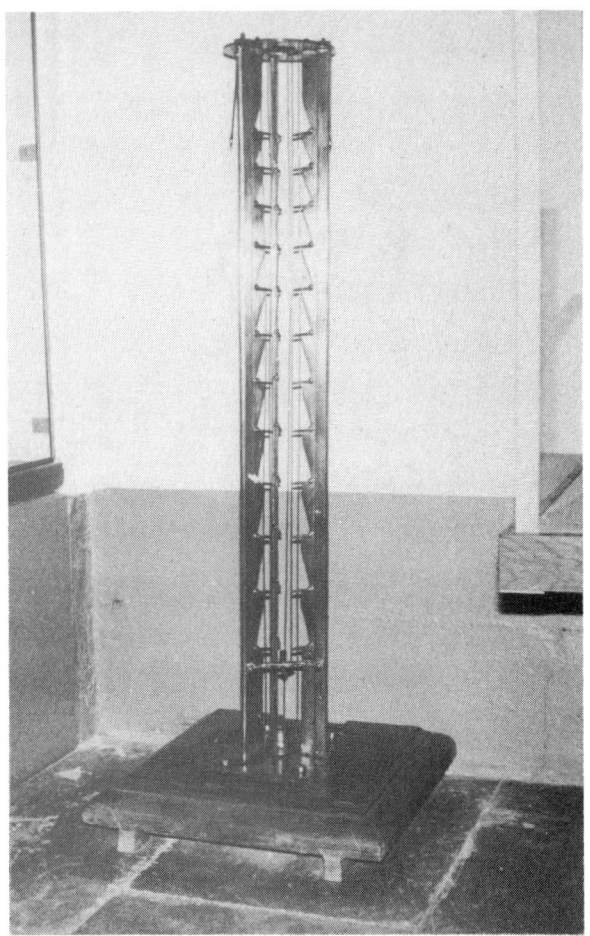

Figure 11 18th Century eprouvette at
the Royal Army Museum, Stockholm.

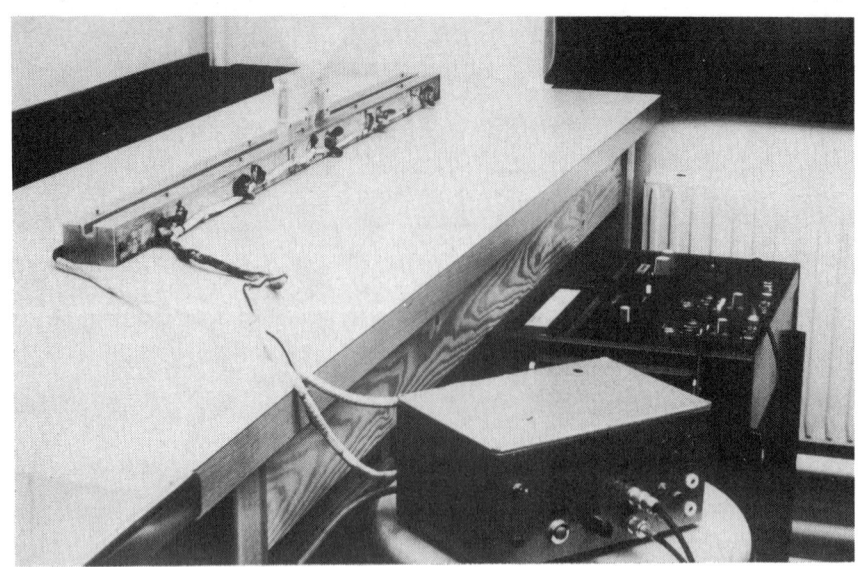

Figure 12   Aluminum groove for experimental determination of propellant burning velocity.

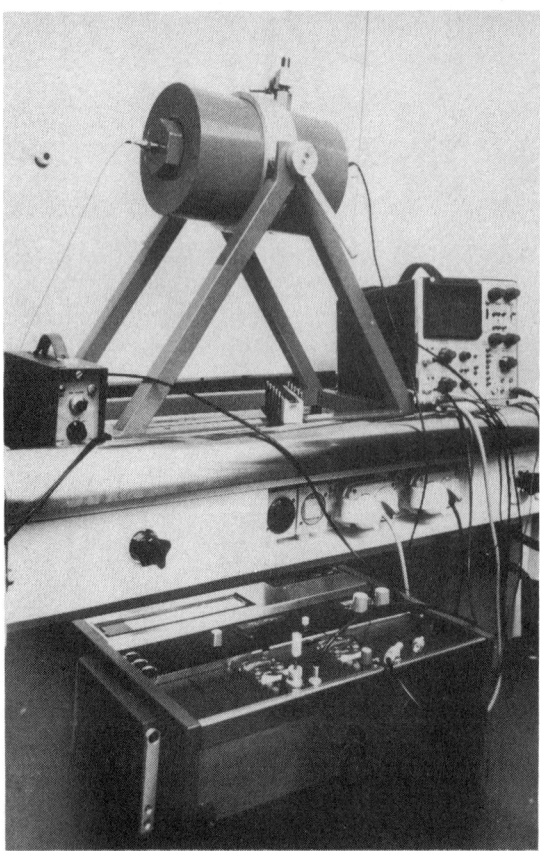

Figure 13   Steel bomb for determination of pressure vs. time characteristics.

RESULTS OF THE ANALYSES

Table 2 contains the results from the analyses and measurements made for the three ancient rocket propellants and two modern blackpowders, of which one, slow-burning, is designated as a rocket propellant.

Table 2

RESULTS OF ANALYSES OF THREE SWEDISH 19TH CENTURY ROCKET BLACKPOWDERS AND TWO MODERN BLACKPOWDERS

	Blackpowder				
	AM 1216 Standard	AM 1212 Vaillant	AM 1219 Signal	S09	Rocket blackpowder
Composition, percent					
KNO_3	67.1	66.8	63.9	76.7	74.5
C	12.1	12.4	24.1	14.0	15.5
S	20.8	20.7	12.0	9.3	10.0
ash	0.7	1.6	0.6	0.3	0.6
humidity	0.9	0.7	1.1	1.4	1.1
Density, $g \cdot cm^{-3}$					
absolute	2.03	2.03	1.89	1.94	1.94
apparent	0.747	0.676	0.685	0.956	0.642
Burning velocity $s \cdot m^{-1}$	3.05	2.61	-	0.492	6.6
Pressure vs. time					
amount propellant burned, g	20.0	20.0	12.1	30.0	30.0
maximum pressure, bar	42.0	37.0	26.5	113.0	85.0
rising time, ms	120.0	75.0	435.0	26.0	96.0
Heat of combustion					
at constant volume, $kJ \cdot g^{-1}$	2.62	2.62	2.43	3.36	3.25

The old rocket blackpowders have a much lower potassium nitrate content than the powders used for comparison and most modern powders in general. Also, the charcoal content is lower (except for the signal rocket) and consequently the sulphur content higher. The usual, modern composition 75:15:10 was used in Sweden earlier, but a lower saltpeter content mm gives a slower-burning powder, as for the signal rocket, and a higher sulphur content gives the powder better keeping properties. As to ash content and humidity, the old blackpowders are quite normal.

Both the absolute and apparent densities were determined on loose powder formed during the defusing of the rockets and thus are of little interest. They might show, however, that the powders have been well pressed, which also should have contributed to their low-burning velocity.

The heat of combustion at constant volume is relatively low for the old black-powders, which can be ascribed to the high sulphur content. The burning velocities of the standard and Vaillant blackpowder are, as expected, low. The signal rocket charge was too small to allow a determination, but a guess from the composition and the rising time by burning in the bomb is that it should have burned at a slower rate than other powders.

Curves from the closed bomb studies are reproduced in Figures 14 and 15. When studying these curves it should be borne in mind that smaller quantities were used for the old blackpowders, which is reflected in lower maximum pressures (and which also have affected the rising times).

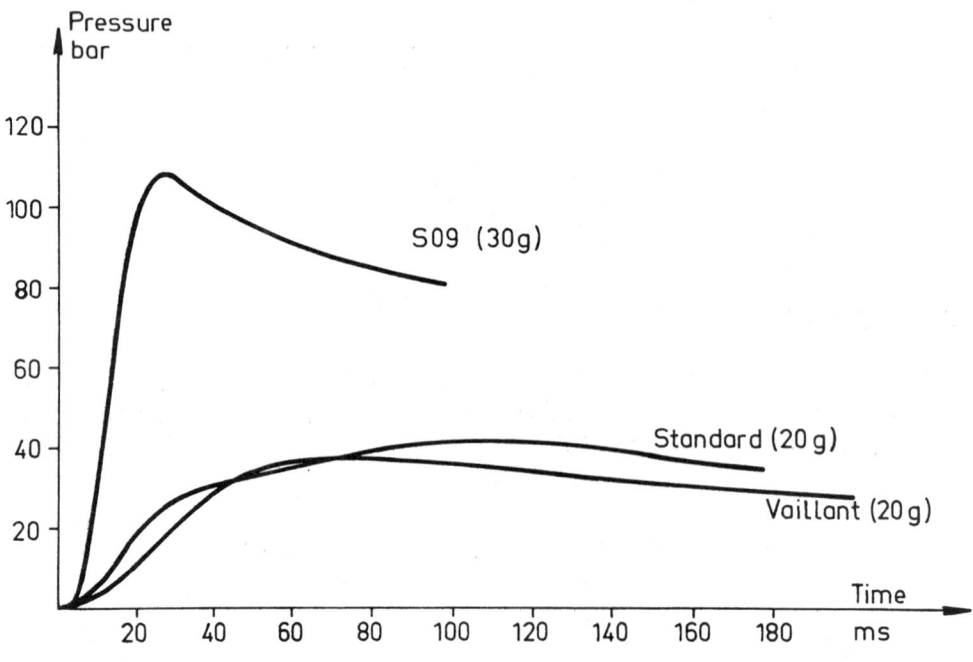

Figure 14 Pressure vs. time for blackpowder from the standard two-inch and Vaillant rockets and the modern blackpowder S09.

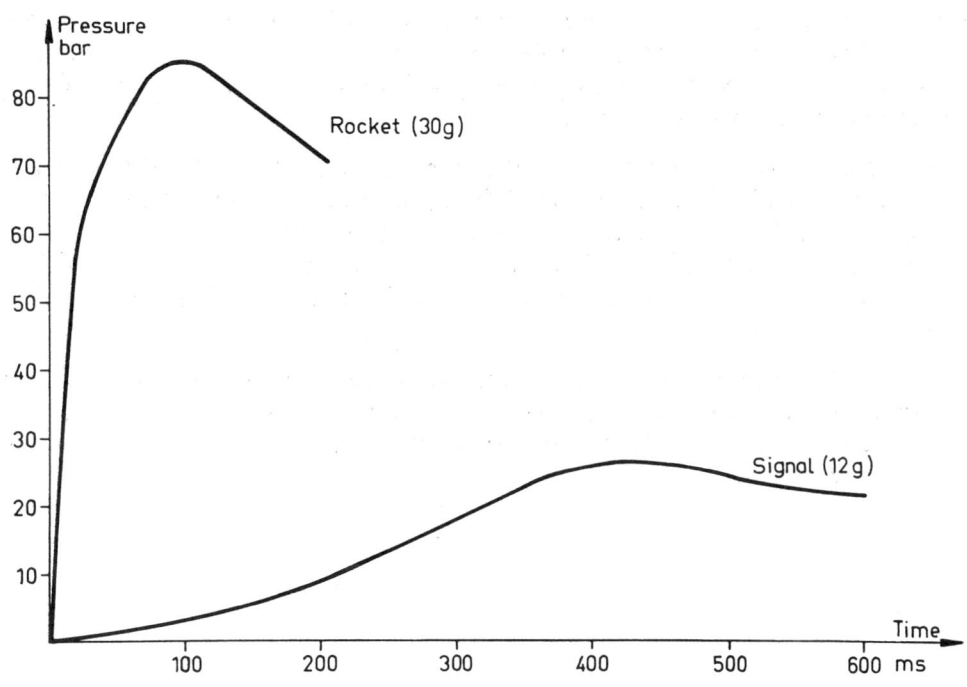

Figure 15 Pressure vs. time for blackpowder from the signal rocket and a modern rocket powder.

ROCKET PERFORMANCE

Based on the heat of combustion in Table 2, two of the typical rocket propulsion characteristics can be computed as theoretical values, theoretical nozzle exit velocity (v_e) and the specific impulse (I_{sp}). These are grouped in Table 3.

Table 3
TYPICAL ROCKET PROPULSION CHARACTERISTICS

Propellant Sample	v_e (m/s)	I_{sp} (s)	I_{sp} (Ns/kg)
Standard	2,282	233	2,282
Vaillant	2,282	233	2,282
Signal	2,198	224	2,198
Reference literature on 19th century propellants	~2,400	~250	~2,400

27

The data in Table 3 would give a theoretical velocity increment of $\Delta V' = 570$ m/s for the standard rocket based on the actual weight properties. However, for the standard rocket the maximum range was approximately 1,000 meters [3] at an elevation of 20 degrees. This leads to the following actual values:

$$\Delta V' = 123{,}5 \text{ m/s}$$

$$I_{sp}' = 47{,}7 \text{ s or } 470 \text{ Ns/kg}$$

$$V_{ef} = 470 \text{ m/s}$$

Comparing the theoretical (v_e) and actual (calculated) nozzle exit velocity (v_{ef}) the efficiency is only 20 percent. It should be noted that these rockets were not designed with a nozzle, but a simple exhaust orifice in an almost flat end-surface.

No launch performance data are known for the delta-winged rocket; but, based on the fact that the rocket-engine itself and the propellant are almost identical to the standard rocket, the range can be calculated to $s_{cal} = 1{,}280$ meters ($\Delta V' = 140$ m/s) based on a somewhat better ratio between useful load and total mass.

CONCLUSION

When the old propellants were compared with modern ones of a relatively good quality, it was found that the poor rocket performances were due to a very inefficient motor design. It has not been possible within the performed investigation to determine the burning time or massflow for an actual rocket, which would have provided valuable additional data like thrust and real nozzle exit velocity. Special considerations due to the fact that the rockets are exhibit items in a museum somewhat limited the possibilities of analysis.

ACKNOWLEDGEMENT

The authors express their gratitude for the support of the Swedish National Defence Research Institute and its staff in performing the chemical and combustion analyses and for photographs. Special thanks are given to the Royal Army Museum in Stockholm and its staff for providing the rockets and other valuable historical information.

REFERENCES

1. Skoog, A.I., "The Swedish Rocket Corps (1933-1945)," in *Essays on the History of Rocketry and Astronautics: Proceedings of the Third Through the Sixth History Symposia of the International Academy of Astronautics*" edited by R. Cargil Hall, National Aeronautics and Space Administration Conference Publication No. 2014, Volume I, 1977, pp. 9-22 and reprinted in *History of Rocketry and Astronautics*, Volume 7, Part I, pp. 9-22. Univelt, Inc., San Diego, 1986.

2. Montgéry, Merignon de, *Annales Maritimes et Coloniales*, Paris, 1825, p. 21.

3. Staf, C. "PM ang. tillverkning af krigsraketer för artilleriet vid Raketkorpsens verkstäder å Marieberg.nära Stockholm" (handwritten manuscript in Swedish dated 1836). The Royal Army Museum Library, Stockholm, Litt. I. H.d.I.n. N:r 36.

Chapter 3

BEGINNINGS OF AIRBORNE AEROMEDICAL
WEIGHTLESSNESS RESEARCH[*]

Harald J. von Beckh[†]

The astronautical pioneers, Tsiolkovsky, Goddard, and Oberth, first considered the possible effects of space flight on humans early in the twentieth century. After World War II, an increasing number of aeromedical investigators became interested in the medical problems of space flight, particularly its most challenging aspect: weightlessness. Until 1950 these efforts remained limited to theoretical deliberations and predictions. Beginning in the early fifties, however, researchers began actively to experiment with zero gravity. Weightlessness was investigated aboard aircraft in vertical diving flights and later by flying Keplerian trajectories. Less accurate simulations of weightlessness using immersion and sub-gravity towers on the ground, complementing the airborne research, yielded additional findings.

This paper examines these early studies, and contrasts the experimental results obtained with the medical data returned in the 1960's when manned space flight became a reality.

INTRODUCTION

I was a pilot and a flight surgeon of the German Luftwaffe in February 1940. At the end of World War II I had over five years of experience in Aviation Medicine. After the war I wanted very much to stay in this specialty. It became obvious, however, that after the war flying in Germany would not be possible for many years, so I volunteered at the Argentine Mission in Genoa to work for the Argentine Air Force.

In Argentina, a country of the southern hemisphere, many physical phenomena differed from the northern part of our globe. For example, due to the Coriolis effect, the water in a washbowl flows clockwise as opposed to counter-clockwise in the northern hemisphere. This was not a particular bother to transplanted pilots, as was the fact of the sun being in the north direction at noon. At first, this somewhat affected our orientation. In helpful contrast, however, was the Argentine Railroad

---

[*] Presented at The Tenth IAA History of Astronautics Symposium, Anaheim, California, U.S.A., October 1976.

[†] M.D., Naval Air Development Center, Warminster, Pennsylvania 18974-5000, U.S.A.

System. All rails originate in Buenos Aires and go fanlike to the west and by law all the railroad stations had their names painted on the roof of the station in big white letters. One of the most important navigational instruments was a railroad timetable which each pilot had in his cockpit. If a pilot wished to orient his position, he would fly at a low altitude and read the name of the railroad station he was over, consult his timetable and navigate to his destination. This maneuver was called in the pilot's jargon "to buy a railroad ticket."

Soon after my arrival in Buenos Aires, I became a consultant in the National Institute of Aviation Medicine of the Argentine Air Force.

THE PRECURSORS OF ASTRONAUTICS

Authors like Edgar Allen Poe (1809-1847), and Jules Verne (1828-1905) treated weightlessness as an interesting aspect of space flight. But the first authors who brought space flight problems in the scientific sphere were the Russian, Konstantin E. Tsiolkovsky (1853-1881), the American, Robert E. Goddard (1882-1945) and the Transsylvania-born German, Hermann Oberth (born in 1894).

THEORETICAL PAPERS ON WEIGHTLESSNESS

In 1950, the Space Medicine Branch of the Aeromedical Association, and in 1951 the International Astronautical Federation were founded.

These times are described in detail in my paper published in the *Journal of Aviation Space and Environmental Medicine* [28]:

The spectacular advances in rocketry during the 1940's stimulated an increasing number of aeromedical investigators to become interested in the biological and medical aspects of space flight. The great majority of the scientific community, however, remained skeptical as to whether space travel would be possible at all.

Showing great foresight, scientific know-how, and not a small amount of courage for those times, Major General Harry G. Armstrong, USAF-MC, organized a Panel Meeting on the topic of "Aeromedical Problems of Space Travel" in November of 1948. The presentations at the meeting held at the USAF School of Aviation Medicine, Randolph Field, Texas, were made by Armstrong, Prof. Hubertus Strughold (who even then was regarded as the "father" of space medicine), and the astrophysicist, Dr. Heinz Haber. Armstrong showed the same foresight a year later when he established a Department of Space Medicine at the School.

At the 20th Annual Scientific Meeting of the Aero Medical Association, held in New York in 1949, two papers were presented pertaining to space flight. The word "space," however, did not appear in the titles because, at that time, "space" was relegated to science fiction writers, and its use would not have been compatible with the serene and dignified atmosphere of the scientific sessions. Thus, the authors, Armstrong and Dr. Paul A. Campbell, respectively, spoke about "Some Aviation Medical Problems Associated with Potential Rocket Flight" and "Cybernetics and Aviation Medicine."

30

The negative attitude concerning "space" very likely existed in most countries. As an interesting parallel, I would like to recount a situation that occurred at the same time in Buenos Aires. At the Aeromedical Institut of the Argentine Air Force I conducted airborne studies on the effects of weightlessness producing brief periods of weightlessness by vertical diving flights in an open cockpit aerobatic biplane (Focke-Wulf 44). The duration of weightlessness was severely restricted by the limited maximal allowable diving speed of the aircraft and by the altitude necessary to recover from the dive at a sufficiently high altitude over the airfield. As the experiments involved some risk, the responsible safety officers took a grim look at these studies, and threatened to ground the aircraft and the investigator several times. To obtain weightlessness of longer duration, it was necessary to fly parabolic (Keplerian) trajectories, and this could be accomplished only with a more powerful aircraft. In the formal request to Headquarters, Argentine Air Force, for the assignment of such an aircraft, the official justification also avoided the mention of "space" flight; rather, it emphasized that periods of weightlessness could occur in some air combat maneuvers. The justification reads:

> "...combination of diving flights and pull outs into parabolas do occur when fighter aircraft make -- for instance -- gunnery runs on bombers. The attacking plane penetrates the fighter escort by high-speed diving from a superior altitude, makes its pass at the bomber from below as he pulls out, then evades the bomber's tail guns by another dive. If this parabolic flight path by accident approximates a Keplerian trajectory, the pilot would experience short periods of weightlessness. Thus, it is desirable to investigate whether these periods of weightlessness affect the pilot's neuromuscular coordination and/or orientation, as has been predicted by several authors."

This diplomatic formulation very likely eased the favorable decision of the official at headquarters, although he may have suspected the real purpose of the flights. The assigned aircraft (Fiat G 55) was deployed with a Fighter Wing at Mendoza, near the Andes Mountains, about 600 miles from Buenos Aires. Only one week after the request had been submitted, this aircraft was ordered to El Palomar Air Base in Buenos Aires. The Aeromedical Institute was notified of the favorable decision when the aircraft had already taken off from Mendoza, so that the investigator had to prepare the protocol and the airborne zero-G instrumentation very hastily.

This rapid assignment of a research aircraft was unprecedented and, for quite a while, was the topic of discussions in the aeronautical circles of Buenos Aires. Jokingly, it was stated that this victory over bureaucratic inertia was only possible because the project was "weightless."

Meanwhile, in the United States, the conception of a space medicine organization merged as a result of a significant meeting. This was the symposium on "Biological Aspects of Manned Space Flight" held at the Medical College of the University of Illinois on 3 March 1950. Armstrong and the late Dr. Andrew C. Ivy, then Vice President of the Chicago Professional Colleges of the University of Illinois, co-sponsored this historic meeting.

This time, the prominent authors no longer had to avoid the word "space," as can be seen from the titles of the lectures: "Space Medicine in the United States Air Force," by Armstrong; "Multi-Stage Rockets and Artificial Satellites," by Dr.

Wernher von Braun; "Physiological Considerations on the Possibility of Life under Extraterrestrial Conditions," by Strughold; "Astronomy and Space Medicine," by Haber; "Orientation in Space," by Campbell; "Bioclimatology of Manned Rocket Flight," by Dr. Konrad Buettner.

The great number of enthusiastic attendees, the spirited discussions, the public response, and the news media coverage were beyond all expectations. Dr. John Marbarger, then head of the Environmental and Aviation Medical Laboratory of the University of Illinois, participated in the organization of the meeting, and edited and published the symposium proceedings in book form at the University of Illinois Press. This book, entitled *Space Medicine -- the Human Factor in Flights Beyond the Earth*, was soon in its third printing. Thus, for space sciences, the year 1950 can be considered as the breakthrough from the science fiction level to accepted scientific status.

The immediate outgrowth of this successful meeting was that the participants and attendees agreed that an organization was necessary to coordinate the exchange information related to space medical research. It was the consensus that this organization should be within the framework of the Aero Medical Association.

Thus, an "Informal Committee Interested in Space Medicine" was formed. Dr. A.C. Ivy kindly agreed to be the pro tem chairman of the group. The first session was scheduled as a luncheon meeting during the 21st Annual Meeting of the Aero Medical Association in Chicago. Strughold and Dr. Gauer were asked to make formal presentations at this luncheon meeting in the Palmer House Hotel on 31 May 1950.

Strughold made the first presentation, which contained the following prophetic remarks:

"It can be predicted that rocket and space flight are in the same state of development as was aviation in 1920, whose field of research, including the medical sciences, experienced an explosive development in the following decades. It appears that the space sciences will develop along similar lines. In order to enable the medical faculty to keep pace with the presumable technical development, it is mandatory to place space medicine on the broadest possible basis and, in this manner, effect a rapid and extensive development."

Haber summarized the physical characteristics of the high-altitude atmosphere and of sealed cabins. Also, he recommended a formal space medical organization. Drs. O.O. Benson, E.J. Baldes, P.A. Campbell, and R.S. Benford participated in the discussion and agreed.

Following the discussion, a motion was made, seconded and passed, to petition the Aero Medical Association for affiliation as a section. A committee was established to prepare the petition for admission to be submitted to the Executive Council; its membership consisted of Drs. Ivy, Marbarger, Benford, Campbell and A. Graybiel.

THE FIRST EXPERIMENTAL PAPER ON WEIGHTLESSNESS

During World War II as a pilot flying Junkers 87 dive bombers I experienced that, when diving nearly vertical, I had the sensation of free fall and weightlessness during the first three to five seconds of the dive. The object was to begin the free fall with minimal speed and then increase the acceleration to prolong the free fall as long as possible, i.e., until the permissible diving speed was reached. I selected a test vehicle, the Focke-Wulf 44. This was a German aerobatic two-seater biplane, which was fabricated in Argentina and was a very common school plane for primary instruction. These experiments began in 1950. It was dangerous to pull out at maximal speed (and sufficient time of weightlessness) and to still have sufficient altitude between the ground and the aircraft. (The Base Commander threatened to ground me on several occasions.) With the Focke-Wulf 44, I made two different series of experiments, one with humans, who had to perform a "cross drawing test" during the diving flight, and second, a series of tests with water turtles (see below).

THE ZERO-G METER

The zero-G meter used in these experiments consisted of an 11-in. long glass tube which was suspended perpendicularly. On the upper extremity was a steel spiral which was fixed on an iron sphere whose diameter was nearly the inner diameter of the glass tube. In the horizontal position, the spiral drew the sphere until a position which roughly corresponded to zero-G and which was marked as such. In the vertical position, the sphere descended to a mark which was designed 1 G.

After the weightless phase and before the aircraft produced the high accelerations of the recovery, the instrument had to be placed in a horizontal position to prevent the high accelerations from ruining its sensitivity.

Although the instrument functioned properly, a better zero-G meter was discovered after a series of flights. This so-called meter consisted of a glove or a ping pong ball, suspended before the pilot, and indicating by floating freely whether there was exact weightlessness present giving the pilot the indications necessary to change the flight parabola.

Much later, in 1958, at Holloman Air Force Base, we had a sophisticated device available for weightlessness flights which consisted of two microammeters. When both needles were on zero, then the parabola was exact. The needles, however, had a noticeable time lag, so that the simple glove and ping pong ball "instruments" were generally preferred.

PUBLICATION AT THE FOURTH IAF CONGRESS IN ZURICH

I published the results at the Fourth International Astronautical Congress in Zurich, 3-8 August 1953; its German title was "Untersuchungen ueber Schwerelosigkeit an Veruschspersonen und Tieren waehrend des lotrechten Sturzfluges" ("Investigations about weightlessness on human and animal subjects during Vertical Diving Flights"). This was the first experimental weightlessness paper ever published. Its enlarged form was published in the *Journal of Aviation Medicine* in June 1954.

On 20 August 1952, I was invited by Dr. Odoris, the Director of the Department of Physiology of the Buenos Aires Medical School, to speak about my experiments in a lecture open to the public. The title of my lecture was "Physiology of Flights at Extreme Altitudes." At the end of the lecture a distinguished gentleman congratulated me and introduced himself: Colonel Roadman, Air Attaché, American Embassy. He asked me if I could give him a copy of my paper. After properly clearing my paper with the Argentine authorities I visited Colonel Roadman in his office at the American Embassy and gave him the paper. Later he showed me the evaluation of my paper by Dr. J.P. Henry, of the Aeromed Lab in Wright-Patterson AFB which stated:

"von Beckh's paper is an example how .... ingenuity can replace resources...."

Roadman later became my superior as Commander of the Aerospace Medical Division.

In 1950, Heinz Haber and Fritz Haber had published an article with the title, "Possible Methods of Producing the Gravity-Free State for Medical Research". My wish was to fly parabolas with an aircraft which was available at the airbase in Mendoza. That was the Fiat G 55-B which was similar to the Messerschmitt 109, with which I was familiar.

On 31 August 1952, I gave a lecture at the Institute of Aviation Medicine to which Brigadier General Feliciano Zumelzu was invited. General Zumelzu was Cuartel Maestro General de Aeronaútica; i.e., he was the Commander of all units of the Argentine Air Force with the exception of the flying units. Also, the surgeon general and his Medical Corps were under him. I described my flights with the Focke-Wulf 44 and stated that it would be desirable to reach a much longer time of weightlessness if I could use a higher performance aircraft like the Fiat G 55. I observed the General during my speech, and he made no favorable indication of my suggestion. After my speech, he congratulated me but said nothing about the availability of the Fiat G 55.

I was therefore very astonished when I received a telephone call three days later from the Base Commander of the Air Base El Palomar (near Buenos Aires) informing me that a Fiat G 55 aircraft from the base in Mendoza had landed in Palomar and was awaiting my instructions. This rapid decision in my favor was unique in the Argentine Air Force. In the aeronautical environment this rapid decision became well known and sensational. It was humorously said that my weightlessness experiment request was approved so quickly because it was weightless. After the phone call, I rushed into a glass blower shop nearby and bought another glass tube for my zero-G indicator, because the glass tube was broken in one of the last Focke-Wulf 44 flights. Then I rushed to the Palomar Air Base. The pilot, Capt. N. Gonzalez, understood the problem of parabola flying immediately and we started the experiments which gave us a zero-G duration of 20 sec., consequently enabling me to enlarge upon my paper significantly. It was published in the *Journal of Avia-*

tion Medicine in 1954 under the title "Experiments and Animals and Human Subjects under Sub- and Zero-Gravity Conditions during the Dive and Parabolic Flight."

This paper was the very first in the literature that contained experimental data of humans and animals under weightless conditions.

Chapter 4

EARLY CONCEPT'S OF AEROSPACE SYSTEMS[*]

A. N. Ponomarev and V. S. Mikhailov[†]

One of the most urgent problems in present-day cosmonautics is the construction of aerospace systems for multiple application.

In turn, the most urgent problem for aviation and cosmonautics historians is the study of the evolution of concepts from which modern opinions have become formulated regarding aerospace systems. In this connection, there is a special interest in studying the ideas, suggested at the initial stage, regarding the theoretical foundations of cosmonautics, i.e., in the first third of the 20th Century.

Even at that early stage the attention of investigators was attracted by the idea of use by spaceships of "lift-drag ratio quality" during atmospheric flight. This possibility was mentioned for the first time in the literature in an article by Esnault-Pelterie in 1913. In the middle of the 1920s, the concept of using the lift-drag ratio had already been published by several investigators. In 1924, F.A. Tsander attempted for the first time to develop the first technical project for a spaceship with lift-drag ratio and carried out an analysis of its advantages over the purely rocket ship. Starting at the end of the 1920s, the concept of using the lift-drag ratio began being discussed in a majority of the scientific works on cosmonautics. It is reflected in the popular writings of that time and even in science fiction books, in whose pages winged vehicles appeared.

From the middle 1920s interest began to appear in the use of atmospheric air for the propulsion of space vehicles. In 1924, K.E. Tsiolkovsky, having pointed out the advantage of using air as an oxidizer, suggested to eject air by "special composite turbines". In the same year, Tsander suggested the use of atmospheric air for increasing the mass of a rocket engine jet.

Subsequently, in publications of Tsiolkovsky, Tsander, and R.H. Goddard, the concept of using atmospheric air in propulsion systems was further developed, and, the details of propulsion systems were specified. These propulsion systems were supposed to be used both for space vehicles and as special first stages in aviation.

---

[*] Presented at The Ninth IAA History of Astronautics Symposium, Lisbon, September 1975.

[†] Committee of the Soviet National Association of Natural Science and Technology Historians, USSR Academy of Sciences, Moscow, USSR.

However, the idea of using atmospheric air in propulsion systems did not get the support of all the investigators in the sphere of astronautics. For instance, H. Oberth and E. Sänger considered it more realistic to focus on the use of rocket engines. Thus, even in the first third of the 20th Century, there were two opposing points of view on the use of atmospheric air in propulsion systems, and this persists to the present.

In publications appearing during the first third of our century the questions were examined of organizing communication with orbital stations by means of regular Earth-space-Earth flights. One of the first to mention this possibility was Tsander, who in 1924 suggested using a winged spaceship for the transport of goods and people to and from interplanetary stations. Supplying orbital stations from Earth or the Moon by means of special transport rockets was suggested also by M. Valier. In 1926, Tsiolkovsky published a plan for the mastering of cosmos in which the supply of the orbital stations was envisaged by means of rockets having a suitable lift-drag ratio. Sänger later pointed out that one of the main problems in the development of rocket airplanes was to establish communication with orbital stations.

Thus, regular transport flights to orbital stations were suggested as far back as the first third of the 20th Century. Moreover, this seemed to be one of the main duties of space transport systems, which in many respects resembles present-day opinions on the use of aerospace vehicles.

Little attention was paid in earlier days to questions of multiple uses of space vehicles. Such questions were then secondary in comparison to the problem of accomplishing space flight. Still, the possibility of multiple use was mentioned. In 1923, Oberth -- speaking of the cost of building a space rocket -- remarked that "with proper handling, it is capable of 100 lift-offs." And in 1929, Tsiolkovsky expressed an opinion on the possibility of using elements of a rocket train.

Thus ideas, which are the basis of the present-day concepts of aerospace systems, were put forward about half a century ago, i.e., long before the development of practical work in this sphere. This reflected the existing tendency in the first third of the 20th Century for aviation methods to be connected with the beneficial use of atmospheric air for cosmonautical enterprises. This process was supported by a whole series of reasons.

Even at the early development stage of the theory of space flight it was determined that the possibility of its accomplishment depended on the ability of spacecraft to develop the required speed, which in its turn, was controlled by the exhaust velocity of combustion products and fuel mass-construction mass ratio. Research conducted at the time revealed limited possibilities of raising these parameters with the use of chemical fuel. The elucidation of this limitation stimulated the search for alternate scientific and technical solutions. Suggestions offered can be divided into two groups:

1. Those involving increasing power-producing possibilities of spacecraft (for instance, combustion of metals, the use of nuclear energy, solar sail, etc.)

2. Those involving increasing the potential possibilities of spacecraft by application of new schemes and construction solutions (for instance, gradation, ground means for boosting, etc.).

It is quite obvious that the founders of space-related rocketry were quite familiar with the widely advertised achievements of aviation. Moreover, many of them were more or less connected with aviation, and some, as for instance Tsiolkovsky and Esnault-Pelterie, were quite active in this sphere. For them, the borrowing of ideas, methods, schemes and constructive decisions from aviation was a natural process.

The use of aviation achievements made it possible to reduce to some extent the number of problems requiring priority solutions and to concentrate the attention of investigators on solution of principal questions.

The desire to use techniques tested in aviation are noticeable in many spacecraft projects. This is evident in the arrangement of spacecraft having lift-drag ratio. In the first third of the 20th Century, various types of aerodynamic arrangements were suggested (with controllable brake panel, with carrying body, and with wings). Of these, the most widely used has become the tested winged airplane scheme.

The tendency to use known and verified principles and construction techniques is also noticeable in suggestions for spacecraft propulsion systems. As examples, suggestions have been made for various modifications of internal combustion piston engines, to be applied to spacecraft in which the thrust build-up should be completely or partially due to the jet effect of exhaust. These, being jet engines in principle, should have remained piston engines in the scheme.

The same example is the modification by Tsiolkovsky of the well-known airplane scheme -- the flying wing. He suggested increasing the lift-drag ratio of the spacecraft during landing to join together several spindle-shaped bodies. It is a remarkable fact that later on Tsiolkovsky seemed to have returned this idea to aviation, by suggesting to apply the scheme -- developed by him for spacecraft -- to airplanes.

In these and in many other examples the tendency is seen to use new ideas in combination with known and perfected schemes and elements, borrowed from aviation practice. The investigators of that time saw in this a possible means of intensifying the development of cosmonautics.

The temptation to use the achievements of aviation coupled with the realization by a majority of investigators of the difficulties in the means of accomplishing space flight have resulted in the appearance, during the first third of the 20th Century, of plans for the development of aeronautics in which it was suggested that airplanes gradually evolve into spacecraft (with construction of a number of intermediate types of space vehicles). In this case, it was assumed that these space vehicles would have an independent value even outside of cosmonautics proper, in particular for resolving problems inherent in aviation.

At that time, the most urgent problem was to find methods by means of which it would have been possible to upgrade considerably the specifications of atmospheric vehicles. The questions connected with this took up a notable place in the work of the cosmonautics pioneers, in which the possibilities were discussed of using rocket engines in aviation and the use of the spacecraft itself or its component parts for transorbital transport flight.

As cosmonautical concepts blossomed in the 1920s, investigators began coupling aviation methods with those of space flight. Particularly during the second half of that decade, increased contacts between cosmonautics and aviation were built up for the benefit of both. During the early 1930s, these ideas were discussed in publications by most space flight investigators, particularly Tsiolkovsky and Tsander. These publications exhibit both novelty and significance.

A majority of ideas developed during the first third of the 20th century applying aviation methods to cosmonautics retain their value even today. However, the forms of implementation expected at that time differed considerably from modern thought. This is primarily explained by the difference in the development levels of science and technology. On the basis of knowledge existing at that time, it was difficult to compare the complexity of implementing different variants of technical solutions and to forecast the emergence of new problems (for instance, involving flight at hypersonic velocities). This frequently caused an over-optimistic evaluation of the possibility of borrowing directly from the then-existing state of aviation know-how. There was also a tendency to under-estimate progress during the difficult period of cosmonautical development.

It is remarkable that, though many investigators assumed development of aviation systems into cosmonautics, their own opinions have undergone a seemingly reverse solution. This process, resembling development of space systems at the present stage, was shown in the fact that methods studied for the solution space flight problems have changed from "purely" rocket ones to a combination with aviation methods. At both stages of the development of cosmonautics (construction of theoretical foundations and practical development) the solution of the principal question regarding the possibility of space flight by means of dynamic rocket methods was followed by the search of ways for perfecting methods typical of aviation technology. Moreover, if during the first third of the 20th century the main stimulus for this was the apparent ease and rapidity of solving the problem of space flight, at present questions of economy and flexibility of using the space systems have become dominant.

Chapter 5

COMPUTER-ORIENTED DYNAMIC MODELING OF SPACECRAFT: HISTORICAL EVOLUTION OF EULERIAN MULTIBODY FORMALISMS SINCE 1750[*]

Robert E. Roberson[†]

The development of Eulerian dynamical formalisms for systems of interconnected rigid bodies is described qualitatively, from their single-body origin in the works of Euler, through the bootless efforts of the 19th Century to modern computer-oriented dynamic simulations. Major emphasis is on the aerospace application area (later extended to terrestrial vehicles), but some parallel developments in biomechanics and the kinematics of mechanisms are included.

INTRODUCTION

In the history of science the focus usually is on the development of physical concepts, while in the history of technology it is on the development of devices and engineering systems. Rarely is it on the evolution of schemes of operation or organization, or on the constructions of mathematical/mechanical descriptions that can be used to analyze physical devices, and by predicting the behavior of systems yet unbuilt, that enable the engineer to bring his creation to a higher state of perfection. I submit that the latter area, the mathematical modeling of technological systems, has historical roots that can be as interesting and illuminating as those of the physical devices themselves.

A particular kind of modeling problem is of concern here. Modern space technology demands that one be able to predict with high accuracy the motion of a vehicle in translation and rotation in the presence of disturbances. We must be able to determine the degree to which the motion can be controlled, the effect of design changes in the system parameters, the mechanical consequences of failures; in general, the dynamical behavior of the vehicle in the light of the qualitative and quantitative requirements of its mission. Furthermore, we must recognize that while some relatively simple spacecraft will behave much like a single rigid body, we

---

[*] Presented at The Eleventh IAA History of Astronautics Symposium, Prague, Czechoslovakia, September 1977.

[†] Professor of Engineering Sciences and Chairman, Department of Applied Mechanics and Engineering Sciences, University of California - San Diego, La Jolla, California, U.S.A.

often must regard the craft as composed of a number of rigid or gyrostatic bodies somehow fastened together into a single entity.

This paper examines the forerunners of modern dynamical descriptions used for spacecraft simulation, both as single bodies and as systems of interconnected bodies. It describes the origins of attempts to construct modern "unified" multibody dynamical formalisms, particularly those called Eulerian formalisms: why they occurred and what underlying philosophy was used. It follows their subsequent development as computer-oriented descriptions, summarizes their current status, and speculates on their future evolution.

THE EIGHTEENTH CENTURY FORERUNNERS

Before the dynamical behavior of systems of rigid bodies can be analyzed, one must be able to give a complete dynamical description of a single body. The ability to do this in terms of differential equations came much later than might be thought. Although Newton solved some important problems of particle motion in his great work, *Philosophiae Naturalis Principia Mathematica,* 1687, he *"gives no evidence of being able to set up differential equations of motions for mechanical systems"* [1, stress his]. Primitive differential equations of first order for the translational motion of a single particle can be found, with some searching, in both [2] and [3]. But prior to 1750, no general procedure was known for writing the differential equations for the rotation of a rigid body.

Before 1750, two problems of rigid body rotation had been analyzed, both motivated by observed phenomena in the real world. One was the rotation of a body turning about a fixed axis, the physical pendulum. The other was the momentary response of a spinning body to a torque normal to its spin axis, the problem underlying the long-known phenomenon of the precession of the equinoxes. I show in [4] that both these cases can be brought within the dynamical framework that then existed and describe in considerable detail the basic work on each.

However, in 1750 Euler found the way to a general one-body theory. He asks in [5] what forces and moments must act on a body to make it take on a prescribed motion. Using what we call Newton's equation of motion (although Newton fathered only the physical principle, not the equation) applied to the "particles" of which the body is constituted, Euler finds the three famous rotational dynamical equations that bear his name today. His equations are involved because he does not use principal axes of inertia, but they are complete and correct. He is not able to do much with them except in very special cases.

The important thing for the historian of technology is that this was the first appearance of rotational dynamical equations seen (by Euler) as an essentially new "principle of mechanics", ranking with the "Newton" equations to form the foundation of mechanics. His viewpoint was correct, for his equations *cannot* be derived from the latter without adding some kind of postulate about internal forces in the body. One may as well postulate the Euler equations themselves as an independent law of motion. For this reason, we often speak of the complete set of dynamical equations for the motion of a rigid body as the Newton/Euler equations. About his equations, Euler himself says:

"It is these three formulas, containing the new principles of mechanics, which one needs to determine the motion of a solid body where the axis of rotation ... does not remain fixed, or directed toward the same spot in the heavens or in absolute space. It is evident that these new principles are sufficient for all imaginable cases of motion that solid bodies can have."

Euler's second major memoir in 1758 [6] begins on a note of despair.

"But although the calculation has succeeded rather well, and I have discovered analytical formulas that determine all the chances that can occur in the motion of a body about a variable axis, their strict application is still subject to difficulties which appear to me to be almost completely insurmountable."

His lament reflects the problems that all succeeding generations of mechanicians have had with these same intractable, nonlinear equations. He then proceeds to rederive the Euler rotational equations *ab initio* without the assumption of a fixed axis as in the memoir of 1750, and to solve the first major problem of general rigid body motion, that of a torque-free body rotating about its center of mass. He tends to view the rotational equations in a more general light than before, but still is concerned primarily with their application in an infinitesimal sense. The details of his solution method in the work of 1768 are given in [4].

Euler's third pioneering memoir [7], considered a companion piece of his 1750 work, was published in 1760. (It is almost impossible to discover the true sequence in which his works were actually written. The publication date is not a reliable guide.) It begins with a statement that he still feels matters are obscure and that further clarification is needed.

"I remark first that the greatest part of this obscurity has its origin in the manner in which one represents the motion of a body turning about is center of gravity, and consequently I shall strive to give a method by which one can form a clear idea of such a motion, whatever it may be."

Thereupon he introduces a parametrization of a rotation by three successive rotation angles, the "Euler angles". In a work on differential calculus dated 1748, he already had shown explicitly how a general rotation of axes could be gotten by three successive rotations about coordinate axes, thereby parametrizing the rotation by three angles. He again writes the Euler dynamical equations and now, for the first time, introduces the kinematical equations that relate the time derivatives of the Euler angles to the three components of angular velocity.

With these three memoirs, Euler's child is put into the world, the parent still dissatisfied with his creation, and left for some years to develop under the care of others. Euler, himself, was to make one other major contribution to the theory in the form of a four-parameter kinematical representation of rotation, but this did not then appear in mechanical guise. In a work of 1770, he plucked such a parametrization from the air to enable him to construct a certain class of magic squares with rotational numbers.

The remainder of the 18th Century saw work on special problems of rotation, almost exclusively by Euler, d'Alembert and Lagrange. The latter published his "Lagrangian formulation" of mechanics in 1764 and made rigid body motion one of

43

his earliest applications. In the early 19th Century, we find a host of embellishments on the basic theory, of major and minor import, by various authors. Much of this was to apply the developing codification of elliptic functions to certain special problems of rotation. Other parametrizations of rotation were tried; e.g., by Cayley, without relieving any of the real difficulties of this problem area. The early 19th Century was a period when the balance still teetered between Eulerian and Lagrangian formalisms for the dynamical equations. Poinsot was one of the last unabashed Eulerians, but the virtues of his work were gradually submerged by the rising Lagrangian tide.

The end of the 18th Century marks the end of the first major period of our history. The principles of mechanics of translation and rotation had been established and were ready to be put to use. But there was little employment to be found. The equations could not (and cannot) be solved in general, so the authors of the 19th Century were, for the most part, reduced to reworking old results in new terms. That century saw the subject of rotation take two paths. One was the further exploration of the classical problems, a path that led to virtual sterility before 1900. The other was the use of rotational dynamics to support advances in technology. This part of the discipline is still alive and flourishing.

MULTIBODY FORMALISMS: NINETEENTH CENTURY

Faced with the difficulties attending the solution of the motion of a single rigid body, it is not surprising that the 19th Century investigators were slow to take up the problem of many coupled rigid bodies. There were no pressing technological problems of the day to motivate an attempt to simulate the motion of a many-body system. And, indeed, even if they wrote the descriptive equations, what could they do with them? Yet, there were at least two authors who did take up the challenge.

The first of these was H. Resal, a well-known French mechanician, author of a five-volume work entitled *Traité de mécanique générale* published during the period 1873-1889 [8]. His approach is based on treating each body of a system as a free body, each acted upon by a set of forces and torques that comprises those from external effects and all those arising from interactions of all the other bodies of the system upon the subject body. For each free body, then, one may write the Newton/Euler dynamical equations and the corresponding kinematical equations. This is the way we still do it today in developing a multibody formalism.

Outlined in modern terms, his approach amounts to the following. Let O be an inertial point and CM^i be the center of mass of the ith body of an n-bodies system. Let ρ^i be the vector from O to CM^i, m^i be the mass of the ith body, H^i be its angular momentum about CM^i, $\mathfrak{z}^i$ be the total force and ζ^i the total torque on the body (the latter about its center of mass) from all sources, internal and external. Resal's scalar dynamical equations are equivalent to

$$m^i \, d^2 \rho^i / dt^2 = \mathfrak{z}^i \qquad dH^i / dt = \zeta^i \qquad (i = 1, \dots , n) \tag{1}$$

These are, in effect, the equations for one body given by Poinsot in 1834, although he had no idea of considering a whole set of such equations simultaneously.

Resal goes on to factor the angular momentum into the scalar product of an inertia dyadic and the angular velocity of the body in question, although, of course, he deals only with scalar forms of the results. Finally, the applied forces and torques are split into external and interaction effects.

In Resal's work the set of dynamical equations he gets are little more than an academic curiosity. He does not really seem to expect to get very far with them. Yet, Eqs. 1 are still our starting point when deriving an Eulerian multibody computer simulation. I refer to them in [4] as the "primitive equations" after they are further expanded in the two respects mentioned above. They are not well-suited for numerical implementation as they stand, but they can be reworked to give equations of another form which are ideal for the purpose.

I now present Otto Fischer of Leipzig as an unsung worker in the field of multibody dynamics. In a series of papers, [9]-[13], he attacks the problem of systems composed of a number of interconnected bodies. He has strong physical motivation and wants answers, so he is led to some of the same modifications of Eqs. 1 that we make today when we want a better basis for computation. His motivation is not technology at all, but physiology. His "system" is the human body, modeled as a number of rigid bodies joined together, and he is interested in describing its mechanics as completely as possible. In the process, he develops almost all of the physical constructs that arise in modern, computer-oriented dynamic models. Lamentably, the work seems to have been completely in vain. Without a computer, he himself could not capitalize on it. It dropped from sight and to the best of my knowledge played no role whatsoever in the rediscovery of the same results, by me and others, that occurred toward 1965. It may be questionable, therefore, whether we can speak of his "contributions", but of his ideas and his understanding of his subject we certainly may speak.

Fischer limits himself to systems interconnected as topological trees, as we all have done in recent years until relatively few months ago.

"The only condition that must be imposed on the system is that if a hinge be disconnected the mechanism falls into two separate parts."

Indeed, he goes significantly further and says that if one has a system with closed loops, it is possible to make cuts to get a uniquely defined system, then impose kinematic constraints. The details of this process are just now being published for Eulerian formalisms in 1977, although they are better known for Lagrangian formalisms. Fischer works out all equations in detail only for two bodies, but he says he knows (as undoubtedly is true) how to do the general case. However, he did not attempt to develop a notation to facilitate generalization and in this one instance current work has taken a significant step in advance. Aside from the computer itself, it is not too much to say that the real difference between the modern formulations and those of the last century is mainly an improvement in "bookkeeping" methods to keep track of the multitude of terms in the equations. Fischer's dynamical equations are founded on Lagrangian rather than Eulerian methods, but for all that his physical interpretations of certain terms are exactly the same. He identifies what we now call "augmented bodies" ("reduzierte Körper") and "barycenters" ("Hauptpunkte"). Hinge points, joints with one and three degrees of freedom, interaction torque models, equilibrium problems, initial acceleration problems, interpretation of the terms in the n-body equations -- he has it all. What a waste that his work was unknown to technology a scant 50 years later!

MID-TWENTIETH CENTURY RENAISSANCE

By the 1950s, two major factors were at work to cause a rebirth of interest in multibody dynamics. The first was the need felt that accompanied the rise of aerospace technology. As soon as it was appreciated that space vehicles often could be modeled as collections of interconnected bodies, the practical utility of multibody dynamics became obvious. The second factor was the fantastically increased capability for digital computation, making it feasible to do large-scale digital simulation of multibody systems. Multibody formalisms existed, of course, both in the Lagrange equations and in the Newton/Euler equations, but now the focus was on recasting these in forms better adapted to computer implementation. In particular, some improvements were in prospect from better choices of variables, others from better notational devices for doing the bookkeeping needed to keep track of the considerable number of terms in the equations.

I like to divide the work done on multibody dynamics during the two decades since the first space flight in 1957 into three major tracks. In each case, working from first principles, the formulation of equations for:

1. A specific, small number of rigid bodies (usually two) within the framework of a specific application, and the construction of special-purpose computer simulation programs based on these

2. An *arbitrary number arbitrarily interconnected* rigid or gyrostatic bodies, and the construction of general-purpose computer simulation programs for treating such systems; this has been done in steps of increasing system generality

3. Interconnected elastic bodies, possibly with some restrictions on number and on the generality of their interconnection and elastic behavior, and the construction of corresponding general-purpose computer simulation programs

Occasionally, the equations in item (1) have been given as special cases of item (2) (e.g., in [14] and [15]). Usually, however, when authors are treating applications of two-body systems, even though they may mention multibody formulations, they return to first principles for their equation (e.g., in [16] and [17]). The equations in item (2) can be gotten as the "rigid body part" of those in item (3) when the latter is developed in a certain way. (See [18], for example.) Conversely, item (2) can be used as a starting point for item (3) in other approaches to the elastic-body problem.

Item (1) is not a unified endeavor, but a series of solutions of special problems. It does not lend itself to a coherent historical review and I doubt that one ever will be done. On the other hand, item (3) is a burgeoning research area at this moment -- a child of the 1970s -- and probably cannot be put into proper historical perspective for yet some years. Therefore, my remaining concern in the present work is with item (2) exclusively.

In pursuing item (2), I focus on Eulerian formalisms, although I cite work that uses the Lagrange equations as a starting point. The evolutions of these formalisms has been shaped by their application areas, each of which tends to emphasize particular features, so I wish to distinguish three major application areas:

1. Aerospace/terrestrial vehicles

2. Biomechanics

3. Mechanisms.

The first of these originated in the dynamic modeling of satellites and other spacecraft of the 1950s, but recent years have seen generalizations motivated by terrestrial vehicles. I discuss this first, leaving aside the second and third areas until some of the central characteristics of such formalisms have been established.

The work devoted to Eulerian multibody systems since 1957 certainly is not unknown or obscure -- indeed, it is widely cited -- but many authors seem to have used their citations mainly as window dressing. I am not aware of any work that has seriously tried to put it into full perspective.

Perhaps the earliest contribution was [19], dated 1958, in which a satellite is supposed to be modeled as follows: The craft consists of a main body to which any number of subsidiary parts are directly attached; rotors, moving particles, gimballess gyros, etc. Topologically, the system interconnection is what has been called a "porcupine" structure. These parts are characterized by mass, inertia (which might be zero), and suitable variables describing the way they translate or rotate (or both) with respect to the main body. The center of mass of the complete system is used as a base point for writing the linear and angular momentum of the system. Although this appears to introduce a variable translation vector into the equations (the distance from the center of mass of the main body to the center of mass of the system generally is a varying quantity), the final results are phrased entirely in terms of the displacement and angular motion variables for the main body together with the *known* position and rotation variables for the relative motions between the subsidiary bodies and the main body. All of the known motion of the main body, in accordance with the philosophy of the paper which treats the motion of subsidiary parts as known disturbances acting on the main body. Results are couched in vector-dyadic terms, not reduced to scalar level.

This work was expanded almost immediately. The vector equations again are used in [20], but with a different philosophy. The internal moving parts now are regarded as control mechanisms rather than producers of disturbances, although the content of the equations themselves is not changed from that of [19]. In [21] (1959), the results are put into scalar form without any modifications in the dynamic model itself. (This has been redone in a somewhat different form in 1966 by [22].) Changes occurring in [23] (1960) are considerably more significant. The assumption of a porcupine structure is abandoned in part. Two classes of parts rather than one are recognized: those parts whose relative motion with respect to contiguous parts are kinematically known and those that are dynamically coupled (e.g., by passive springs and dampers) to its contiguous parts. The important restriction still remaining is that any dynamically coupled parts still are restricted to a porcupine structure relative to the main body, although the kinematically driven parts may form an arbitrary network. However, the statement is made that the system structure "is not hard in principle to generalize", and the work goes on to cite some specific examples where "a more general formulation ultimately may be of interest." As regards the results of the work, equations are again left at the vector-dyadic level and not all relative derivatives are written out explicitly. The highest derivative terms are not all grouped on the left, reflecting the still-prevailing motivation of analyzing the disturbances on the main vehicle produced by the relative motion of internal parts. However, interaction torques that are functions of relative motion are left explicit, as required for applications of the moving parts for control. When the equations are summed over the bodies, the interaction forces and torques add to zero and the results reduce to those of [19].

In 1962, [24] replows the ground of [19] with the difference that the center of mass of the main body rather than the center of mass of the system is the base point for writing rotational equations. This is claimed to have two advantages, both specious. The first is that "the reference point does not wander through the system but is located definitely once for all." In fact, it makes no difference whatsoever what point is used, as long as the work is done correctly, for ultimately all terms are expressed in terms of body-fixed or otherwise known quantities. The use of the system center of mass as base point, on the contrary, has the advantage that its own translational motion is far simpler than that of other points. The second claim is that "the inertia tensors for all moving bodies are evaluated with respect to axes embedded in the individual bodies instead of ... the main body. Thus, the inertias are always constant." Actually, the first part of the statement is true for all approaches, while the second part concerning constancy is never true in the required resolution into main body axes, except for bodies of very special shape and/or relative motion.

In connection with this work, we see the first explicit mention (in [25]) of the multibody formulation being made the basis of a computer program, the details of which are not described. The historian faces grave difficulties in trying to assess the computer implementation of any of the formalisms. He seldom can say what was going on behind the closed doors of the aerospace industry during this time and this is where most computer simulations were born and lived their lives. Rarely have any been described adequately in the archival literature.

The next work in the area is that of Abzug [26]. He devotes part of a chapter on attitude control (in a textbook growing out of a short course at the University of California, Los Angeles) to a formulation of the dynamical equations. He chooses the base-points for the bodies as in [23]: arbitrary for the main body; at the centers of mass of the other bodies. Indeed, except for notational details, the two works are much alike. Both have the equations at a vector level from which considerable reduction is needed before implementing them on a computer. (However, Abzug does write out all relative derivative terms explicitly.) Both distinguish dynamically from the kinematically excited relative motion. In some respects, the interconnection topology seems more general in Abzug's work, for the interaction forces and torques are introduced between all bodies. However, a porcupine structure is implicit in the way translational dependent variables are defined, for these locate all the subsidiary parts with respect to a base-point in the main body.

In 1967, Sandler [27] states the need for flexible computer programs to study satellite attitude motion and goes on to say that "such flexibility may be realized by developing a computer program that simulates the basic satellite body and calls subroutines that simulate the effects of auxiliary component bodies ... In this way a satellite configuration may be changed by replacing computer subroutines ... The subroutines serve to determine the reaction on the basic body due to the auxiliary bodies." Considering rotation alone, his starting point is, in effect, Eq. 1b above. The dH^1/dt terms apparently are not manipulated in his approach other than to replace H^1 by $I^1 \cdot \omega^1$. All manipulation is confined to the right side, i.e., to the external and internal torques. There are no pure torques at the common point of two bodies, only the torque of an interaction force, which somewhat limits generality. His assumed system is a porcupine and he says that he "does not consider reaction torques due to gimbal constraints" (apparently reflecting his view of the most likely way a system would fail to be a porcupine). The work is philosophically close to [19] and [23]. Although it is directed toward the needs of computer simulation, no discussion of a program is included.

We can cite other works in this same general period. First, [28] (1965) is based on the same system model as [19]. It derives an expression for kinetic energy, which had not been given in [19], and rephrases the total angular momentum of the system about its center of mass, which had. It also gives explicitly the instantaneous inertia dyadic for the system about its center of mass, a step toward treating the whole class of kinematically excited cases under the rubric "pseudo-one-body" problems, as I have done in [4]. Second, [29] applies Abzug's equations to a spinning body carrying a number of particles sliding in grooves as a crude model of a manned vehicle. On the whole, though, there are very few later citations to the work described previously. We can say -- fairly, I think -- that the impetus toward a multibody dynamical formalism for spacecraft led to results in 1958-1960 that were not substantially improved for the next 5 years. The first half of the 1960 decade was a period of consolidation, minor changes in viewpoint, and relative quiescence. But in 1965, activity on the subject again burst forth and a train of generalizations began that created the pedestal on which rest today's dynamic simulations.

Two papers, [30] by Hooker and Margulies and [31] by Roberson and Wittenburg, usually are cited as fountainheads for that flow of activity. Most subsequent investigators do not realize that both had a common origin, for the story behind it has not been published previously.

In 1964 -- I do not recall the exact date -- Margulies and I met in a two-day working session in my office at the University of California, Los Angeles. At that time we decided that the construction of a general-purpose computer program designed to model very broad classes of interconnected rigid or gyrostatic body systems, with special attention to those encountered in spacecraft simulation, was a desirable and feasible goal. (Neither of these characteristics was at that time obvious.) We set forth the properties that both our modeled system and our computer program should have. The latter related to ways the program might be made general and flexible without undue loss in efficiency. The former related mainly to the degree of generality that was appropriate to the interconnection topology and mechanisms. We decided that the simulation should be limited to tree-connected systems, inasmuch as this seemed to cover most aerospace applications. (At the same time, we recognized that further generalization probably would have to be accomplished by cutting branches in any more general network until only a tree was left and then rejoining the cut branches by suitable kinematical constrains. At this point, we were, unknowingly, starting to rediscover Fischer.) Furthermore, we felt that initially focus should be on systems in which contiguous bodies share one or more hinge points in common, again because this seemed enough for the applications in which we were then interested. Thereupon we separated, each to pursue the problem in his own way.

Margulies is a geometer by profession and his collaborator, the late Robert Hooker, had interests embracing an orientation toward digital computation. Their approach, viewpoint, and phraseology in [30] reflect these personal backgrounds. The work is excellent and has stood the test of time, even though further generalizations have been laid upon it since. Its basic characteristics are as follows: It applies to tree systems of rigid bodies in which there is only rotation, no translation, between contiguous bodies. Fischer's augmented body and barycenter are rediscovered. Their "main result" is a set of equations left in vector-dyadic terms in which the dependent variables are the absolute angular velocities ω^1 of the several bodies. The equations contain some second derivatives of barycentric vectors (locating the interbody attachment points with respect to the barycenters) which are not written out in scalar form. Thus, not all the highest derivative of the ω^1 are explicit. A vector-dyadic form of the gravitational torque terms is included.

Although the equations are not reduced to scalar terms, they were used immediately by Hooker as a starting point for a computer simulation. (This work has not been documented in the archive literature.) There is no assumption about the kinematics of the interbody connections, except that these be purely rotational, up to the point where the authors describe one method for eliminating unwanted constraint torques. This method, because it raises the order of a matrix that must, in effect, be inverted, is not very efficient. It has since been supplanted by a method that reduces the order instead. As originally presented, the Hooker/Margulies formulation works best if all connections between bodies have three degrees of rotational freedom. At this point, the philosophy behind the use of the equations seems to have swung from one in which all subsidiary parts are kinematically excited (as in [19]) to one in which they all satisfy dynamic equations, for kinematic excitation is not mentioned explicitly.

In developing [31], I initially worked alone. With a personal background that was more algebraic, my approach to shaping the multibody dynamical equations had the flavor of a formal algebraic process. To give the structure of the system a quantitative characterization, I introduced a system graph. Although this was not the first usage of graph theory in mechanics -- the first may have been in the work of Kron several decades ago, but I have not attempted to trace back this part of the subject -- the way the system is structured by the graph and the way the incidence matrix and its left inverse are used in reducing the dynamical equations probably are among the more useful contributions of this publication. My reworking of the primitive equations was somewhat heavy-handed and I was initially guided through the several cycles of compaction of terms, followed by a decomposition into simpler groupings, more by algebraic intuition and aesthetics than by any physical interpretation of the terms. The development improved significantly when my collaboration began with J. Wittenburg, then a graduate student at UCLA. This has continued up to the present in as active a form as geographical constraints permit, to the point where it is almost impossible to separate our individual contributions to later work. Nevertheless, I can state that in [31] most of the interpretive insight, certain derivations, and the reconciliation of our work to [30] was due to Wittenburg.

Like [30], [31] postulates a tree structure and rotational connections between contiguous bodies (limited to exactly three degrees of freedom in its original form). The latter differs in its use of a system graph and in not pursuing cases of reduced freedom in the connections. Furthermore, rather than leaving results in a vector-dyadic form, it phrases them explicitly in terms of matrices of scalars. Associating physical quantities with the vertices or arcs of a graph leads to notational conventions which I believe are superior. The main result of this work was a matrix equation of the general form

$$R \, dy/dt = D(y,t) \tag{2a}$$

where y is a dynamical state vector of order three times the number of bodies in the system, whose elements are angular velocity components of the n bodies, and R is a (generally variable) coefficient matrix whose elements are derived explicitly from the basic properties of the bodies and system geometry. The matrix on the right side contains interaction forces and torques as well as those arising from external effects, together with a large number of miscellaneous terms (Coriolis, centripetal, etc.). Explicit results are gotten for the effective torque of an inverse square gravitational field. Clearly. Eq. 2a is in the form of the matrix algebraic equation $Ax = b$. It first must be solved for x (i.e., for y) by an appropriate technique, noting that R is symmetric and positive definite. Then Eq. 2a takes the form

$$dy/dt = Y(y, t) \tag{2b}$$

which can be used directly as the dynamical part of a digital simulation. The kinematical differential equations still must be added, although they were ignored in [30] as well as in [31]. The formalism first described in [31] has been further described, explained, and elaborated in [32], [33], [34], and [46].

APPLICATIONS AND GENERALIZATIONS

What followed thereafter for general-purpose dynamic simulations of multi-rigid-body systems based on these two publications of 1965 and 1966? Multibody dynamics is inseparable from computation, so we should look first at the progress of digital simulation. There are three major sources of information: company reports,

51

governmental reports, and the archival literature. The first, because they are usually unavailable to the general public and often are ephemeral, do not constitute publication in the traditional sense. Thus, I do not cite the several items of this kind of which I am aware. The second, typically designed for external use and readily available in libraries, should be considered at least "quasi-published". Unfortunately, a fair amount of work in the past decade seems to fall into the first category. One cannot assess the degree to which it rests upon or was influenced by the references discussed heretofore.

An early application is that of Farrell and Newton reported in [35] and [36] dated 1968 and 1969, respectively. These refer back to both [30] and [31], saying in [36] that "Hooker and Margulies astutely noted that the formulation lends itself to a systematic organization involving certain physically meaningful vector and matrix quantities, many of which are time-invariant." I second this observation, feeling that it is an important contribution of [30] even though, strictly speaking, this had been anticipated by Fischer. Farrell and Newton go on to say: "Further investigation by Roberson and Wittenburg produced a computational basis so explicit that the dynamic differential equations follow almost directly after specifying basic parameters of each structural member and of the orbit." Their program, described in [35], is indeed based on [31]. The thrust of [36], on the other hand, is to compare the results of a particular dynamic simulation using a Lagrangian formulation with another in which the spacecraft is modeled by a 26-body discrete system in accordance with the Eulerian formalism of [31]. It can be reported that the agreement between the results of the two methods were excellent, but it should be recognized that their discrete model owed its good quality largely to their perspicacity and insight into the art of discretization.

Other applications blossomed. Wittenburg devoted himself to the problem of the equilibrium of multibody systems in an inverse square field, first in his Ph.D. dissertation and then in [37] and [38], the latter devoted especially to some numerical considerations. Reference [39], also from his dissertation, reviews and further illuminates a number of points in [31]. It should be noted that [37] and, to a lesser degree, [39] both consider the relationship that exists between Lagrangian and Eulerian formulations. Wittenburg then based [40] and [31] in analyzing the effects of impulse on multibody systems. A work by Boland, Samin and Willems [41] (1973), concerned with the stability of equilibrium of certain multibody systems, also used [31] as a starting point.

As regards computer programming, I already have cited [35]. Another work is [42]. It refers to both [30] and [31], but actually builds on the former. Finally, [43] really gets down to practical matters and gives FORTRAN coding for a simulation program. This work is perhaps the last of the Jet Propulsion Laboratory series of reports by Likins and various coauthors written about the modeling of multi-rigid-body systems. It was at about that date that elastic effects began to develop their increasing prominence.

Perhaps the first important generalization of [30] was by Hooker [44] in 1970. His work has two major features. First, it shows the desirability of discarding the absolute angular velocities as dependent variables in favor of the angular velocity of a reference or "main" body together with the relative angular velocities relating all contiguous bodies. Second, it describes how the order of Eqs. 1 can be reduced when removing unwanted interaction torques. Both of these ideas have been incorporated in all subsequent work on the Roberson/Wittenburg formalism as well. In [44] the system is still assumed to be hinge for point-connected and the results are still left in vector-dyadic form.

As regards generalizations of [31], the restriction on interconnections to rotation about a hinge point is removed in [45]. Relative translation and rotation in the joint are treated in their full generality, leaving the assumption of a free structure as the only significant limitation of modern multibody Eulerian formalisms. This restriction, too, has been lifted recently, as described in [47]. Both of these advances are important when applying the formalism to the modeling of terrestrial vehicles, as has begun to be done in the mid-1970s. A discussion of a digital simulation program to implement the most general form of the Roberson/Wittenburg formalism is contained in [48]. Finally, a formalism has been constructed on a very similar conceptual basis by Ossenberg-Franzes. It differs mainly in its unique notational conventions for doing the necessary bookkeeping, which leave little or nothing to the user's memory, making explicit many properties (e.g., the resolution frame for vectors) that are implicit in the usual Roberson/Wittenburg development. The user must decide whether he wishes to master this notation, described in detail in [49] and in a more summary way in [50].

BIOMECHANICS

Meanwhile, a completely different application area was motivating its own developments in multibody dynamics. Perhaps this evolution should have stemmed from the work of Fischer early in the century, but in fact it began anew.

The first I have seen in the recent (post-Fischer) archival literature -- the aerospace literature, incidentally -- on the modeling of the human body as a system of interconnected rigid bodies is [51]. The author divides each arm and leg into the three obvious pieces, treating the hands as point masses, models the trunk as two bodies, an upper and a lower, and adds the head for a total of 15 bodies. Obviously, the system is a tree. Although the point is not made explicit, the bodies are all point or hinge connected, undergoing only relative rotation except for the neck, the connection between the head and upper trunk, which can undergo relative translation as well. (This is presumably the mode of relative motion mainly related to whiplash injuries.) These modeling assumptions are common to the other works in this area of biomechanics, although the body is not always modeled in so many pieces. Much of the literature is concerned with various kinds of walking problems and focuses specifically on the lower extremities attached to a one-body trunk. The gamut of modeling assumptions runs from the simplicity of [52], where the body is modeled as a single main body supported on two massless, rigid legs, to the relative sophistication of [51].

Another noteworthy characteristic of this body of literature is that it often emphasizes the inverse problem of mechanics, much like the 17th and 18th Century literature of mechanics. Because the "laws" of human body motion, e.g., walking, are not known, one must observe the motion and infer the forces and torques rather than postulate the latter and find the motion by solving a set of differential equations. This certainly underlies the way the equations are treated in this research area. When they are written and explicit, they are at the level of Eqs. 1 without further manipulation except to distinguish internal from external forces and torques. The latter are modeled *a priori*; the former are to be inferred.

I shall not review the pertinent literature of this field, extending from about 1967 to the present, for the dynamical developments do not go very far and the main complexities lie in the modeling of internal forces and torques, as well as the control laws for the interactions. The beginning seems to have been a work on the synthesis of a biped locomotion machine, citations to which, however, lead one only to an extended abstract, the full paper with substantive material apparently not having been published. (It undoubtedly was reflected in whole or part in a later published work by the same authors.) A work of 1976 [53] is worth mentioning because it demonstrates both the model (trunk plus two two-body legs) and the dynamical equations (the primitive equations left at a vector level, quite reminiscent of Sandler's equations in [27] in current usage, and because the reader who is genuinely interested can use this reference to carry himself back through all of the intervening literature.

Beyond this, I feel compelled to cite only two other papers because of their direct and explicit involvement with the multibody dynamical model. First, [54] actually discusses an algorithm for the solution of the inverse problem, set up as a problem in mathematical programming. Second, [55] has a more complete discussion of the dynamical equations than most other works in this field. Although its equations partake of many of the characteristics discussed under Applications and Generalizations above, they differ in one significant respect. All internal force and torque components are retained, including those corresponding to the kinematically-locked modes of relative motion. This obviates a somewhat complicated (and tedious, if the right path isn't used) reduction of the equations and allows them to keep a deceptively simple form.

Perhaps the two most recent works in this area that are especially noteworthy because of their completeness are [56] and [57]. In particular, they include computational logic as well as the conversion of trees into systems with closed loops and both add to the brief list of references I have given here.

MECHANISMS

Until about the past decade there has been far more attention paid to the kinematics of mechanisms than to their dynamics. The events that have begun to push the field toward dynamics are familiar ones: an increasing need for dynamic analysis motivated by increasing performance requirements on mechanisms and the rise of the digital computer as a tool to do the work. However, mechanism dynamics differs from the applications discussed previously in an important way. Rather than system interconnections with closed loops being exceptional, here they are the rule. To treat such systems, the traditional approach has been to identify generalized coordinates for a specific system and to treat this system as a special case, using the Lagrangian formulation of mechanics. This does not lend itself very well to the construction of general-purpose computer programs that can be used to treat broad classes of systems by one algorithm without any program modifications.

Because of the difference in approach and results, my comments on this subject will be brief. They are confined to a few of the closer points of contact. Citations are only illustrative, for an exhaustive survey is beyond the scope of this work.

A pertinent work from 1967 is that of Chace [58]. He refers to the problem of having to solve a set of linear algebraic equations at every integration step (true regardless of which dynamic formulation is used) as described following Eq. 2a above. His intention is to relieve this problem by using relative coordinates (i.e., a minimal set) rather than the full set of six coordinates for each body which then are subject to constraints. A generic form (summation over j, m is implied)

$$a_{ij}(x, \dot{x}, t)\ddot{x}_j + c_{im}(x)\lambda_m = g_i(x, \dot{x}, t) \tag{3}$$

is given for the dynamical equations, where the λ are Lagrange multipliers. These are consistent with equations gotten in later generalizations of [31], though arranged in slightly different form (i.e., not as the first order equation, Eq. 2b). He gets these from a Lagrangian approach. Perhaps the most significant difference from the path that starts with [31] is that the ingredients of Eq. 3 are not written out explicitly. Quantities needed for this equation come from kinetic and potential energy functions that are not developed explicitly for a general system. Thus, although Chace does describe a computer algorithm in general terms, I do not feel that the work in [58] can really be characterized as computer-ready. His introductory remarks mention several programs, generally in the unpublished category, having various degrees of generality.

In 1971, [59] continues along related lines. It includes some discussion of a computer program at a rather general level. Relative coordinates also are used in [60] to get dynamical equations. It is assumed that the interconnection topology of the bodies is a straight line, whence certain simplifications in notation are possible. At the conclusion, there is still some way to go to get explicit scalar equations having the form of Eq. 2b. Finally, I would cite [61], for its discussion of a unified approach is Lagrangian and, as usual, an algorithm for choosing generalized coordinates is not given in advance, but is left to the user. This work seems to be a good reflection of the state of the art in its area in 1972.

SUMMARY OF STATUS AND OUTLOOK

Eulerian dynamical formalisms are particularly well adapted to the needs of general-purpose digital computer programs for simulating the motion of many-rigid-body systems. Although some attention was given to such systems in the last century, marked interest in them has developed mainly during the two decades since 1958, the principal motivation being the needs for digital simulation of spacecraft modeled as systems of interconnected rigid or gyrostatic bodies. Such simulations later were broadened to encompass terrestrial systems such as high-speed trains. Two other application areas for similar systems have been biomechanics and the dynamics of mechanisms. Biomechanics concerns tree systems, while mechanisms normally involve closed loops and traditionally have been approached through constrained Lagrangian dynamical equations.

Stimulated by the aerospace/terrestrial vehicle application area, very flexible and general programs have been constructed, based on Eulerian formalisms. These can handle broad classes of systems algorithmically. Most are confined to cases where contiguous bodies undergo relative translation and the interconnection topology is a tree, but programs exist in which both of these restrictions are relaxed. Unfortunately, although the underlying analytical formalism has been documented to at least some extent, one must say that existing dynamic simulation computer programs are rather poorly documented in the archival literature and probably will remain so, inasmuch as many of them are confined to a cloistered existence behind the walls of industrial organizations.

In a real sense, one may regard this area of investigation as almost complete. Ironically, as such simulation programs have reached a state of mature development, interest in them as working tools has diminished. The "action" has moved elsewhere, into the area of multibody *flexible* systems. Nevertheless, physical systems do exist in which valid modeling can be done under the assumption of body rigidity. For these, the dynamic simulation formalisms and programs I have described should continue to serve a very useful purpose.

REFERENCES

1. C.A. Truesdell, "A program toward rediscovering the rational mechanics of the Age of Reason", *Arch. Hist. Exact Sci. 1* (1960-1962), 3-36.

2. L. Euler, *Mecanica sive Motus Scientia Analytice*, Petropoli, 1736 (2 volumes).

3. J. d'Alembert, *Traité de dynamique*, Paris, 1743.

4. R.E. Roberson, *Dynamics and Control of Rotating Bodies*, to be published.

5. L. Euler, "Découverte d'un nouveau principe de mécanique", *Mém. Acad. Sci. Berlin 6* (1750), 185-217, 1752. *Opera Omnia II/5*, 81-108.

6. L. Euler, "Du mouvement de rotation des corps solides autour d'un axe variable", *Mém. Acad. Sci. Berlin 14* (1758), 154-193, 1765. *Opera Omnia II/8*, 200-235.

7. L. Euler, "Du mouvement d'un corps solide quelconque lorsqu'il tourne autour d'un axe mobile", *Mém. Acad. Sci. Berlin 16* (1760), 176-227, 1767. *Opera Omnia II/8*, 313-356.

8. H. Resal, *Traité de mécanique générale*, Gauthier-Villars, Paris, 1873-1889 (5 volumes).

9. This item embraces a series of eight very lengthy papers on muscle statics and dynamics and the human gait by O. Fischer (one with coauthor W. Braune) published over the period 1893-1901 in *Abhandlungen der mathematisch-physischen Klasse der königlich sächsischen Gesellschaft der Wissenschaften*, volumes 20-23, 25, 26.

10. O. Fischer, "Über die reduzierten Systeme und die Hauptpunkte der Glieder eines Gelenkmechanismus und ihre Bedeutung für die Technische Mechanik", *Z. f. math. Phys. 47* (1902), 429-466.

11. O. Fischer, "Über die Bewegungsgleichungen Räumlicher Gelenksysteme", *Abh. k. sächs. Ges. Wiss., math.-phys. Cl. 29* (1906), 269-354.

12. O. Fischer, *Theoretische Grundlagen für eine Mechanik der lebenden Körper*, Teubner, Leipzig, 1906.

13. O. Fischer, *Kinematik organischer Gelenke*, Fried. Vieweg u. Sohn, Braunschweig, 1907.

14. G.M. Connell, "Degree-of-freedom requirements for hinged multibody satellites", *J. Spacecraft Rockets 6* (1969), 501-503.

15. G.M. Connell, "Equilibrium attitude error of gravity gradient satellites", *Astronaut. Acta 15* (1969-1970), 169-180.

16. T.L. Edwards and M.H. Kaplan, "Automatic spacecraft detumbling by internal mass motion", *AIAA J. 12* (1974), 496-502.

17. C. Grubin, "Docking dynamics for rigid-body spacecraft", *AIAA J. 2* (1964), 5-12.

18. P. Boland, J.C. Samin and P.Y. Willems, "Stability analysis of interconnected deformable bodies in a topological tree", *AIAA J. 12* (1974), 1025-1030.

19. R.E. Roberson, "Torques on a satellite vehicle from internal moving parts", *J. Appl. Mech. 25* (1958), 196-200. Supplement, pp. 287-288.

20. R.E. Roberson, "Principles of inertial control of satellite attitude", *Proc. IX International Astronautical Federation* (Amsterdam, 1958), Springer-Verlag, Wien, 1959, 33-43.

21. R.E. Roberson, "A unified analytical description of satellite attitude motions", *Astronaut. Acta 5* (1959), 347-355.

22. W. Schiehlen, "Über den Drallsatz für Satelliten mit im innern bewegten Massen", *ZAMM 46* (1966), T132-T134.

23. R.E. Roberson, "Attitude control of satellites and space vehicles", in *Advances in Space Science*, Vol. 2, F.I. Ordway, III (Ed.), Academic Press, New York, 1960, 351-436.

24. C. Grubin, "Dynamics of a vehicle containing moving parts", *J. Appl. Mech. 29* (1962), 486-488.

25. N.H. Beachley, "Inversion of spin-stabilized spacecraft by mass translation -- some practical aspects", *J. Spacecraft Rockets 8* (1971), 1078-1080.

26. M.J. Abzug, "Active satellite attitude control", Ch. 8 in *Guidance and Control of Aerospace Vehicles*, C.T. Leondes (Ed.), McGraw-Hill, New York, 1963, 331-425.

27. S.H. Sandler, "Dynamic equations for connected rigid bodies", *J. Spacecraft Rockets 4* (1967), 684-685.

28. B.T. Fang, "Kinetic energy and angular momentum about the variable center of mass of a satellite", *AIAA J. 3* (1965), 1540-1542.

29. C.F. Harding, "Manned Vehicles as solids with translating particles: I", *J. Spacecraft Rockets 2* (1965), 465-467.

30. W.W. Hooker and G. Margulies, "The dynamical attitude equations for an n-body satellite", *J. Astro. Sci. 12* (1965), 123-128.

31. R.E. Roberson and J. Wittenburg, "A dynamical formalism for an arbitrary number of interconnected rigid bodies, with reference to the problem of satellite attitude control", *Proc. Third Congress IFAC* (London, 1966), Butterworth, London, undated, Vol. 1, Book 3, Paper 46D, 9 pp.

32. R.E. Roberson and J. Wittenburg, Lectures 10-14 in *Dynamics of Flexible Spacecraft*, R.E. Roberson (Ed.), International Centre for Mechanical Sciences Courses and Lectures No. 103 (Udine, 1971), Springer-Verlag, Wien, 1972, 99-154.

33. J. Wittenburg, "The dynamics of systems of coupled rigid bodies. A new general formalism with applications", in *Sterodynamics*, Centro Internazionale Matematico Estivo, I Ciclo 1971, Bressanone (June 1971), G. Grioli (Ed.), Edizioni Cremonese, Roma, 1972, 273-352.

34. J. Wittenburg, *Dynamics of Systems of Rigid Bodies*, B.G. Teubner, Stuttgart, in press.

35. J.L. Farrell, J.K. Newton and J.J. Connelly, "Digital program for dynamics of non-rigid gravity gradient satellites", NASA Contractor Report CR-1119, Washington, 8 August 1968.

36. J.L. Farrell and J.K. Newton, "Continuous and discrete RAE structural models", *J. Spacecraft Rockets 6* (1969), 414-423.

37. J. Wittenburg, "Gleichgewichtslagen von Vielkörper-Satellitensystemen", *Abh. Braunschweigischen Wiss. Ges. 20* (1968), 198-278.

38. J. Wittenburg, "Die numerische Bestimmung stabiler Gleichgewichtslagen von Vielkörper-Satellitensystemen", *Ing.-Arch. 39* (1970), 201-208.

39. J. Wittenburg, "Die Differentialgleichungen der Bewegung für eine Klasse von Systemen starrer körper im Gravitationsfeld", *Ing.-Arch. 37* (1968), 221-242.

40. J. Wittenburg, "Der Stoss auf ein System gelenkig gekoppelter, starrer Körper", *Ing.-Arch. 39* (1970), 219-229.

41. P. Boland, J.C. Samin and P.Y. Willems, "Stability of interconnected rigid bodies", *Ing.-Arch. 42* (1973), 360-370.

42. G.E. Fleischer, "Multi-rigid-body attitude dynamics simulation", Jet Propulsion Laboratory, Technical Report 32-1516, Pasadena, California, 15 February 1971.

43. G.E. Fleischer and P.W. Likins, "Attitude dynamics simulation subroutines for systems of hinge-connected rigid bodies", Jet Propulsion Laboratory, Technical Report 32-1592, Pasadena, California, 1 May 1974.

44. W.W. Hooker, "A set of r dynamical attitude equations for an arbitrary n-body satellite having r rotational degrees of freedom", *AIAA J. 8* (1970), 1205-1207.

45. R.E. Roberson, "A form of the translational dynamical equations for relative motion in systems of many non-rigid bodies", *Acta Mech. 14* (1972), 297-308.

46. J. Wittenburg, "Automatic construction of nonlinear equations of motion for systems with many degrees of freedom", in *Gyrodynamics*, P.Y. Willems (Ed.), Springer-Verlag, Berlin, 1974, 10-22.

47. R.E. Roberson, "A multibody Eulerian dynamic simulation as a design tool for attitude dynamics and control", *Proc. Conference on Attitude and Orbit Control Systems* (Frascati, October 1977), to appear.

48. R.E. Roberson, "Digital dynamic simulation of vehicles modeled as many-body systems: current status", in *Vehicle System Dynamics*, to appear in 1977.

49. F.W. Ossenberg-Franzes, "Bewegungsgleichungen von Mehrkörpersystemen unter Berücksichtigung translatorischer und rotatorischer Differenzbewegungen", Dissertation, TU München, 1972.

50. F.W. Ossenberg-Franzes, "Equations of motion of multiple body systems with translational and rotational degrees of freedom", in *Gyrodynamics*, P.Y. Willems (Ed.), Springer-Verlag, Berlin, 1974, 201-207.

51. E.P. Hanavan, Jr., "A personalized mathematical model of the human body", *J. Spacecraft Rockets 3* (1968), 446-448.

52. A.A. Frank, "An approach to the dynamic analysis and synthesis of biped locomotion machines", *Med. Biol. Eng. 8* (1970), 465-476.

53. M.A. Townsend and T.C. Tsai, "Biomechanics and modeling of bipedal climbing and descending", *J. Biomech. 9* (1976), 227-239.

54. M. Townsend and A. Seireg, "Optimal trajectories and controls for systems of coupled rigid bodies", *J. Eng. Ind., Trans. ASME 94* B (1972), 472-482.

55. M.A. Townsend, "State space characterization of complex rigid body systems subject to control", *J. Eng. Ind., Trans. ASME 95* B (1973), 465-470.

56. M. Vukobratovic' and J. Stepanenko, "Mathematical models of general anthropormorphic systems", *Math. Biosci. 17* (1973), 191-242.

57. Yu. Stepanenko and M. Vukobratovic', "Dynamics of articulated open-chain active mechanisms", *Math. Biosci. 28* (1976), 137-170.

58. M.A. Chace, "Analysis of the time-dependence of multi-freedom mechanical systems in relative coordinates", *J. Eng. Ind., Trans. ASME 89* B (1967), 119-125.

59. M.A. Chace and Y.O. Bayazitoglu, "Development and application of a generalized d'Alembert force for multifreedom mechanical systems", *J. Eng. Ind., Trans. ASME 93* B (1971), 317-327.

60. T.A. Sherby and J.F. Chmielewski, "Generalized vector derivatives for systems with multiple relative motion", *J. Appl. Mech. 35* (1968), 20-24.

61. P.N. Sheth and J.J. Uicker, Jr., "IMP (Integrated Mechanisms Program), A computer-aided design analysis system for mechanisms and linkage", *J. Eng. Ind., Trans. ASME 94* B (1972), 454-464.

Part III

DEVELOPMENT OF LIQUID- AND SOLID-PROPELLANT ROCKETS, 1880-1945

Chapter 6

ORGANIZATION AND RESULTS OF THE WORK OF THE FIRST SCIENTIFIC CENTERS FOR ROCKET TECHNOLOGY IN THE USSR[*]

I. A. Merkulov[†]

Rocket technology is the technical base for contemporary achievements of cosmonautics. The USSR's successes in launching the first artificial Earth satellites and the first automatic interplanetary stations to the Moon, Venus and Mars, in accomplishing the first orbital manned flight and other outstanding accomplishments in the area of the study and exploration of space, were due to a significant degree to the early start of work on rocket technology.

At the IAF [International Astronautical Federation] congresses, beginning with the 18th Congress, which took place in Belgrade in 1967, in a number of reports, many questions on the history of Soviet space rocket technology have already been dealt with. In the present report, an attempt is made to tell about all the largest organizations that were working in the USSR in the 1920's and 1930's in the field of rocket technology. At the same time, it was kept in mind that in those years all the various work on the development of scientific rockets, combat rockets and jet engine planes was considered as one scientific problem. This problem was frequently designated by the term "the problem of jet propulsion." The theoretical bases for all these highly diverse branches of technology were included in a concept -- the theory of jet propulsion. Therefore, in dealing with the results of the activities of the first scientific centers, which worked in the field of jet propulsion, it has been recognized as expedient to note all the variety of their achievements in the field of the problem of jet propulsion.

N. I. TIKHOMIROV'S JET PROPULSION LABORATORY

The first Soviet scientific research and experimental design organization for the development of jet engines and rockets was established in Moscow in March 1921 on the initiative of the engineer-chemist, N.I. Tikhomirov, and at first was

---

[*] Presented at The Eleventh IAA History of Astronautics Symposium, Prague, Czechoslovakia, September 1977.

[†] Committee of the Soviet National Association of Natural Science and Technology Historians, USSR Academy of Sciences, Moscow, USSR.

called the "Laboratory for the Development of the Inventions of .I. Tikhomirov." It was located on Tikhvinskaya Street in the two-story building No. 3, where a pyrotechnical and chemical laboratory and a machine shop were set up [1, p. 101]. Its task was the development of rockets that operated on smokeless powder.

N.I. Tikhomirov and his talented assistant, V.A. Artemyev, who had begun working on the improvement of powder rockets even before the First World War, performed a large amount of work on the selection of the composition of smokeless powder, on working out the technology for the production of powder charges and on the study of the process of their combustion in jet engine chambers. They involved in this work a number of scientific institutes, mainly in Leningrad. And at the beginning of 1924, the first models of charges with nitrocellulose-trinitrotoluene (TNT) powder were produced. The biggest contribution to the development of the methods for obtaining such powder was made by O.G. Filippov and S.A. Serikov.

In March and April 1924, V.A. Artemyev conducted tests at the main artillery firing range in Leningrad of projectiles with rocket engines installed on them, which worked on smokeless powder. During the tests, 21 projectiles were launched and a ten-fold increase in distance was obtained in comparison to the initial projectiles without rocket engines [1, p 102].

Inasmuch as the basic work on rocket engines using smokeless powder was conducted in Leningrad in 1927, the laboratory was transferred completely to this city. In the documents of that time, it was frequently called N.I. Tikhomirov's Jet Propulsion Laboratory. Through the efforts of its staff in 1928, the first Soviet rockets using smokeless powder were developed. On 3 March 1928, successful launches took place at the Scientific Testing Artillery Firing Range (STAFR). As a result of the immense achievements in the development of rockets with solid-propellant engines (SPRE), N.I. Tikhomirov's Jet Propulsion Laboratory was expanded in June 1928, when it received the name the Gas Dynamics Laboratory (GDL).

THE GAS DYNAMICS LABORATORY

In 1928, the GDL was located on the STAFR and made widespread use of its laboratories and shops. In 1932, it obtained 12 rooms in the central section of the Main Admiralty and the Ioanovskiy Ravelin building in the Petropavlovsk Fortress. With each passing year, the number of GDL associates increased. In September of 1930, there were 23 people working there, at the end of 1931 -- 77, in December of 1932 -- 120 and at the beginning of 1933, the number of associates grew to nearly 200 people [1, pp 103-105]. In April of 1930, the permanent leader of the laboratory, N.I. Tikhomirov, died and B.S. Petropavlovskiy became chief.

An important event in the development of Soviet rocket technology was the organization, on 15 May 1929, within the make-up of the GDL upon the initiative of V.P. Glushko, of a subunit on electrical and liquid-propellant rocket engines [LPRE] and rockets. This subunit, which soon grew into a large branch, was the first state scientific organization for space-oriented rocket technology.

In 1931, in the make-up of the GDL, there were seven sectors operating: G.E. Langemak headed the sector on powder rockets, V.P. Glushko -- the sector on solid-propellant rockets [SPR], V.I. Dudakov -- the sector on aviation use of powder rockets, N.A. Dorovlev -- the mortar sector, I.I. Kulagin -- the sector on powder production, Ye. S. Petrov -- the production sector, and V.A. Krasovskiy -- the administrative management sector [1, p 105].

The GDL successfully continued the work begun by N.I. Tikhomirov on the development of rockets using smokeless powder. Under the supervision of B.S. Petropavlovskiy, a study was conducted on the laws of combustion of powder charges in rocket chambers, and the design elements of the rocket engines, the rockets and the launching devices, were worked out. In 1930-1931, in the GDL, 82mm and 132mm caliber powder rockets were developed that were intended to be used as jet propulsion rockets. And in the summer of 1932, the first official firings in the air of the RS-82 rockets from the I-4 aircraft were conducted. In that same year, tests were begun on arming the R-5 aircraft with the RS-82 and RS-132 rockets and the TB-1 aircraft with the 132 and 245mm caliber jet propulsion rockets [1, p 104].

Under V.A. Artemyev's supervision, in the GDL, flares, signal flares and propaganda rockets using smokeless powder engines were demonstrated.

In evaluating the results of the GDL's work in the field of powder rockets, Academician V.P. Glushko wrote: "By the end of 1933, the GDL had had large-scale achievements in the development of rockets using smokeless powder. In all, in the GDL by the end of 1933, nine types of various caliber and purpose rockets had been developed and adopted.

B.S. Petropavlovskiy, G.E. Langemak and V.A. Artemyev are the main authors of these developments begun earlier by N.I. Tikhomirov" [1, p 107].

In the GDL, work on rocket launching of the U-1, TB-1 and TB-3 aircraft was carried out successfully under the supervision of V.I. Dudakov. On 14 October 1933, state tests were conducted on the TB-1 aircraft equipped with smokeless rocket engines. Thanks to the action of the SPRE, the length of an aircraft's take-off run was reduced by 77 percent. work was also carried out on rocket catapulting and deceleration of aircraft [1, pp 104-105].

Highly successful was the GDL's work on electric rocket engines (ERE) and LPREs. In 1929-1931, V.P. Glushko designed the world's first electrothermal rocket engine and LPRE: the ORM, ORM-1 and ORM-2, which were developed and tested in those same years. In 1932, the ORM series of LPRE's from ORM-4 to ORM-22 were constructed.

In 1932, one of the leading scientists from TsaAGI [The Central Aerohydrodynamics Institute -- CAHI], Professor V.P. Vetchinkin, attended the ORM-9 engine tests in the GDL. In his own review, he wrote: "In the GDL, the main part of the work for the realization of the rocket -- the solid propellant jet propulsion engine -- was performed ... From this point of view, the GDL's achievements (mainly those of Engineer Glushko) must be recognized as brilliant" [5, p 13].

Simultaneous with the development of the LPRE in the GDL, work was carried out on the development of rockets. In 1932, a plan for a rocket based on the design of Glushko, the RLA-100 with a lift altitude of 100 km, was developed there. Its launch weight amounted to 400 kg. The nitric acid LPRE with a reinforced universal joint should have developed a thrust of 3,000 k during an operating period of 20 sec. The production of three sets of the RLA-100 rockets was started at the Machine Building Plant in the city of Perm, but was never completed [17, p 712].

In order to speed up the flight tests of the engines with thrusts up to 300 kg, checks of the rocket launch and control methods were developed in the GDL in 1933, and stand test firings of the RLA-1 and RLA-2 rockets for vertical flight to an altitude of 2-4 km from the launch table without a guidance device were prepared and conducted. Plans were made and work begun on the RLA-3 guided rocket. Within its body there was an instrument compartment with two gyroscopic devices, which guided it using pneumatic servo devices and the mechanical drafts of two pairs of air vanes located in the tail unit.

In 1933, there were test stand firings of the ORM-23 through ORM-52 engines in the GDL. The results of the GDL's work on the development of LPRE's were expressed in the following manner by Academician V.P. Glushko:

> "By the end of 1933, in the GDL, they overcame the basic difficulties associated with ensuring the reliable operation of LPRE's. Hypergolic and pyrotechnical ignition, centrifugal burners, a spirally finned nozzle dynamically cooled by the fuel component, the internal cooling of the walls of the combustion chamber by the fuel screen, the successfully selected construction materials made it possible to achieve the repeated operation of engines at a pressure in the chamber of 20-25 ATA and a specific impulse of 200-210 sec using a nitric acid-kerosene fuel. This was supported by the official tests conducted in 1933 on the ORM-50 engine with a thrust of 150 kg and the ORM-52 with a thrust of 300 kg, which were intended for rockets, hydroplane torpedoes and aircraft. Over the course of 10 launches, the ORM-50 model worked 314 sec and remained whole. The ORM-52 model worked 533 sec. during 29 launches and maintained its operations capacity [3, pp 112-113]".

As a result of the work of the GDL staff, the foundations for subsequent Soviet rocket engine construction were laid. From inside the GDL walls came the basic staffs that formed the creative collective of the Experimental Design Bureau, the GDL-EDB, which developed the powerful LPRE's for all Soviet launch vehicles that have flown into space.

JET PROPULSION STUDY GROUP

In September 1931, at the Central Council of the USSR Osoaviakhim [Society for Promoting Defense and Aviation and Chemical Construction], within the make-up of the Air Technology Bureau, the Jet Propulsion Study Group [GIRD -- JPSG] was organized. Its first chairman was F.A. Tsander. The group promoted scientific propaganda on the problems of rocket technology and paid a lot of attention to the training of rocket construction personnel. In the spring of 1932, in the JPSG engineering and design courses on rocket technology were organized -- a type of short-term institute.

In April of 1932, the JPSG obtained space in the basement of building No. 19 on Sadovo-Spasskaya Street in Moscow, which became the birthplace of the first Soviet liquid propellant rockets [LPR]. There the necessary experimental and testing and production base was established and the basic work was conducted. The successful activities of the JPSG led to the fact that in 1932 the group was transformed from a social organization into a state scientific research organization, which was headed up by S.P. Korolev since 1 May 1932 [25].

Within the JPSG, four design units were organized. The first developed the LPRE's, and in particular, the ORM-2 oxygen alcohol aviation LPRE, and designed the GIRD-10 LPR. This unit was headed up by Tsander. The second JPSG unit, led by the experienced aviation designer, M.K. Tikhonravov, designed LPR's and LPRE's and developed the pumping unit for feeding fuel into the LPRE chamber.

The third unit, headed up by Yu. A. Pobedonostsev, developed and tested on the stand and in flight the world's first ramjet engines -- the GIRD-08. The JPSG's fourth group, headed by S.P. Korolev and Ye. S. Shchetinkov, designed the world's first winged LPR, the GIRD-06, and began conducting flights tests on the BICh-11 airframe designed by B.I. Cheranovskiy, for which Tsander's unit developed LPRE's [7-13].

All four units were part of the JPSG's first department, which was entrusted with the scientific research and testing and experimentation work. The Second Department took care of the administrative and managerial work. The third department was the mass organization department and conducted scientific and technical propaganda on rocket technology. The fourth department was called the JPSG's pilot production department [11, 12].

The USSR's first rocket range for test flights of rockets was established in the forest in the vicinity of Nakhabino Station outside Moscow.

The first Soviet LPR was the "09" rocket designed by M.K. Tikhonravov. Its flight on 17 August 1933, represented an important step in the formation of Soviet rocket production. On 6 November, the second flight of the updated model of the rocket, designated "13," took place. And on 25 November they launched in Nakhabino the second JPSG rocket, the design of which was started under the supervision of Tsander, the GIRD-10. During 1933, the JPSG staff designed and built two more LPR's, the "07" and the "05," which subsequently made several flights. The latter, which had completed flights using the 12k oxygen-alcohol LPRE, is well-known under the name "Aviavnito" [The All-Union Scientific and Engineering Technology Society of the Aviation Industry].

The example of the tests on the first LPR, the GIRD-09 in 1933, tells convincingly of the care exercised during the testing of the rockets. In the archives, 17 documents on the testing of the rocket units, 3 on the testing of the engines, 25 on the rocket combustion tests and 7 on rocket launches have been preserved [17]. In the following year, tests were continued and a number of ground tests were conducted, as well as three rocket launches into the air [18]. In those cases the rockets ascended to an altitude of 1,500 m.

The solution by the JPSG staff of the problem of developing an LPR exerted a great deal of influence on the further development of rocket technology in the Soviet Union.

JET PROPULSION SCIENTIFIC RESEARCH INSTITUTE

The JPSG's successful work on LPR's and the GDL's work on the development of LPRE's and SPR's were the basis for the organization within the Soviet Union of the world's first Jet Propulsion Scientific Research Institute (JPSRI). It was established by a resolution of the USSR Council of Labor and Defense in October 1933, based on the GDL and the JPSG, and joined the system of the People's Commissariat for Heavy Industry. In the JPSRI, they developed a broad front of complex scientific research and planning and design work on all the basic directions of rocket technology.

In the JPSRI, they continued the work begun in the JPSG on LPR's. Flight tests were conducted on the "13" rocket, during which it reached an altitude of 1,500 m, and there were launches of the "07" and "Aviavnito" rockets. Four more LPR's were designed in 1936-1937, with various LPRE's, based on the "09" rocket designed by M.K. Tikhonravov.

The JPSRI staff continued the GDL's work on smokeless powder rocket engines. Here, they completed the development of the RS-82 and RS-132 powder rockets, which were intended to be installed on aircraft. They were installed on the IL-2 [Ilyushin], Yak [Yakovlev] and La [Lavochkin] aircraft.

In the JPSRI, they also developed the BM-13-16 mobile rocket launches, the so-called guardian mortars that played an exceptionally large role during the years of the Second World War.

A large achievement of the JPSRI staff was the development of the nitric acid-kerosene and oxygen-alcohol LPRE's. The staff of LPRE specialists, trained in the GDL, continued on the JPSRI under the supervision of Glushko to develop the family of ORM engines.

Over the years 1934-1938, single-chamber and twin-chamber designs with thrusts of up to 600 kg were developed. The ORM-53 through -70 engines operated on nitric acid, while the ORM-101 and -102 used tetranitromethane as the oxidizer. Of particularly great importance was, at that time, the development of the ORM-65 engine, which was officially tested in 1936. It operated on nitric acid and kerosene. The amount of its thrust was controlled during the flight from 50 to 175 kg. It was intended for the RP-318-1 rocket plane and the 212 winged rocket, both designed by Korolev. The ORM-65 engine was the homeland's best LPRE of the time.

In the JPSIR, in 1937, they developed the first GG-1 gas generator. It produced 40-70 hp from gas with a pressure of 20-25 ATA and a temperature of 450-580 degrees C for supplying power to a turbine or a piston engine, which start the fuel pumps going.

In the JPSRI, they completed the construction of the world's first winged LPR, the "06," designed by Korolev. And on 23 May 1934, it completed its first test flight. The institute's staff designed and built three more types of winged rockets with LPRE's: the 216, the 212 and the 301 and one winged rocket with an SPRE [15].

The most interesting rocket was the 212 model designed by Korolev. It had automatic launching, stabilization and guidance systems. The wing span amounted to 8.06 meters and the area to 4.7 m^2. The payload size was 30 kg. The estimated flying range was 50 km [15].

In the JPSRI, under the supervision of Yu. A. Pobedonostsev and M.S. Kisenko, three series of flight tests of the "08" ramjet engine, placed in the body of an artillery shell, were conducted in the years 1934-1936 [26].

In the JPSRI, under the supervision of Pobedonostsev, they developed and operated successfully the USSR's first supersonic wind tunnel with a (Töpler) unit, which made it possible to visualize the gas flow.

Extremely interesting was the work on the development of and the flight tests for the homeland's first rocket plane, the RP-318-1, designed by Korolev. In 1937-1938, ground tests of this rocket plane were conducted using the ORM-65 LPRE. And in 1939-1940, the JPSRI, in conjunction with the Special Design Department (SDD) of the "Aviakhim" [Aviation Chemicals] Plant, conducted flight tests of the RP-318-1 using the RDA-1-150 engine, a modification of the ORM-65. On 28 February 1940, a rocket plane piloted by the SDD test pilot, V.P. Fedorov, was lifted in to the air on a tow line behind the R-5 airplane. Having separated from the tow plane, Fedorov turned on the LPRE at an altitude of 2,600 m. The rocket plane, gathering speed, overtook the aircraft and flew on ahead with confidence.

These tests became a significant event in the history of human flight in rocket-propelled aircraft.

In the JPSRI, they developed and successfully tested in flight the RDD-604 and RAS-5521 rockets designed by L.S. Dushkin. They became the largest LPR's developed and tested in the USSR until the end of 1940.

These rockets had the KRD-600 compound [combined] engine. It was an LPRE, into whose chamber nitrocellulose powder was stuffed. During a launch of the engine, at first the solid fuel is burned. At the same time, the plugs covering the outlet spill ports are burned up. By the end of the combustion of the powder, when the pressure in the combustion chamber was less than that in the tanks with the liquid fuel components -- nitric acid and kerosene, these latter items began to flow into the chamber and the engine shifted from solid-propellant operation to liquid-propellant operation. During the combustion of the powder, the maximum thrust was equal to 3,850 kg. During the LPRE operation phase, the thrust amounted to 1,278 kg.

The RDD-604 rockets had a launch weight of 180-187 kg, including a payload of 30 kg. The fuel tanks system with the solid-propellant gas generator (SPGG) weighed 52-59 kg. The rocket was launched at an angle of 55 degrees to the horizon using a carriage whose ramp had a length of 8.5 m [19].

In January of 1940, flight tests of 8 RDD-604 rockets took place. The first two rockets, launched on 5 and 9 January, completed successful flights over distances of 17 km and 17.5 km. Particularly successful were the flights completed by rockets nos. 5, 7 and 8, which covered a distance of more than 19 km [19].

The successful flights of five LPR's over distances of 17-20 km represented a significant achievement for Soviet rocket technology on a level with the highest achievements of the world's rocket production of that time.

In 1940-1941, three more series of flight tests were conducted on the 604 rocket. During these tests, the rockets flew over distances of 20 km.

The 521 rocket was intended to be launched both from the ground and from an aircraft. Its design was similar to that of the 604 rocket.

On 6 August 1940, there were flight tests of 5 RAS-521 rockets [20]. They were launched into the air from a plane standing on the ground. In order for them to fly the maximum distance, it was necessary to launch them at an angle of 55 degrees. But, because of the limited dimensions of the firing range, the rockets were launched at an angle of 30 degrees and flew a distance of 11 km. The tests of the rockets reinforced the large successes achieved in the development of rocket production during the testing of the RDD-604 rockets.

STRATOSPHERIC COMMITTEE

After the JPSG became part of the JPSRI, within the Military Science Committee (MSC) of the Central Council of the USSR Osoaviakhim, in January of 1934, they organized a Jet Propulsion Section, which the social activist group of the Moscow JPSG joined. I.A. Merkulov was chosen head of the section and O.S. Oganesov was chosen as his deputy. The active work in the section was carried out by Professors K.L. Bayev, V.P. Vetchinkin, K.A. Putilov, and engineers V.P. Glushko, L.S. Dushkin, G.E. Langemak, A.F. Nistratov, V.N. Prokofyev and M.K. Tikhonravov.

In March of 1934, the Osoaviakhim Central Council, desiring to involve the broad circles of the scientific and technical community in creative participation in the the study and exploration of the stratosphere, organized a Committee for the Study of the Stratosphere, which for short was called the Stratospheric Committee. This committee operated successfully for more than four years. The Jet Propulsion Section became a part of it.

In the Jet Propulsion Section, six rockets were designed, three of which were built. They were the rocket designed by A.I. Polyarnyy using an oxygen-alcohol LPRE, which was originally designated the R-1 and later received the designation "Osoaviakhim," the rocket designed by A.F. Nistratov and I.A. Merkulov (the R-2) with an LPRE operating on a three-component fuel (liquid oxygen, alcohol and water), which was called the three-component rocket -- TR-2, and the ramjet rocket (the R-3) designed by Merkulov, called the ramjet rocket -- VR-3. The interesting projects developed by Ye. S. Parayev and V.N. Prokofyev for LPR's unfortunately, were not realized. The sixth was a design for a three-stage rocket with an SPRE for all the stages, developed by A.F. Nistratov and received a high evaluation from Professor V.P. Vetchinkin [24].

The Jet Propulsion Section of the Osoaviakhim Central Council was a social scientific organization. Its staff successfully conducted theoretical research, design work, the publication of collected works entitled "Jet Propulsion," and scientific propaganda on rocket technology and cosmonautics. The section trained engineers in rocket technology. But the Osoaviakhim Central Council's Stratospheric Committee did not have its own production base and therefore, the section's developments that were of great interest were handed over to industry for further development. Thus, in 1936, the unit headed up by A.I. Polyarnyy, in its entirety, including all the designers, mechanics and workers, joined the newly organized KB-7 [design bureau].

In 1937, the group of specialists working on the theoretical problems of ramjet engines and on designing ramjet rockets went to the "Aviakhim" Plant, where the designs developed in the Jet Propulsion Section were realized. The standing firing tests of the three-component LPRE rockets, the TR-2, were conducted under the supervision of Nistratov in the ONIL [Joint Scientific Research Laboratory -- JSRL].

"AVIAKHIM"

One more collective of scientists and designers, which conducted work on rocket technology, was organized on the initiative of A. Ya. Shcherbakov, the Special Design Department (SDD) of the "Aviakhim" Plant. The SDD was established to develop a number of interesting inventions in the field of high-altitude aviation, which were produced in the Jet Propulsion Group of the Kharkov Council of Osoaviakhim. The SDD specialists developed the design of the sealed cockpits, which were installed on mass-produced aircraft. They implemented the method proposed by A. Ya. Shcherbakov of high-altitude towing of chains of gliders behind an aircraft.

In 1937, the work on ramjet rockets and aviation ramjet engines was transferred from the Osoaviakhim Central Council, Jet Propulsion Section to the SDD. Sixteen ramjet rockets were built there and in the period from February through May 1939, their flight tests were conducted at the airfield near Planernaya Station outside Moscow. The rockets built at the "Aviakhim" Plant were the world's first ramjet rockets. They were also the first Soviet two-stage rockets.

In the years 1939-1940, the world's first aviation ramjets, designed by Merkulov, the DM-2 and DM-4, were developed and flight-tested at the "Aviakhim" Plant [22]. These engines were installed as auxiliary engines on the I-152 and I-153 aircraft designed by N.N. Polikarpov. For the ground tests and completion of the engines, a special steel wind tunnel, the AT-2, with a length of 12 m and an operational section diameter of 1 m, was constructed. The official tests of the I-152 aircraft with two DM-2 ramjets were conducted over the Central Airfield M.V. Frunze in Moscow on 25 January 1940. In all, over the period of the flight tests, 74 flights were made. They were carried out by the test pilots P. Ye. Loginov, A.V. Davydov, A.I. Zhukov and N.A. Sapotsko. (The results of the flight test were dealt with in detail in Professor Yu. A. Pobedonostsev's report at the 19th IAF Congress in 1968).

In 1939-1940, the SDD, together with the JPSRI, conducted flight tests on the RP-318-1 rocket plane designed by S.P. Korolev. The chief engineers for these flight tests were A. Ya. Shcherbakov and A.V. Pallo. The tests of the rocket plane were conducted by SDD pilot V.P. Fedorov.

KB-7 DESIGN BUREAU

In 1936, the KB-7 Design Bureau was organized in Moscow to develop LPR's. It was located on Aviation Pereulok, where a well-equipped experimental base had been constructed. The bureau's chief was L.K. Korneyev. His deputy was one of the pupils and closest assistants of F.A. Tsander, the talented scientist and designer A.I. Polyarnyy who was the scientific supervisor of all of KB-7's developments.

KB-7 continued the work on the Osoaviakhim rocket, which retained its own designation there (it was also designated the R-06).

On 11 April 1937, the Osoaviakhim rocket completed its first successful flight [35, p 4]. On 25 August 1937, flight tests for more models took place in Leningrad. These were the first official tests of a Soviet LPR.

The rockets were launched at an angle to the horizon of from 65 degrees to 88 degrees. In each of the launches, the engine operated for 1-18 sec. During the third and fourth launches -- at an angle of 70 degrees and 65 degrees, respectively -- the flight range amounted to 6 km and 5 km, respectively [27, p 11].

In KB-7, five more types of LPR's were constructed. All of them had oxygen-alcohol LPRE's. The design of one of them -- the R-03 -- was begun by L.K. Korneyev, even before the establishment of KB-7. The bureau's staff, under the supervision of A.I. Polyarnyy, developed the design of this rocket in detail, constructed 10 models of it and tested them in April of 1937, together with the R-06 rocket.

For the purpose of seeking methods of ensuring the stability of the rockets in flight, in KB-7 they constructed the R-04 and ANIR-5 LPR's and the R-07m powder rocket.

The R-04 device was a rotating rocket. It was supposed to rotate on the launching carriage at up to 2,000 rpm. Also, in order to have additional rotation during the flight, four powder charges were installed in its nose section.

In 1938, from 25 to 28 February, tests of 6 R-03 and 2 R-06 rockets took place in Pavlograd. In addition, 6 R-07m powder rockets were tested. All the rockets were launched at an angle of 65 degrees or 75 degrees. Four R-06 rockets completed successful flights at a distance of from 4,000 m (R-03-7) to 6,800 m (R-03-8). The Osoaviakhim R-06 rockets underwent their last flight tests on 28 February, having completed a flight at a distance of 3,100 m [27, pp 60-70].

In the document on the tests of these rockets, the following was stated as a conclusion:

"It can be stated that KB-7 in its own work with the LP's, developed on the basis of the theory of the Soviet scientist, K.E. Tsiolkovsky, attained significant achievements" ... [27, pp 60-70].

In 1938, six ANIR-5 rockets were prepared in KB-7. In order to increase the flight stability, in accordance with P.I. Ivanov's suggestion, gyroscopes were installed on them which were firmly attached to the body of the rocket. Research on the movement of the rockets with the gyroscopes was conducted by Academician A.N. Krylov. In its own design, the ANIR-5 rocket resembled the R-06 rocket, in which a gyroscope was installed and corresponding changes were made to the stabilizers. Prior to the launch, the gyroscope was rotating at the rate of 19,000 rpm.

Of interest was the R-05 rocket, developed to reach an altitude of 50 km. It was proposed that its stability in flight be ensured by increasing the take-off velocity from the carriage of 40-50 m/s using two launching SPRE's with a total thrust of 1,250 kg/s. The R-05 rocket was intended for the USSR Academy of Sciences' Geophysics Institute, whose director, Academician O. Yu. Schmidt, expressed great interest in it and participated in the discussion of its parameters and instrumentation.

In KB-7, four more LPR designs were developed: the ANIR-6, the ENIR-7, the R-05g and the design for a two-stage R-10 rocket, with a calculated flight altitude of 100 km.

THE "OSOAVIAKHIM" JET PROPULSION GROUP

The development of rocket technology in the USSR was of a broad public nature. In the 1920's and 1930's, in the study of the theory of jet propulsion, its development and first design research on rocket craft included a large number of scientists, inventors, engineers and a particularly large number of interplanetary flight enthusiasts. In 1924, in Moscow, the Society for Interplanetary Communications was formed. In many cities of the Soviet Union, mainly ones with institutions of higher learning, they began to establish groups to study the theory of interplanetary communications. Several of these groups operated successfully over the course of a number of years and from them came the specialists who subsequently became the prominent scientists and designers in the field of rocket technology. For example, in Kharkov in 1925, on the initiative of A. Ya. Shcherbakov, a group of rocket technology enthusiasts was organized at the Kharkov Aviation Institute. This group corresponded with K.E. Tsiolkovsky and carried out successful work on the study of the theoretical bases for rocket technology. A similar group operated successfully under the the supervision of Professor N.A. Rynin in Leningrad. A similar group was organized at the Moscow Aviation Institute under the supervision of F.A. Tsander.

From the beginning of the 1930's, the Osoaviakhim -- a volunteer society and one of whose main tasks was the promotion of the development of aviation -- conducted a lot of work on scientific propaganda on rocket technology and the theory of space flight.

In September 1931, as has already been mentioned above, the JPSG was organized in Moscow within the system of the USSR Osoaviakhim Central Council. In November of the same year, a JPSG (GIRD) was organized within the system of the Leningrad Oblast Council of Osoaviakhim (LenGIRD). Soon after the Moscow and Leningrad groups, JPSG's were organized in many other cities of the Soviet Union. JPSG work was carried out in Kharkov, Gorkiy, Yerevan, Baku, Kiev, Tbilisi, Rostov-on-the-Don and dozens of other cities. Supervision of the activities of all the JPSG's was implemented by the Moscow group headed by S.P. Korolev, which, as of 1932, began to be called the Central [group] -- CJPSG as well.

After the transfer of the CJPSG into the make-up of the JPSRI and the organization in Moscow of the Jet Propulsion Section into the make-up of the Military Science Committee of the Osoaviakhim Central Council, in other cities, within the make-up of the Military Science Committee of the Osoaviakhim, jet propulsion sections or groups were established which continued and developed the work begun in the JPSG's.

The Osoaviakhim jet propulsion sections in the cities of Leningrad, Kharkov and Gorkiy operated the most successfully.

The LenGIRD was headed up by the talented engineer, V.V. Razumov. The staff of the LenGIRD built and tested in flight a number of powder rockets designed by V.V. Razumov with SPRE's designed by V.A. Artemyev and made plans for an LPR based on a design by V.V. Razumov using a rotation LPRE designed by A.N. Shtern, which operated on liquid oxygen and benzene.

After its reorganization and transfer into the make-up of the Leningrad MSC, the Jet Propulsion Section completed the construction of V.V. Razumov's LPR, conducted stand firing tests of its engine and in order to check the rocket's stability, implemented its twisting using an SPRE. Then the Leningrad Jet Propulsion Section, under the supervision of Professor M.V. Machinskiy, designed another series of original LPR's.

Of extreme interest were the activities of the Kharkov JPSG and the Jet Propulsion Section of the Kharkov MSC. A lot of energy in the organization of the work on rocket technology there was expended by A. Ya. Shcherbakov, Professor Dakhov and the young enthusiast, V.I. Rozov. The Kharkov Jet Propulsion Section built a series of powder rockets, tested them in wind tunnels and in flight. Academician G.F. Proskura rendered a great deal of assistance to the Jet Propulsion Section of the Kharkov MSC [21].

The jet propulsion group of the Gorkiy MSC gathered together a large group of scientists, engineers and young inventors.Particularly active in the Gorkiy MSC were Professor K.A. Putilov and the talented inventor, B.R. Pastukhovskiy. In the

Gorkiy MSC, in accordance with a design by engineer Ivanov, they built an original design LPR.

The MSC's in other cities of the USSR conducted propaganda work on the scientific bases of rocket technology and cosmonautics.

A great service of the JPSG's and Osoaviakhim MSC's was the mobilization of broad circles of the scientific, engineering and inventors' communities for the working out of questions on the use of rocket technology to solve pressing problems of that time -- research on the stratosphere and the development of high-altitude aviation, which at the same time were of paramount importance also as the first step on the path to the realization of flights into space.

The brief enumeration listed here of the scientific research and experiment and design organizations, which worked on the development of rockets, speaks of the wide scale which the work in the field of rocket production attained in the 1930's in the USSR. The work of the first scientific centers for rocket technology is a graphic example of how, in the USSR in the first years of the country's industrialization, a successful struggle was carried on for technological progress and for the development of the most advanced and progressive branches of science and technology.

The results of the work of the first Soviet organizations for rocket technology made it possible to draw highly substantial conclusions:

In the 1930's, in the USSR, reliable designs for LPRE's, which operated on a variety of fuels with a high boiling point and cryogenic fuels, were developed.

Over the first decade in the development of Soviet rocket production, rockets of all the well-known types -- single-stage and two-stage, ballistic and winged, ground-launched and air-launched -- were built and tested in flight.

In the USSR, rockets were developed with all the well-known types of jet propulsion engines -- solid-propellant rocket engines (SPRE) and hybrid engines that worked on solid fuel and liquid oxidizers, LPRE's and ramjets.

In 1939-1940, in the USSR, flight tests were conducted on piloted craft with aviation ramjets and LPRE's.

BIBLIOGRAPHY

1. Glushko, V.P., "The Role of the Gas Dynamics Laboratory (GDL) in the Development of Rocket Technology," Vestnik an SSSR, 1972, No 2, pp 100-108.

2. Glushko, V.P., "The Contribution of the Leningrad Gas Dynamics Laboratory (GDL) to the Development of Rocket Technology. Report to the 13th International Congress on the History of Science (Moscow, 1971)," in the collection "Iz istorii aviatsii i kosmonavtiki" [From the History of Aviation and Cosmonautics], Issue 17-18, Moscow, 1972, pp 35-43.

2. Glushko, V.P., "The Development of Liquid-Propellant Rocket Engine Production and its Influence on Science and Technology in the USSR," Vestnik an SSSR, 1973, No 12, pp 110-121.

4. Glushko, V.P., "The Development of Soviet Space Rocket Engine Production," Izvestiya an SSSR, Energetika i Transport [Power Engineering and Transportation], 1974, No 5, pp 3-28.

5. Glushko, V.P., "Raketnyye dvigateli GDL-OKB" [The Rocket Engines of the Gas Dynamics Laboratory's Experimental Design Bureau], Moscow, 1975.

6. Ivanov, N.V., "The First Soviet Rocket Technology Organization," in the book "Idei Tsiolkovskogo i problemy kosmonavtiki" [Tsiolkovsky's Ideas and the Problems of Cosmonautics], Moscow, 1974, pp 67-72.

7. Tikhonravov, M.K., Biryukov, Yu. V., "The Realization of K.E. Tsiolkovsky's Ideas in the Work of the GIRD [Jet Propulsion Study Group]," in the book "Idei Tsiolkovskogo i problemy kosmonavtiki," Moscow, 1974, pp 58-66.

8. Tikhonravov, M.K., "The Role of K.E. Tsiolkovsky in the Development of Rocket and Space Technology. Report to the 13th International Congress on the History of Science (Moscow, 1971)," in the collection "Iz istorii aviatsii i kosmonavtiki," Issue 17-18, Moscow, 1972, pp 186-193.

9. Pobedonostsev, Yu. A., Merkulov, I.A., "The Realization of K.E. Tsiolkovsky's Ideas in the Work of the GIRD," Trudy vi chteniy K.E. Tsiolkovskogo. Sektsiya "Problemy raketnoy i kosmicheskoy tekhniki" [The Problems of Rocket and Space Technology], Moscow, 1973, pp 19-29.

10. Biryukov, Yu. V., "K.E. Tsiolkovsky and the First Steps of Soviet Rocket Production," in the book "Idei Tsiolkovskogo i problemy kosmonavtiki," Moscow, 1974, pp 73-79.

11. Biryukov, Yu. V., Komarov, V.M., "On the Matter of the Organization and Activities of the Jet Propulsion Study Group of the USSR Osoaviakhim Central Council," in the collection "Iz istorii aviatsii i kosmonavtiki," 1974, Issue 24, pp 52-81.

12. Pobedonostsev, Yu. A., Merkulov, I.A., "On the 40th Anniversary of the Moscow Jet Propulsion Study Group (GIRD [JPSG])," in the collection "Iz istorii aviatsii i kosmonavtiki," Issue 24, Moscow, 1974, pp 8-16.

13. Raushenbakh, B.V., Biryukov, Yu. V., "JPSG Chief S.P. Korolev -- the Founder of Practical Cosmonautics," in the collection "Iz istorii aviasii i kosmonavtiki," Issue 24, Moscow, 1974, pp 17-24.

14. Korolev, S.P., "The Flight of Jet Propulsion Craft in the Stratosphere," Trudy vsesoyuznoy konferentsii po izucheniyu stratosfery, Leningrad-Moscow, 1935, pp 849-855.

15. Korolev, S.P., "Winged Rockets and Their Use for Manned Flight," in the book "Pionery raketnoy tekhniki. [The Pioneers of Rocket Technology] Vetchinkin, Glushko, Korolev, Tikhonravov," Moscow, 1972, pp 452-475.

16. Sokolskiy, V.N., "A Concise Outline of the Development of Rocket Technology (up to the End of the Second World War)," in the collection "Iz istorii aviatsii i kosmonavtiki," Issue 26, Moscow, 1975, pp 113-144.

17. Arkhiv an SSSR [Archives of the USSR Academy of Sciences], Sec. 4, Cat. 14, D. 50.

18. Ibid, D. 53

19. Ibid, D. 75.

20. Ibid, D. 78.

21. Ibid, D. 213.

22. Shcherbakov, A. Ya., "Ramjet Flight Tests on Planes Designed by N.N. Polikarpov in 1939-1940," in the collection "Iz istorii aviatsii i kosmonavtiki," Issues 3, Moscow, 1965, pp 40-49.

23. Merkulov, I.A., "The Realization of K.E. Tsiolkovsky's Ideas in the First Soviet Rockets," Trudy x chteniy K.E. Tsiolkovskogo. Sektsiya "Problemy raketnoy i kosmicheskoy tekhniki," Moscow, 1977.

24. Merkulov, I.A., Nistratov, A.F., Romanenko, B.N., "The Realization of K.E. Tsiolkovsky's Ideas in the Work of the Osoaviakhim Central Council's Jet Propulsion Section," Trudy ix chteniy K.E. Tsiolkovskogo. Sektsiya "Problemy raketnoy i kosmicheskoy tekhniki, Moscow, 1975, pp 147-155.

25. Tsentralnyy arkhiv dosaaf SSSR. Prikazy po lichnomu sostavu. Otdel vozdushnogo flota. Prikaz po tss Osoaviakhima ot 14 iyulya 1932 G. [The Central Archives of the USSR Voluntary Society for the Promotion of the Army, Air Force and Navy. Orders Regarding Personnel. The Air Force Department. The Order Regarding the Osoaviakhim Central Council of 14 July 1932].

26. Merkulov, I.A., "The First Experimental Research on JPSG Ramjets," in the Collection "Iz istorii aviatsii i kosmonavtiki," Issue 3, Moscow, 1965, pp 22-32.

27. Arkhiv an SSSR, op. cit., D. 61.

28. Ibid, D. 59.

29. Komarov, V.M., Sadovoy, G.A., "On the Influence of K.E. Tsiolkovsky's Ideas on the Development of the Rocket Technology Enthusiasts Movement in the USSR (the '20's and '30's)," Trudy v chteniy K.E. Tsiolkovskogo. Sektsiya "Problemy raketnoy i kosmicheskoy tekhniki," Moscow, 1971, pp 95-108.

Chapter 7

GENESIS OF LIQUID HYDROGEN PROPULSION
THROUGH 1945[*]

John L. Sloop[†]

Experimental research using liquid hydrogen as fuel for aircraft and rockets began in the United States in 1945 and continued sporadically during the 1950s. In 1958 and 1959, decisions were made to develop a rocket engine and upper stages of launch vehicles using liquid hydrogen. The subsequent developments of Centaur and Saturn launch vehicles were key elements in the success of American manned and unmanned space missions and transformed liquid hydrogen into a practical fuel with a great potential for wider energy applications.

The decisions to use liquid hydrogen would not have surprised the great Russian rocket pioneer Konstantin E. Tsiolkovsky (Figure 1), for he proposed a liquid hydrogen-liquid oxygen space rocket in 1903, five years after the first liquefaction of hydrogen by James Dewar. This paper is concerned with the origins of U.S. interest and experiments with liquid hydrogen, the possible links with earlier work, and why liquid hydrogen was not used earlier as a propulsion fuel [1].

Of Tsiolkovsky's many contributions to rocket technology, perhaps the best known is his theory of rocket flight based on the laws of motion. The Tsiolkovsky equation helps to explain the advantages and disadvantages of using liquid hydrogen. Tsiolkovsky showed that the velocity of a rocket vehicle is directly proportional to the velocity of the exhaust. Hydrogen excelled over all other stable chemical fuels in achieving high exhaust velocity, an advantage quickly realized by Tsiolkovsky and others who followed him.

The Tsiolkovsky equation also has a term containing the ratio of initial to final mass of the vehicle. In this term, hydrogen appears as a disadvantage because its low density requires a large-volume tank which adds to the final mass and penalizes performance. Thus, hydrogen's advantage of high exhaust velocity is partially offset by an increase in the final mass because of its low density.

---

* Presented at The Eleventh IAA History of Astronautics Symposium, Prague, Czechoslovakia, September 1977.

† Consultant, Bethesda, Maryland, U.S.A.; formerly National Advisory Committee for Aeronautics and National Aeronautics and Space Adminstration.

During his career, Tsiolkovsky's enthusiasm for using hydrogen waned, especially when he became engrossed in rocket-powered aircraft, which are volume-limited. A year before his death in 1935, he discussed rocket fuels and concluded that "hydrogen is unsuitable because of its low density and storage difficulties when in liquid form [2]."

Figure 1 Konstantin E. Tsiolkovsky

Another rocket pioneer, Robert H. Goddard (Figure 2), was also attracted to hydrogen-oxygen because of its high-energy potential. In 1909, he calculated that the energy released from 45 kilograms of hydrogen-oxygen was sufficient to propel a 1-kg payload to infinity. In 1910, he wrote about producing hydrogen-oxygen on the Moon. Goddard, however, was considering the combination in the same way as a solid propellant; that is, burning discrete charges. When he began experimenting with continuous burning in 1921, the practicality of the gasoline-liquid oxygen combination attracted him. By 1923, he had operated a test rocket with gasoline-liquid oxygen and three years later became the first to fly a liquid-fueled rocket. His achievement clearly demonstrated the feasibility of using a cryogenic fluid -- liquid oxygen -- in flight. He did not experiment with liquid hydrogen, however, because of its low availability and handling problems. For the same reasons, he was amazed to learn in 1939 that the National Advisory Committee for Aeronautics (NACA) was considering liquid hydrogen for a flight application [3]. NACA, however, did not get around to such experiments until the 1950s.

Figure 2   Robert H. Goddard

Returning to the 1920s, still another rocket pioneer, Hermann Oberth (Figure 3), published the first of his series of books on interplanetary flight in 1923. He proposed a multistage vehicle using alcohol-water with liquid oxygen in the first stage and liquid hydrogen-liquid oxygen in the upper stages. He also proposed the use of pressure-stabilized, thin-wall tanks as a practical means of achieving low tank mass for liquid hydrogen. Both his upper-stage propellants and the thin-walled tanks were adopted in the U.S. space program. Oberth was primarily a theoretician but apparently he experimented with a gaseous hydrogen-oxygen burner though not with liquid hydrogen [4].

To sum up, all three rocket pioneers -- Tsiolkovsky, Goddard, and Oberth -- were attracted to and proposed the use of liquid hydrogen-liquid oxygen because of its high heat content, but theoretician and experimentalist alike saw the disadvantages of hydrogen's low density, limited availability, and handling difficulties.

Parallel to rocket considerations there were other activities that used hydrogen. The best known was in lighter-than-air flight, the first practical application of gaseous hydrogen that started in 1783. From 1900 to 1937, thousands of passengers were carried in large hydrogen-filled dirigibles yet there were accidents and these ended the era of the giants. The last and best remembered was the Hindenburg, filled with 200,000 m^3 of hydrogen, which burst into flames after a transatlantic flight to the United States. Thirty-six people lost their lives in the accident.

Figure 3 Hermann Oberth

Not so well known were early attempts to use dirigible buoyancy gas as fuel in its engines instead of venting it. Paul Haenlein patented this concept in 1872 and successfully used coal gas in a Lenoir engine in the first flight using an internal combustion engine the same year. Haenlein also considered hydrogen, but no record has been found that he tried it. Others did, however, following World War I, in Italy, Great Britain, Germany, and the United States. These were of limited success as hydrogen has a tendency to produce detonations or knock in piston engines [5]. These lighter-than-air applications added to the technology of generating, storing, and handling hydrogen which was further enhanced by the greatly expanded use of hydrogen in hydrogenation processes.

A second parallel activity involving hydrogen was scientific investigations of low-temperature phenomena that began to move more rapidly during the second half of the 19th Century with the race to liquefy the so-called permanent gases. Hydrogen was liquefied in 1898 by Dewar and helium in 1908 by Kamerlingh Onnes. Dewar also developed an efficient cryogenic storage vessel bearing his name. From these and other low-temperature experiments, liquefiers were developed which made liquid hydrogen available in small quantities.

The earliest rocket experimenter to use liquid hydrogen appears to have been Walter Thiel at Kummersdorf in Germany, during the 1937-1940 period. According to recollections of Wernher von Braun, Thiel tried a number of propellant combinations, among them liquid hydrogen-liquid oxygen and liquid hydrogen-liquid oxygen and fluorine mixtures in a small (200 newton) engine:

> "As to Thiel's liquid hydrogen tests with this set-up, I remember seeing liquefied (outside) air dripping from the supercold liquid hydrogen line. In discussing liquid hydrogen's potential, Thiel fully endorsed Oberth's earlier optimism, but pointed out that tightness of plumbing connections was a critical problem and the ever-present explosion hazard caused by the accumulation of leaked-out hydrogen gas in an unvented structural pocket would require extreme care in the design of a liquid hydrogen-powered rocket or rocket stage [6]."

The exploratory work with hydrogen went no further as development concentrated on the A series of rockets. Thiel transferred to Peenemünde to work for von Braun and was killed in 1943 during a British air raid. The German A-4 (V-2), using Oberth's alcohol-water mixture with liquid oxygen, established beyond all doubt the feasibility of using a cryogenic fluid in a rocket vehicle.

A parallel flight activity influencing interest in fuels other than high-octane gasoline was the development of jet engines for aircraft. Hans von Ohain was the first to use hydrogen in a turbojet engine. Employed by Heinkel in 1936 to develop a turbojet and pressed for time, von Ohain used gaseous hydrogen as a fuel of convenience. In early 1937, tests showed that the engine ran "outstandingly well with respect to quick throttle changes (almost like a piston engine) [7]." The test impressed Heinkel and gave von Ohain time to develop a gasoline combustor for his engine. Whether or not this transient use of hydrogen in a turbojet stirred interest elsewhere is not known. It is conceivable, however, that it may have influenced NACA's 1939 interest in liquid hydrogen with atmospheric air which so surprised Goddard.

The advent of German V-weapons and the effectiveness of a small number of jet interceptors against Allied bombers brought swift realization to the United States of how far behind it was in these new technologies. Part of the lag in developing jet aircraft was a decision to concentrate on the mass production of tried and proven piston engine planes rather than rely on the potentially superior but untried jet engine. Teams of Allied scientists and engineers followed in the wake of advancing armies in Europe, gathering technical data from documents and interrogations of Germans involved. Among those interrogated was Wernher von Braun and his concepts of future space missions caused considerable interest [8]. Less known was another interrogation of von Braun in which he discussed Thiel's brief experiments with liquid hydrogen and problems from plumbing leakage [9].

In late 1944 and early 1945, as war pressures on U.S. aeronautical laboratories began to ease, fuel researchers at the Army Air Force's Wright Field began to plan long-range projects. How much they may have been influenced by prior work is conjecture. They were well aware of hydrogen's advantages and disadvantages from general studies and from occasional research studies or suggestions. In the early 1920s, for example, the NACA translated a German paper by P. Meyer on fuels lighter than gasoline [10]. Meyer discussed hydrogen but apparently only considered it in gaseous form for he concluded that the heavy tanks required would not be feasible for aircraft. They were also aware of a British suggestion forwarded to them in 1942 by the NACA. It was written by F.E. Simon, a physicist who fled Germany before the war and had brought a hydrogen liquefier to Oxford's Clarendon laboratory. Simon proposed to use liquid hydrogen as a means for increasing aircraft range [11]. As the total hydrogen liquefaction capacity in the United States was only a few hundred liters per day, Simon's suggestion was dismissed as utterly impractical, particularly in wartime.

Figure 4 Professor Herrick L. Johnston (right) and Gwynne A. Wright with hydrogen liquefier at Ohio State University, ca. 1945

In the long-range planning at Wright Field, the chief civilian engineer of the power plants laboratory, Opie Chenoweth, suggested to his colleagues that research be undertaken to increase the energy content of aviation fuels. Although hydrogen was not a good fuel for piston engines because of its tendency to cause knock, jet engines did not have this restriction. At Ohio State University in nearby Columbus, Professor Herrick Johnston had a fine cryogenics laboratory and was a leading authority on liquefying hydrogen (Figure 4). He had a liquefier capable of producing 25 l of hydrogen per hour. Which of the several researchers involved at Wright Field put all these together is not known, but on 1 July 1945, Ohio State University began a study of liquid hydrogen for aircraft and rockets under contract to Wright Field [12]. From interviews and communications with several of the principals involved, a reasonable conclusion is that this hydrogen research was initiated as a normal consequence of the laboratory's research operations, evolving from group considerations rather than from the inspiration of an individual or reaction to a new piece of information [13]. Initial studies led to successful testing of liquid hydrogen-liquid oxygen experimental rocket engines (Figure 5).

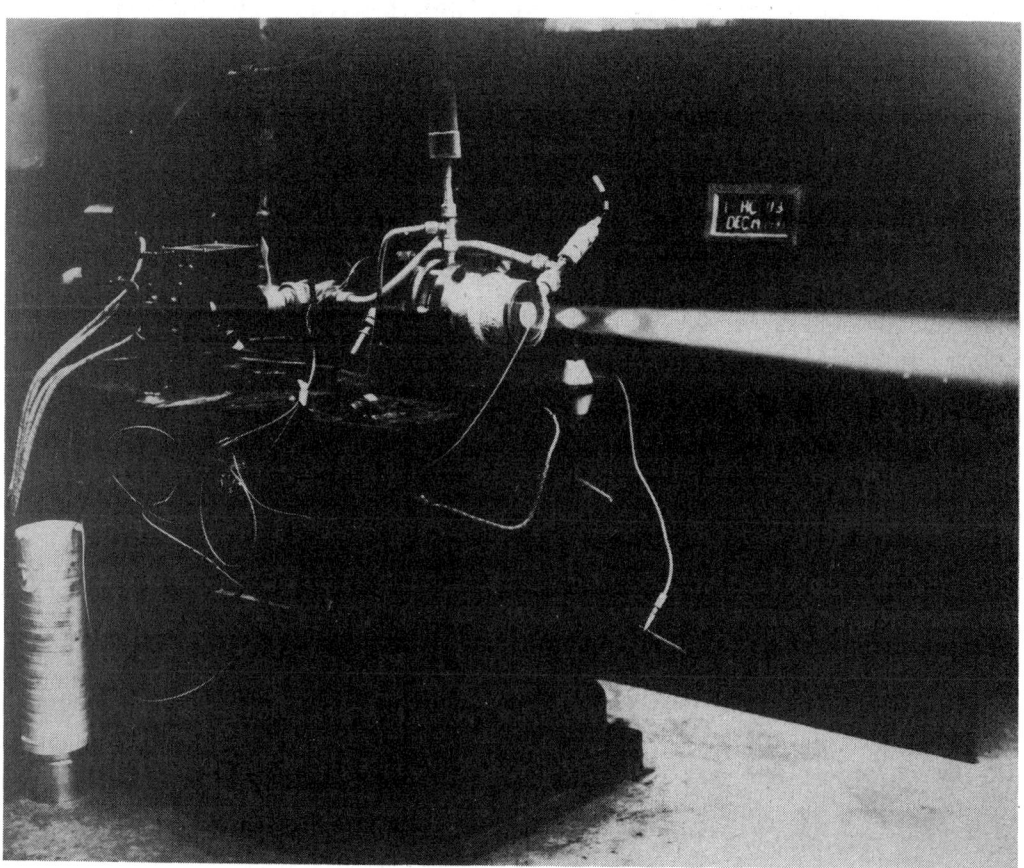

Figure 5 Liquid hydrogen-liquid oxygen experimental rocket engine regeneratively cooled by liquid hydrogen, Ohio State University, December 1949. Note frost on outside of rocket combustion chamber.

Like the Army Air Force, the Navy was stirred by German jet propulsion developments. In one action, it sponsored a study of fuels for jet propulsion by Alexis W. Lemmon, Jr., which he reported in May 1945 [14]. Lemmon found that hydrogen-oxygen gave the highest exhaust velocity of any propellant combination he studied but he rejected it because of its low density.

In July 1945, a young Marine lieutenant, Abraham Hyatt, reported to the Navy's Bureau of Aeronautics after completing a technical intelligence mission. Hyatt brought along German technical documents, including von Braun's space predictions, which stimulated the staff, particularly Lt. Robert Haviland and Cmdr. Harvey Hall. Both began studies of space projects and made proposals for satellites but they took different courses on the launch vehicles. Hall, who had a doctorate in physics, began educating himself in rocket theory. He worked out the Tsiolkovsky equation from the laws of motion and began to explore the extremes of exhaust velocity and mass ratio. At the time he was unaware of the newly-issued Lemmon report. He simply went to his chemistry textbooks in search of high-energy reactions and there he found hydrogen and oxygen, whose heat of combustion had been measured by Lavoisier and Laplace in the 18th Century and by others many times since. Hall was also totally unaware that he was repeating the same steps that Tsiolkovsky had taken almost a half century earlier and arriving at the same conclusion; that is, an initial enthusiasm to use liquid hydrogen [15]. As a result of Hall's initiatives, the Navy let a contract with the Aerojet Engineering Corporation for an experimental investigation of a liquid hydrogen-liquid oxygen rocket [16]. Unlike the Air Force contract with Ohio State, which was a general investigation, the Navy contract was directed toward using liquid hydrogen-liquid oxygen in a single-stage-to-orbit booster for a satellite.

In conclusion, the U.S. Air Force and Navy became interested in liquid hydrogen as a rocket fuel in 1945, both independent of each other and of other work, as well as for different reasons. Consideration of liquid hydrogen is a logical outcome of any study of high-energy fuels; low density, low availability, and handling difficulties were the chief obstacles which prevented an application from the time Tsiolkovsky first suggested it until after Sputnik.

REFERENCES

1. This paper is based on research conducted by the author for a larger study: *Liquid Hydrogen as a Propulsion Fuel, 1945-1959*, (NASA SP-4404, 1978).

2. *Collected Works of K.E. Tsiolkovsky*, ed. A.A. Blagonrovov, vol. 2: *Reactive Flying Machines*, NASA Technical Translation F-237 (Washington, 1965), p 513.

3. Robert H. Goddard, *The Papers of Robert H. Goddard*, ed. Esther C. Goddard and G. Edward Pendray, 3 vol. (New York: McGraw-Hill, 1970), pp 1237-38.

4. Hermann Oberth, *Ways to Spaceflight*, (Munich: Oldenbourg, 1929), NASA trans. TTF-622, 1972, pp 22,369.

5. U.S. Patent 130915, 27 Aug. 1872; Paul Haenlein, Zeitschrift für Luftschifffahrt 1, No. 8 (1888): 84; "Aeronautical Engineering Supplement. *The Aeroplane* 18 (18 Feb. 1920): 362.

6. Wernher von Braun statement to author, 8 November 1973.

7. Hans von Ohain statement to author, 21 May 1974.

8. One of von Braun's predictions, a space mirror, was published in *Life* 19 (23 July 1945): 78-80.

9. Clauser, Klemperer and Ridenour, "Report on the Interrogation of Professor von Braun," Douglas Aircraft Co., July 1946. Unfortunately, a copy of this report has not been located although its information about hydrogen leakage was referenced in a later report (1947) on hydrogen.

10. NACA Technical Note 136.

11. F. E. Simon, "Liquid Hydrogen as a Fuel for Aircraft," Clarendon Laboratory, Oxford University, 16 April 1942, 10 pp. Sent to NACA, 5 May 1942. Sent to Wright Field, 30 June 1942. A copy has not been located but the suggestion is mentioned by Nancy Arms, *A Prophet in Two Countries: The Life of F.E. Simon*, (New York: Pergamon, 1966), p 105. Robert F. Kerley remembers the reaction to it. Kerley to author, 29 January 1974.

12. "Liquid Hydrogen Propellant for Aircraft and Rockets," AFP 431952, Project MX-558, Contract W33-038-ac-11101 (14552) 1 July 1945-30 April 1948.

13. Opie Chenoweth to author, 23 January 1974; John Duckworth to author, 25 January 1974; interview with Opie Chenoweth and Weldon Worth, Dayton, 7 June 1974; Robert Kerley to Monte Wright, NASA History Office, 14 May 1976.

14. Alexis W. Lemmon, Jr., "Fuel Systems for Jet Propulsion," (Washington: U.S. Navy, 1945).

15. Telephone interview with Abraham Hyatt by R. Cargill Hall, 21 January 1970, NASA History Office; interview with Hyatt, El Segundo, 26 April 1974; telephone interview with Harvey Hall, 31 October and 6 November 1973; R. Cargill Hall, "Earth Satellites, a First Look by the United States Navy in the 1940s," XXI International Astronautical Congress, Constance, West Germany, 9 October 1970.

16. George H. Osborn, Robert Gordon, and Herman L. Coplen, "Liquid Hydrogen Development, 1944-1950," XXI IAC, Constance, West Germany, 9 October 1970. Hydrogen research at Aerojet before 1945 has not been documented. Interview with George James, Washington, 19 July 1973.

Chapter 8

HISTORY OF DEVELOPMENT OF FIRST SPACE ROCKET ENGINES IN THE USSR[*]

V. I. Prishchepa[†]

The power base for cosmonautics at the present time is made up of liquid propellant rocket engines (LPRE), whose operating principle was laid down back in 1903 in the classic work of K. E. Tsiolkovsky [1]. Among the complex problems that had to be solved in order to achieve space flight, the paramount one was the problem of developing the chamber for the LPRE unit, which directly creates the thrust (Figure 1). The problem lay in the development of a design that would function reliably under conditions of high mechanical and thermal loads, ensuring at the same time the efficient conversion of the potential chemical energy of liquid rocket fuel into kinetic energy of the jet gas stream. The technical ideas expressed by Tsiolkovsky served as a good foundation for the beginning of the practical work on the solution of the indicated problem.

Tsiolkovsky proposed burning a fuel under a pressure of several thousand atmospheres, and then dispelling the obtained gas in a continuously expanding nozzle that would extend the entire length of the rocket, until the temperature and elasticity values were "completely negligible," right down to the conversion of the combustion products "into liquid and even into ice crystals, which rush out of the tube with startling speed" [2, pp 102, 107]. At the same time, practically all the thermal energy generated during the combustion of the rocket fuel would be converted into the kinetic energy of the jet stream flowing out of the nozzle.

The efficiency of a rocket engine is determined by the amount of thrust obtained from 1 kg of fuel expended in 1 sec. This parameter, called the specific impulse, during the engine's operation under calculated conditions is numerically equal to the jet stream velocity. Together with the thrust, the specific impulse is the paramount parameter of the rocket engine, inasmuch as, according to Tsiolkovsky's well-known formula, it is associated by means of a direct proportional relationship with the velocity attained by the rocket upon the complete expenditure of its fuel.

---

[*] Presented at The Tenth IAA History of Astronautics Symposium, Anaheim, California, U.S.A., October 1971.

[†] Committee of the Soviet National Association of Natural Science and Technology Historians, USSR Academy of Sciences, Moscow, USSR.

The high temperatures, pressures and gas velocities in the chamber determine its high thermal factor. The value of the heat flux density (i.e., the amount of heat crossing a unit of the chamber surface over a unit of time(is nearly constant along the length of the combustion chamber, then increases with a sharply pronounced peak in the nozzle throat, after which it decreases, reaching a minimal value when it exits from the chamber (Figure 1).

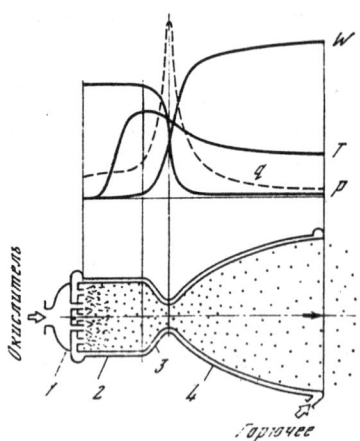

Figure 1 Diagram of chamber of contemporary LPRE and the parameters which characterize its operating process.
(1) the spray injector, (2) the combustion chamber, (3), (4) the subsonic and supersonic sections of the nozzle respectively; (p), (T), (W) the pressure (kg/cm^2), temperature ($^\circ$K) and the velocity (m/s) of the combustion products, (q) the density of the heat flux (MWt/m^2).

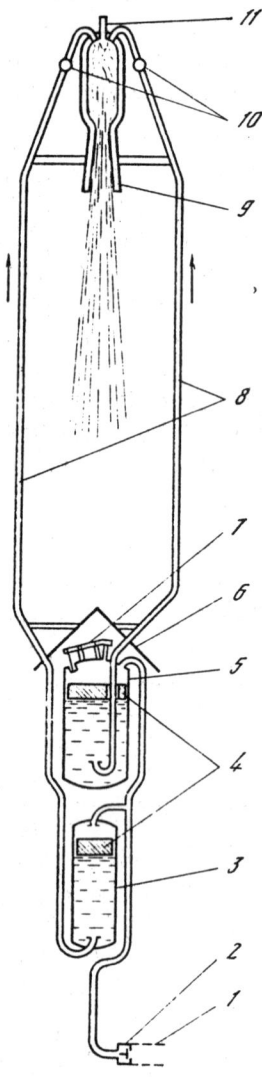

Figure 2 The first liquid propellant rocket, 1926 (launch weight, 4.6 kg).
(1) ground tank hose, (2) check valve, (3) tank with gasoline (benzine), (4) floating stopper valve, (5) tank with liquid oxygen, (6) protective shield, (7) safety valve, (8) feed pipes, (9) chamber with synthetic corundum refractory lining, (10) needle valve, (11) igniter.

In order to keep the chamber structure intact, Tsiolkovsky proposed cooling it with the liquid fuel itself, running the fuel components in the casing along the chamber wall before feeding them into the combustion area [1]. Such a method, called regenerative cooling, is widely used in contemporary LPRE's and is now the most reasonable one. However, its realization was by far not a simple matter. In fact, the introduction of regenerative cooling not only substantially complicated and increased the deadweight of the chamber structure, but also required additional fuel pressure (in order to compensate for hydraulic losses in the cooling system), which complicated the task of developing the feed units.

In addition, in the 1920's and 1930's, when the tests with LPRE's had begun, they did not have sufficiently accurate methods for calculating the heat transfer processes for the LPRE's operating conditions. Therefore, the first experimenters began with the simplest of single-section chambers. And so that these chambers could endure at least several seconds of operation, they were made on a large scale out of heat-conducting metals, immersed in water or in fuel tanks, and placed so that they would be surrounded by the air flow in fuel tanks, and placed so that they would be surrounded by the air flow in flight and so on. R.H. Goddard, who had begun experiments on developing LPRE's earlier than others, was the first to try lining the chamber with refractory material [3, pp 195f]. It was precisely such a chamber that was installed in his first LPR, which was launched on 16 March 1926 (Figure 2).

In order to facilitate the task of developing a workable chamber, many designers went for a reduction in the temperature of the combustion products by over-enriching the fuel mixture with fuel oil or ballasted water. Of course, at the same time, the specific impulse of the chamber was also reduced. Goddard, and after him H. Oberth in Germany, proposed cooling the chamber by creating next to the wall a stream of a relatively cold liquefied gas layer [3, p 201; 4, p 470]. To this end, for example, part of the fuel should be fed to the combustion arc along the wall of the chamber. Such a cooling method was called curtain or "internal" in contrast to the "external" regenerative method.

In our country, the practical work in the field of LPRE's and LPR's was begun in 1929 by the Leningrad Gas Dynamics Laboratory (GDL). The group of LPRE specialists, headed by the young scientist and current academician, V.P. Glushko, tested the most diverse chamber designs on stands and, finally, in 1933, developed LPRE's capable of operating continuously over the course of dozens of seconds. In addition, these engines could be used repeatedly. The "Experimental Rocket Motors," the ORM-50 and ORM-52, with which we are concerned, developed thrusts of 150 and 300 kg, respectively. Their chambers had (curtain) and regenerative cooling [5, pp 181, 185]. The curtain was created by the centrifugal fuel injectors located on the steel cylindrical combustion chamber by feeding a small part of the atomized liquids onto the wall. Judging from the fact that the chamber did not burn through for a long time, the curtain, carried along by the gas flow, was retained also in the area of the nozzle. In addition, it was intensively cooled by the stream of oxidizer, which flowed through the conduits formed by spiral ribs on the internal steel wall and covered it with split aluminum bushings (Figure 3). Thanks to the spiral conduits, the velocities and the path of the cooling liquid were increased, the surface area washed by it increased and, as a result, reliable cooling was achieved. Glushko obtained a patent for a chamber with spiral ribbing and split bushings [5, pp 228-230]. This design was widely used in native and foreign LPRE's in the 1930's and 1940's.

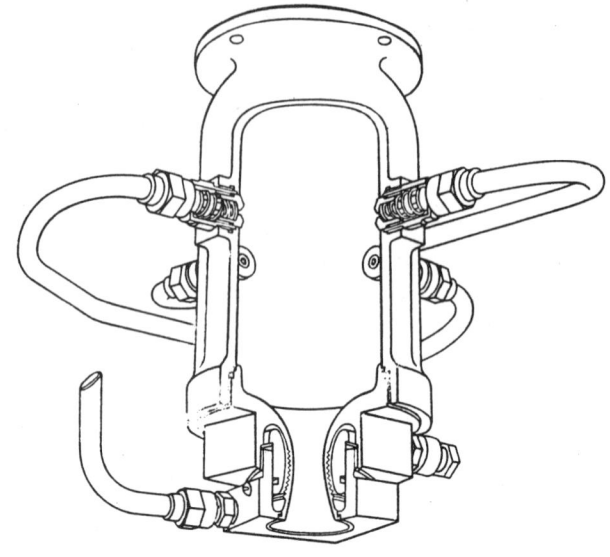

Figure 3   Chamber of the ORM-50 engine, 1933

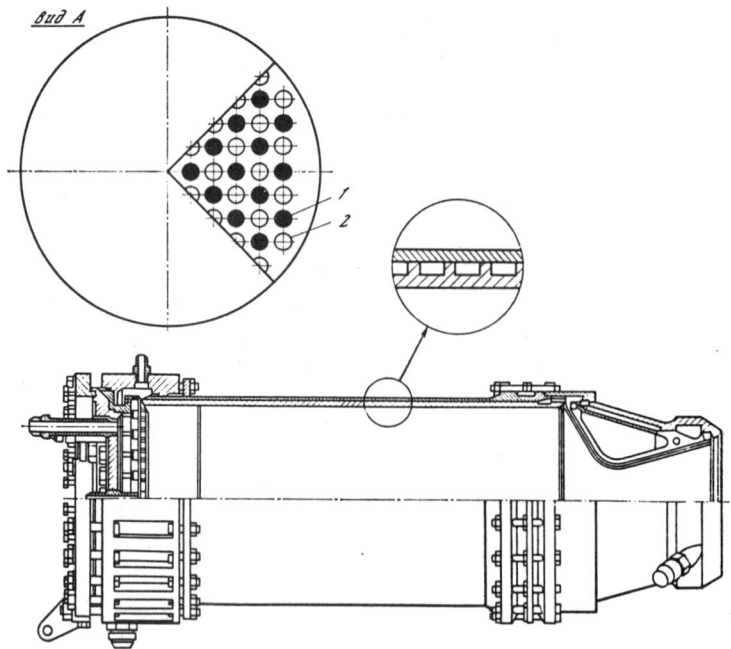

Figure 4   Chamber of the RD-1M engine, 1946. Placement of the injectors in the head (view from the side of the nozzle): (1) oxidizer, (2) fuel.

92

The ORM-50, ORM-52 and subsequent LPRE's developed by the group under the supervision of Glushko in the 1930's operated on a two-component propellant in which the oxidizer was nitric acid and the fuel was tractor kerosene. These cheap products were widely used in the economy and did not cause as much inconvenience in use as liquid oxygen and even more so hydrogen. It is important to note that, although in theory, according to the specific impulse, fuel with a nitric acid oxidizer is worse than oxygen, in fact, Glushko's engines turned out to be more efficient than all the others. This is explained by the fact that the GDL group managed not only to solve the problem of reliable cooling of the chamber, but also to ensure a high-quality fuel mixture atomization, i.e., a good intermingling of the atomized fuel components. Thus, the properly prepared mixture burned at a pressure of 20-25 kg/cm^2, which was a record for that time. Upon leaving the nozzle, the combustion products expanded to the normal atmospheric pressure. As a result, the specific impulse amounted to 2,110 m/s.

The design solutions contained in the ORM-50 and ORM-52 were developed further in the Soviet LPRE's developed towards the end of the Patriotic War [World War II]. Among them was the USSR's first mass-produced LPRE, the RD-1 (in the final version it was called the RD-9Z), designed by Glushko and produced by an experimental unit in a quantity of more than 200 copies [6]. This engine, which underwent static tests, developed a thrust of 300 kg and had an operational life of 1 hr., which was limited by the wear and tear on the fuel pumps. They were power-plant driven pumps. These pumps were used on the domestic LPRE's first and cut down greatly on the size of the fuel tanks. The RD-1 was intended as an auxiliary aircraft engine to supplement the basic (piston) engine unit.

During the war, in the JPSRI, they also developed an LPRE for the basic power plant of the BI series aircraft. This LPRE, with a thrust of 1,100 kg, designed for forced feeding of a nitric acid-kerosene, at first did not satisfy the given technical requirements, and the main reason here turned out to be the not completely successful design of the chamber, which did not provide adequate cooling and high-quality fuel mixture atomization. A.M. Isayev, one of the inventors of the BI aircraft, himself undertook to redo the engine, and as a result of the creative use of all domestic experience, this talented designer managed to develop a reliable LPRE with a high performance level. It was called the RD-1 (i.e., the same as Glushko's engine) [7, pp 24-31].

In 1946, A.M. Isayev improved his own engine, having increased its operating life to 1 hr. and having lowered the hydraulic losses in the lines (for the purpose of reducing the feed pressure). The chamber of this modified engine, the RD-1M, contained a head with dozens and dozens of injectors, placed in a "chessboard" arrangement (Figure 4). At the same time, the outermost oxidizer injectors sprayed the liquid towards the center of the head and at the corners of the chessboard were fuel injectors with increased flow rates [7, p 34]. Thus, the chamber wall operated not only at a lowered temperature, but in a reducing medium, which was an additional guarantee against a burnthrough. The numerous injectors, placed evenly on the cheese head (in the first version of the RD-1 the head was reminiscent of the shape of a marquee), ensured a good intermingling of the fuel components; however, because of the intensive curtain cooling (which disrupted the homogeneity of the mixture), the specific impulse of the LPRE was reduced by 60 m/s and amounted to all of 1,920 m/s. Subsequently, they were able to reduce this shortcoming in the new fuel mixture atomization system to a minimum, and the technical ideas, tested in the design of the RD-1M's injector head, were widely used in Soviet LPRE's.

The designs of the LPRE's developed during the war years reflected to a large degree the level of aviation engine production of that time. Their parts were based on the same technological equipment as the parts for piston engines. The chambers of the LPRE's used up quite a bit of labor in their production and they required a skilled work force. For example, in order to get the internal wall with ribs, a lathe operator had to carve out the complex shaped surfaces and to cut in them 16 and 24 starting threads. Just like piston motors, the LPRE designs were made as teardownable items with numerous connecting parts. In order to seal the end joints between the internal and external walls, which move relative to one another during operation due to unequal heating, it was necessary to install compensators in the form of bellows, self-sealing lead gaskets, and so on. For reasons of durability, the chamber parts had to be made of steel and made large. It is true that the use in one of the German aviation LPRE's (the BMW 109-718 engine) of a head built according to the same principle as that of the RD-1M, made it possible to make widespread use of a lightweight duralumin alloy. However, the specific impulse of this LPRE amounted to only around 1,750 m/s -- which is approximately 200 m/s less that that of the RD-1 designed by Glushko [8, p 348].

Along with the aviation LPRE, the great technological achievement of the 1940's was the powerful LPRE developed in Germany for the A-4 ballistic rocket with a range of nearly 300 km. The chamber of this engine, which operated on a liquid oxygen -- aqueous solution of ethyl alcohol propellant combination developed a thrust of up to 29 tons. The specific impulse of the LPRE amounted to 2,280 m/s with an initial combustion products pressure of 15 kg/cm^2. A high-quality fuel mixture atomization in the chamber was achieved thanks to the head with the so-called pre-combustion chambers -- sleeves with injectors in the bottom and in the conical walls. Individual jets of the mixed fuel, entering the combustion area from the pre-combustion chambers, became mixed among themselves prior to combustion (Figure 5). Among a number of other elements, the pre-combustion chambers had been invented several years before the beginning of the A-4's development. The various versions of them were described, for example, in the book by G.E. Langemak and Glushko, published back in 1935 [9, pp 91-97]. The engine chamber of the A-4 rocket was peculiar in that it was produced from smooth (non-ribbed) sheet metal shells, which formed the external and internal walls, which were joined into a whole by welding over several hoops. At the same time, a section of the hoops had openings for feeding fuel from the cooling system into the gas stream for the purpose of creating a cooling curtain.

In comparison with the aviation LPRE chambers, such a design was a step forward. However, by the second half of the 1940 decade, its limited possibilities had become clear. During the indicated time period, in the USSR and abroad, research work had begun that was aimed at the development of rocket boosters capable of covering distances of thousands of kilometers, and later of completing flights into space. Calculations indicated that based on the technological level attained in the A-4, in order to launch a satellite with a mass of several kilograms, it would be necessary to have a five-stage rocket with a launch mass in the hundreds of tons (see, for example, [10]). In order to seriously talk about the goal set, it would be necessary to increase the specific impulse of the LPRE by a factor of approximately 1.5 and reduce (at the least, by half) the mass of the engine and all the other rocket components.

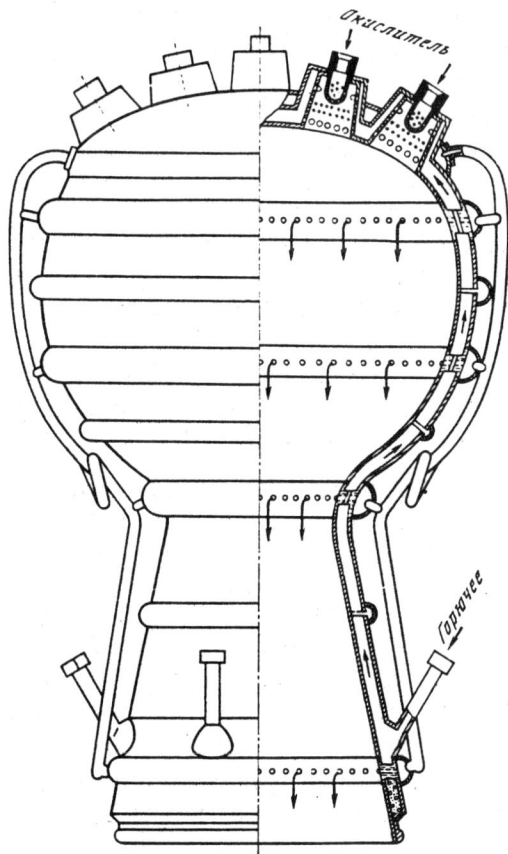

Figure 5 Engine chamber of the A-4 rocket, 1942

Work in this direction was begun in our country in 1946-1947 by the Experimental Design Bureau of the GDL [GDL-EDB], headed by Glushko. The project studies (see, for example, [11]) indicated that the required specific impulse of the LPRE could be attained by using a liquid oxygen -- kerosene propellant combination together boosting of the operating pressure in the combustion chamber up to the level of 50 kg/cm^2. At the same time, however, it was necessary to thicken the external wall of the chamber and the mass of the chamber increased substantially. Indeed, the problem of cooling the chamber seemed to be unsolvable.

The fact is that in comparison to the A-4's engine, the initial temperature of the gas in the chamber was increased by 900 K and the density of the heat flux increased by a factor of three. In order to cool the combustion wall, in accordance with the laws of heat transfer, it was necessary to make it very thin. But then it would be crumpled by the pressure of the fuel flowing in the regenerative cooling system. It would be possible to reduce the heat fluxes by intensification of the curtain cooling, but this reduction would be attained at the cost of a reduction in the specific impulse.

As in many other instances, the prerequisites for the solution of the problem that had arisen were contained in the early developments of rocket technology's pioneers. Let us make a small excursion into the history of the LPRE. In 1933, in the GDL, the ORM-48 LPRE was designed with a nozzle made from the ribbed steel wall and a copper jacket, which were joined into a single whole by soldering [12, p 11]. The soldering was done using a hard solder along the tops of the spiral ribs made on the steel wall (Figure 6). Thus, closed conduits were obtained for the passage of the coolant. Ordinary water was used for this and the ORM-48 engine itself was intended for experiments to determine the nature of the gas pressure change along the nozzle.

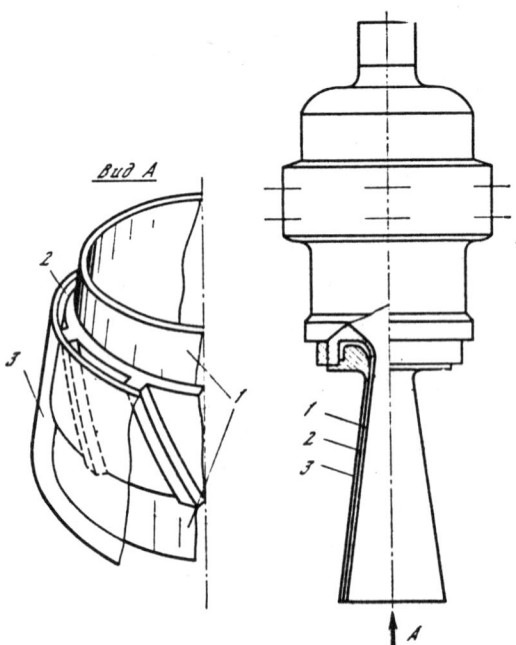

Figure 6 The ORM-48 engine, 1933. Nozzle section: (1) combustion wall, (2) band of ribbing on the combustion wall, (3) jacket.

In the middle of the 1930's, chambers with integral bodies of various design were also developed by E. Sänger in Germany. In 1934, he tested (and a year later

96

patented) a chamber with a body made of winding copper tubes, joined together with solder, and a chamber close in design to the ORM-48. The body of the latter contained a bronze internal wall with milled ribs to which the jacket parts were soldered on the outside [13, pp 236-237].

Veterans of rocket technology remember that, at the end of 1942, chambers with whole bodies interested Isayev. Over the course of 1943, under his supervision, nozzles were designed, similar in design to the nozzle of the ORM-48, as well as a furnace for soldering, equipped with a heating air-kerosene burner and a system for developing a reducing hydrogen medium. By the end of 1944, approximately 10 nozzles had been produced in this furnace. All this work was due to the burnthroughs of the BI aircraft's LPRE chambers. Isayev discovered the reason for the burnthroughs in the deformation of the chamber's combustion wall, which led to a local increase in the space between the walls and a reduction in this place of the velocity of coolant. However, with the development of the RD-1, the chamber of which did not burn through, the work on soldering came to an end. (In addition, Isayev's small group could not produce the sufficiently large furnaces necessary to solder the entire chamber.)

At the end of 1944, Isayev's group tested a chamber, the cylindrical portion of which was produced from two sheet metal shells, welded along the ends. The space between the shells was fixed using longitudinal wires placed inside, which were welded along the ends of the shells. After several launches at a reduced operating level, this chamber lost stability and burned through at a 90 kg thrust level [7, p 38]. Nevertheless, the work on chambers made from sheet metal material continued, inasmuch as the fate of the EDB's subsequent plans depended to a large degree on their result. Isayev recalled later [7, pp 41-42]:

"If the EDB had had a good production base available, and its workers had a good idea about the possibilities for well set-up mass production with a high level of technology, it is probable that their designs would have been different. But the EDB workers ... had available a very small number of general-purpose machine tools, the simplest welding equipment, they experienced difficulties with the forge shop and in general they did not have a foundry ... Every production order was pinched to the minimum and fulfilled late. Therefore, the designer's first task was to achieve maximum simplicity and to develop a design which would not require special equipment, would be produced from on-hand materials and did not require exploitation of new technological processes. Simplicity ... as it seemed, yielded also reliability in operation".

They managed to develop an operationally capable sheet metal chamber after a head with curtain cooling injectors was worked out. The heat fluxes, recorded during the operation of chambers with this head, turned out to be so low that the designers decided to weld a jacket to the combustion wall over the entire surface with spot welding through connecting bands. They constructed the injector head on the form of a block made from three bottoms (which formed collectors for the oxidizer and the fuel), joined by welded seams. The internal and middle bottoms were joined, in addition, through laminated tubular injectors for the oxidizer (Figure 7) [7, p 43]. Tests of the chamber with this design (U-1250) took place in the summer of 1946. At a pressure of 17 kg/cm^2, a thrust of 1,300 kg and a specific impulse of 2,050-2,090 m/s were obtained. This gave Isayev's group a reason to plan a whole series of similar chambers with thrusts in the range of 400-9,000 kg, an operating pressure of 16 kg/cm^2 and a specific impulse of 1,960-2,110 m/s. It was proposed that the LPRE's with these lightweight chambers, intended for pressure-feed of a nitric acid-kerosene fuel, would satisfy all the needs of the developing rocket technology, beginning with aviation engines up to engine units for long-range rockets [7, pp 50-52].

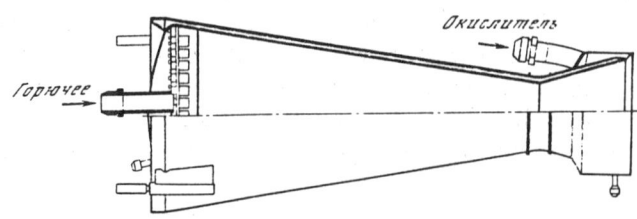

Figure 7 The U-1250 engine chamber, 1946

Having noted the erroneousness of such a point of view, it is necessary to point out, however, that the chambers with a weld design, developed by Isayev's group, hastened the development of contemporary designs, which are capable of operating under conditions of high pressures, temperatures and heat fluxes, developing a high specific impulse in the absence of limitations on a practical introduction of chambers with firmly interconnected shells was the danger that such chambers would fail because of thermal stresses arising as a consequence of the large difference in the temperatures of the two shells. Isayev's welded chambers aided in overcoming this danger to a significant degree.

In 1948, the GDL-EDB group made plans for chambers in which the ideas outlined in the design of the ORM-48 and subsequent Soviet LPRE's were realized on a contemporary technological level. In these chambers, the joining of the walls was accomplished using a high-temperature solder along the tops of the ribs milled in the combustion wall. The chamber heads had multilayer bottoms with injectors soldered into them. At the final stage of the chamber production process, the individual sections of the body and the head were welded into a single whole with circular seams. As a result, an integrated soldered-welded design was obtained (Figure 8) [14, p 12]. In such a so-called design with frequent connections, the walls could have a small width, since, thanks to the numerous thin ribs, the individual conduits obtained for the passage of the coolant were narrow. Thus, the combustion wall could be produced from a relatively flimsy, but still highly heat-conductive copper alloy, and the jacket from highly durable alloys, for example, alloy steels.

Tests of the first of the new design chambers took place in the GDL-EDB in mid-1949. These chambers, which operated on an oxygen-kerosene fuel and developed a thrust of 7 tons with an initial gas pressure of 60 kg/cm^2, were intended for development of technological processes and also for research on questions concerning cooling and fuel mixture atomization. At the same time, in an experimental chamber of similar design with a thrust of 50 kg, prospective rocket fuels were tested. The GDL-EDB, jointly with specialized SRI's, conducted expanded research in the field of the technology of soldering layered designs made from homogeneous and heterogeneous materials. As a result, a method was worked out for vacuum soldering of chamber joints in a neutral protective medium (nitrogen). In order to obtain quality solders of the joinings, the experimental production unit of the GDL-EDB drew up plans for and produced special electric furnaces, which provided high speed heating, a small drop in temperature during the process of loading the joints and a constant temperature during the soldering process. For the combustion wall, it was necessary to develop a special heat-resistant alloy (chromous bronze) which combined high thermal strength and operating properties. Also exploited were new types of rustproof and alloyed steels and a new solder based on silver and copper was developed which ensured a high degree of heat resistance for the soldered joinings and so on [15].

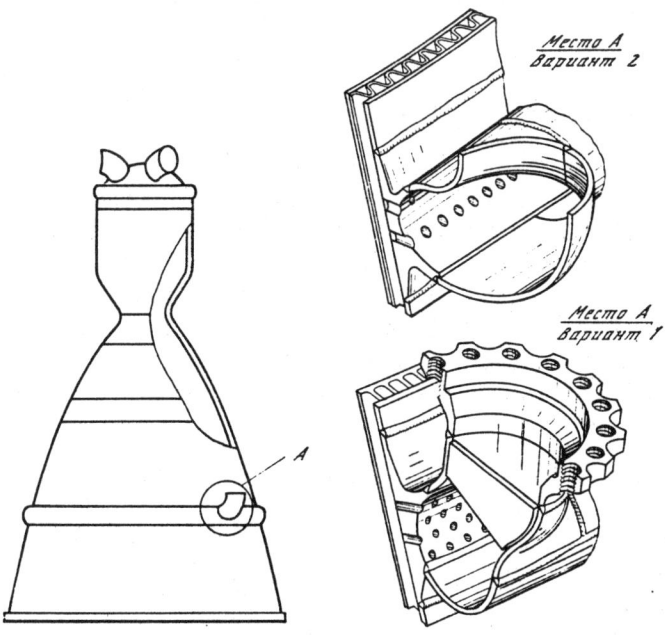

Figure 8   Soldered-welded chamber designed by the GSL-EDB

In addition to the chamber with a ribbed internal wall, in the GDL-EDB they developed a design version with smooth shells, connected using a middle corrugated wall. It can be produced, for example, from copper alloys or well stamped low-carbon steels. Such a design, much simpler to produce, is based on less stressing operating conditions. For example, in the combustion area and in the area of the nozzle throat, the connection between the walls can be accomplished using ribs and at the exhaust section of the nozzle, where the heat fluxes are not as intense, using corrugation. The research conducted in 1954 on chambers with soldered-welded designs and the experience obtained during the production of the large, full-sized joints were important factors in the successful development of the RD-107 and RD-108 engines, which ensured space flight in 1957. In each of the 20 basic chambers of the five LPRE's of the Sputnik launcher, nearly 70 kg of high-caloric oxygen-kerosene fuel was burned in 1 sec. At the same time, gases were formed with a pressure of 50-60 kg/cm^2 and a temperature of 3,500 K, which then dilated in the nozzles to 0.3-0.4 kg/cm^2, speeding up to nearly 3,000 m/s. The chamber developed a thrust of 23 tons with an all-up mass of only 143 kg; the length of the entire chamber was 1.9 m, the diameter of the nozzle at the exhaust point amounted to 0.72 m and the combustion chamber to 0.43 m. In each liter of volume in the combustion area, there were up to 10 MJ of heat per second and the density of the heat flux entering into the wall of the chamber amounted to 17 MWt/m^2. Under these conditions, without the adoption of special measures, the design would burn up in the computed seconds.

With the development of the chambers with a soldered-welded design, there appeared broad possibilities for increasing the LPRE's specific impulse by increasing the operating pressure and using efficient rocket propellants; along with this, there was a substantial reduction in the relative dimensions and in the specific mass of the engine (the mass of the design per unit of thrust). The indicated measurements to a specific degree are illustrated in Figure 9, in which the chamber of the A-4 rocket is represented in comparison to the soldered-welded chambers of the GDL-EDB designs for the period 1957-1962.

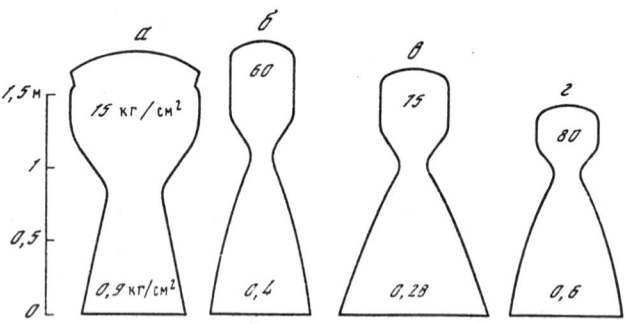

Figure 9 The chambers of various LPRE's. (a) the A-4 rocket chamber, 1943 (thrust - 28 tons, specific impulse - 2,300 m/s, mass - 450 kg); (b) RD-107 chamber, 1957 (23 tons, 3,141 m/s, 143 kg); (c) RD-219 chamber, 1961 (45 tons, 2,898 m/s, 127 kg); (d) RD-111 chamber, 1962 (41 tons, 3,157 m/s, 136 kg).

A high operating pressure and an efficient rocket fuel were necessary conditions but not sufficient for obtaining a high specific impulse. No less important was the need to reduce to a minimum the energy losses (in friction, heat transfer and so on) in all phases of the chamber's operating process, including the atomization of the fuel components by the injectors, their mingling, combustion and the subsequent expansion of the gases formed in the nozzle. This difficult task was solved by the joint efforts of designers, technologists and scientists, specialists in the various fundamental sciences. Their cooperation was an important factor in the development of an LPRE, which was supported by the development of the design of so substantial a part of the chamber and the entire engine as the jet propulsion nozzle.

The LPRE's of the 1930's and 1940's were intended to operate in the lower layers of the atmosphere. Therefore, their nozzles were designed for the expansion of the gases to a pressure, equal or close to that of the normal atmosphere. The relatively low thrust values and the low degree of gas expansion made it possible to use conical nozzles with small expansion angles. These nozzles were simple to produce, had relatively small dimensions and mass and were characterized by small energy losses in the gas stream. Nevertheless, even at the beginning of the 1930's, in the GDL-EDB, there were proposals for more improved nozzles -- ones with profiles which would ensure the same degree of gas expansion as the conical ones, with a shorter length. The indicated proposal was the result of experiments set up in 1930 for the purpose of determining the optimum parameters for the chamber's operating process and the geometric characteristics of the nozzles: a powder engine, equipped with two different nozzles, installed diametrically opposite one another, was suspended on a differential pendulum and tested [5, pp 103-109].

During the development of the first space LPRE's (the RD-107 and RD-108), in which gas expanded from a pressure of 50-60 kg/cm^2 to 0.34-0.40 kg/cm^2, the use of curved nozzles of relatively simple configuration -- shaped like arcs of circles, yielded a notable gain in axial dimensions and engine mass. From the beginning of the 1960's, in the GDL-EDB designs (the RD-119 with a gas expansion from 80.5 to 0.063 kg/cm^2 and the RD-219 -- from 75 to 0.28 kg/cm^2), they began to use nozzles with an angular inlet (into the supersonic part), that were suggested by the JPSRI jointly with the USSR Academy of Sciences' Computer Center. The development in the GDL-EDB (jointly with the aforementioned center) of nozzles with an experimental profile aided in the further improvement of the LPRE's characteristics. Such nozzles have been used, in particular, in the RD-111 and RD-253, where the operating gas expanded from a pressure of 80 to 0.5 kg/cm^2 and from 150 to 0.62 kg/cm^2, respectively [16, p 16].

In researching the problem of the selection of the optimum parameters for the operating process, the GDL-EDB specialists turned their attention to the circumstance that an increase in pressure would lead to a reduction in the dimensions of the chamber. The given circumstance was an additional factor which determined that the development of LPRE's would be in the direction of boosting the operating process. On this path, the school of rocket engine production, which was associated with the activities of the GDL-EDB, undoubtedly occupied a leading position [16, p 15]: over the 10-year period, which concluded with the development of the first space engines, the pressure in the chambers of the powerful LPRE's increased by a factor of 4, and in recent years -- by the same amount again. The engines of the first half of the 1960's operated with combustion chamber pressures of up to 75-80 kg/cm^2 (in the rated mode). With the development in 1965 of new engines (for example, the RD-253 for the Proton rocket boosters), this indicator increased two-fold at one stroke.

Chambers with a pressure higher than 100 kg/cm^2 have the peculiar feature that the fuel components enter into their combustion area in a different aggregation state: usually liquid fuel from the regenerative cooling system and the exhaust generator gas, which represents the products of the combustion of the oxidizer with part of the fuel. The latter is produced in a special unit -- the gas generator, and is used to drive the turbines, which turn the centrifugal fuel pumps (the turbines together with the pumps form a turbopump unit). In chambers with pressures up to 100 kg/cm^2, instead of exhaust generator gas, liquid oxidizer flows to the injectors: the post-turbine gas is discarded into a separate exhaust pipe. The transition with the increase in pressure from the "liquid-liquid" system to the "liquid-gas" system or the system with afterburning of generator gas is explained by the condition of balance between the capacities of the fuel pumps and the turbine. In accordance with this condition, with the increase in pressure in the chamber (and, consequently, the fuel feed pressure), an ever increasing part of the fuel is supposed to be used to obtain the generator gas, and its disposal in an exhaust pipe becomes a disadvantage since it leads to a reduction in the result specific impulse of the LPRE.

The necessity of afterburning of the generator gas, like the subsequent chamber pressure increase, did not require principal changes in the soldered-welded design of the chamber developed for the first space LPRE's. They improved and altered only individual parts, materials and technological processes (in particular, substantial changes were endured in the soldering process and the corresponding technological equipment). The use of the latest achievements in the field of the general metallurgy, weldings, thermal process soldering and gas dynamics, along with the results of purposeful scientific research and the accumulated design experience made it possible to realize the merits of the soldered-welded design of the chamber to an ever greater degree. An idea of this can be obtained from an examination of Figure 9 and the following data on the chambers of the RD-216 and RD-253 engines.

The first of the indicated LPRE's, developed in 1960 (and used since 1964 in the Cosmos and Intercosmos rocket boosters), uses a non-afterburning system; the second, developed 5 years later, belongs to the family of engines with afterburning. In both LPRE's, one type of fuel is used (in the RD-253 one with a higher calorific value). They develop an identical thrust on the ground (150 tons), which is created in the RD-253 in a single chamber with a mass of 400 kg, while in the RD-216 it is done by four identical chambers with a total mass of 508 kg. With a substantially greater thrust, the RD-253 chamber is characterized by the smaller dimensions of the combustion area: diameter of 430 mm and length of 238 mm compared to 480 and 300 mm for each chamber of the RD-216. With regards to the specific impulse, the RD-253 chamber significantly exceeds the RD-216 chamber: by 326 m/s during operation on the ground and by 210 m/s in a vacuum.

During the development of the chambers for the RD-216 engine, which contain combustion products with a pressure of 75 kg/cm^2 and a temperature of 3,050 K, it turned out to be possible to use the most simple version of the soldered-welded design: the steel shells of the chamber are joined using corrugated spacers (aligned in the subcritical part of the nozzle spirally -- for the purpose of intensification of the regenerative cooling). The peripheral injectors, through which part

102

of the fuel flows into the combustion chamber, are used to set up the internal curtain cooling.

In the RD-253, the chamber operates under immeasurably more stressful conditions than in the RD-216, which is explained by the substantial increase in thrust along with the decrease in the dimensions of the combustion area, and also the increased pressure (150 kg/cm^2) and temperature (3,400K) of the combustion products. Regarding the degree of stress of the operating process in the chamber of the RD-253, this can be judged by the following indicators: more than 350 g of fuel are dispersed each second across 1 cm^2 of the cross-section of the combustion chamber (seven to eight times more than in the RD-107 and RD-108), and a 1 cm^3 section of the combustion area produces nearly 5 tons of thrust (13 to 15 times more than in the first space engines). The density of the heat flux entering into the wall of the RD-253's chamber amounts to 120 MWt/m^2. Under such stressful conditions, the corrugated spacers can be used only in the structure of the exhaust section of the nozzle, which is the least loaded section with respect to heat. In the remaining section of the chamber, an internally milled wall, produced from highly heat-conductive bronze, is used. The indicated wall is protected from burnthrough by the liquid gas film formed by the fuel entering into the combustion area from the regenerative cooling system via two rows of openings. In addition, (by means of spraying), a high-temperature, heat-insulating coating of zirconium dioxide has been deposited on the internal surface of the bronze wall. In this connection, it must be remembered that refractory compounds based on available ceramics had been developed and successfully used in experimental chambers of the GDL-EDB back at the beginning of the 1930's [5, pp 78-95].

Since the time of the development of the first space engines, the soldered-welded chambers designed by the GDL-EDB have formed the basis for the domestic LPRE's. These lightweight, compact units operate under pressures in the hundreds of atmospheres, endure temperatures of 4,500 K and are resistant to the effects of any chemically corrosive products [17, p 20]. Thus, thanks to the development of ideas contained in the works of the pioneers in cosmonautics and the technical solutions realized in the early designs of the LPRE's, space flight became feasible, as did the subsequent successes of Soviet cosmonautics.

BIBLIOGRAPHY

1. Tsiolkovsky, K.E., "Space Research using Jet Propulsion Devices (1903)," in the book "Pionery raketnoy tekhniki [Pioneers of Rocket Technology]: Kibalchich, Tsiolkovsky, Tsander, Kondratyuk. Izbrannyye trudy [Selected Works]," Moscow, 1964, pp 23-53.

2. Ibid, "Supplement to parts 1 and 2 of the above-named work," pp 96-107.

3. Goddard, R., "Supplement to a Report to the Board of Trustees of Clark University on the Work conducted from June of 1921 through August of 1923," in the book "Pionery raketnoy tekhniki: Ganswindt, Goddard, Esnault-Pelterie, Oberth, Hohmann. Izbrannyye trudy," Moscow, 197, pp 193-202.

4. Oberth, H., "A Rocket in Space," in the book "Pionery raketnoy tekhniki: Ganswindt, Goddard, Esno-Peltry, Oberth, Hohmann. Izbrannyye trudy," Moscow, 1977.

5. Glushko, V.P., "Put v raketnoy tekhnike [The Path in Rocket Technology]. Izbrannyye trudy," Moscow, 1977.

6. Prishchepa, V.I., Shkolnikov I. Ye., "Thirty Years since the Time of the Demonstration Flight of an Aircraft with the RD-9Z LPRE designed by V.P. Glushko (1946)," in the book "Iz istorii aviatsii i kosmonavtiki" [From the History of Aviation and Cosmonautics], Moscow, 1976, Issue 29, pp 99-104.

7. Isayev, A.M. "Pervyye shagi k kosmicheskim dvigatelyam" [The First Steps Towards Space Engines], Moscow, 1979.

8. Stemmer, J., "Raketenantriebe" [Rocket Engines], Zürich, 1952.

9. Langemak, G.E., Glushko, V.P., "Rakety, ikh ustroystvo i primeneniye" [Rockets, their Construction and Use], Moscow, Leningrad, 1935.

10. Klauzer, F., "Flights beyond the Limits of the Earth's Atmosphere," in the book "Fizika i khimiya reaktivnogo dvizheniya" [The Physics and Chemistry of Jet Propulsion], Moscow, 1949, Collection 2, pp 183-197.

11. Glushko, V.P., "On the Development of Powerful Jet Propulsion Engines which use Liquid Fuel," in the book "Raketnaya tekhnika" [Rocket Technology], 1948, Edition 2, pp 1-15.

12. Glushko, V.P., "Albom konstruktsiy ZhRD" [Album of LPRE Designs], Moscow, 1958, Part 1.

13. Sänger-Bredt, I., Engel, R., "The development on regeneratively cooled liquid rocket engines in Austria and Germany, 1926-42," in "First Steps Toward Space," Washington, 1974, Smithsonian Institute Press, pp 217-246. Now published as Vol. 6, AAS History Series, San Diego, California, 1985, Univelt, Inc.

14. Bychkov, V.N., Nazarov, G.A., Prishchepa, V.I., "Kosmicheskiye zhidkostno-raketnyye dvigateli" [Space Liquid Rocket Engines], Moscow, 1976.

15. Prishchepa, V.I., Bratenkov, Yu. A., Shkolnikov, I. Ye., "Certain Questions on the Development of the Engines for the First Space Rocket," Trudy X chteniy K.E. Tsiolkovskogo. Sektsiya "Problemy raketnoy tekhniki," Moscow, 1977, pp 184-193.

16. Prishchepa, V.A., "The Realization and Development of K.E. Tsiolkovsky's Ideas in the GDL-EDB," Trudy XIV Chteniy K.E. Tsiolkovskogo. Sektsiya "Problemy raketnoy i kosmicheskoy tekhniki," Moscow, 1980, pp 12-22.

17. Glushko, V.P., "The Development of Soviet Space Rocket Engine Production," Iizvestiya an SSSR, energetika i transport, [Power Production and Transportation], 1974, No. 5, pp 3-29.

Part IV
ROCKETRY AND ASTRONAUTICS AFTER 1945

Chapter 9

BEGINNINGS OF ROCKET AND MISSILE ACTIVITIES IN SWITZERLAND[*]

Nik A. Schliep[†]

Missile engineering on an industrial basis was started in 1948 by Oerlikon Bührle Machine Tools Company and its sister company Contraves AG. At the beginning, static firings with a 600 kg thrust propulsion unit were made. Kerosene and nitric acid were used as propellant. The airframe was built in a bonded lightweight construction to the maximum extent permitted at that time. This was the first time that bonding procedures with resin had been used.

In 1950, the first unguided rocket launches were made at Lake Constance. For recovery purposes the rockets were equipped with a parachute system. The first guided launches were made in the Swiss Alps with a limited impulse and full-range flights were carried out in 1952 at the Holloman Air Force Base in Alamogordo, New Mexico, U.S.A., with the cooperation of the U.S. Army. Relating to continuous progress in propulsion technique the first tests with solid propellants were started. This activity finally led to the high-altitude research sounding rocket Zenit. The highlight of the motor with a total impulse of 100,000 kgsec was a concentrically cast boost and sustain phase for programming the thrust level. As in the past, bonded metal structure technology was used for the entire combustion chamber because of weight-saving purposes. Swiss scientists, Prof. J. Geiss from the University of Berne, known for his solar wind experiments on the first Moon landings, and the Swiss astronomer Prof. Golay developed experiments for Zenit's maiden flight.

The paper points out the Swiss pioneer spirit to develop liquid propelled and solid fuel rockets, the early bonding technology leading to advanced lightweight designs for spacecraft structures, and the philosophy used for parachute recovery systems.

Aerospace activities in Switzerland cannot be compared with those occurring in countries like the United States or the USSR. Switzerland is one of the ten member states of the European Space Agency (ESA) whose industry is working on various satellite projects and the European launch vehicle Ariane. However, our

---

[*]   Presented at The Tenth IAA History of Astronautics Symposium, Anaheim, California, U.S.A., October 1976.

[†]   Manager, Aerospace Department, Contraves AG, Zürich, Switzerland.

country can claim to have played a rather important role after World War II in the field of rocket and guided missile development.

Initial steps in rocket technology in Switzerland were made with systematic development and testing of a liquid propulsion system using a self-made test layout, by the Swiss engineer Josef Stemmer in 1956. He measured the thrust with a dynamometer on a movable sled as well as the velocity of gases in various expansion nozzles. Several propellants, such as gasoline with oxygen and acetylene with oxygen, were investigated. Chamber pressures up to 50 atm and nozzle exit velocities up to 3,800 m/sec were measured. Parallel to these static tests, first flight tests with a model airplane were made near Zürich in April 1941. The model, equipped with a rocket motor producing 23 kg thrust, reached a maximum speed of 193 km/h. Stemmer was a scientist and engineer, a man who worked with the right ratio of theoretical background and practical experience. He, as so many other scientists and experimenters, suffered from limited funding.

Rocket engineering on an industrial basis was started in 1947 by Oerlikon-Bührle Machine Tools Company and its sister company Contraves AG, Zürich. The two companies decided to develop at their own expense a liquid rocket propelled missile having a weight of 250 kg and a thrust of 600 kg. Two main tasks had to be fulfilled in parallel: building an airframe and building a propulsion unit. In late 1947, the first static firings with an experimental motor of 600 kg thrust was carried out (Figure 1). Kerosene with nitric acid as oxidizer were used as the propellant. At first, due to safety reasons, the test runs were limited to a burning time of up to 5 sec. The basic idea was to attach the complete propulsion system, including the propellant tanks, to the aft section of the airframe so that development time could be gained and flight tests could start as early as possible. The test runs with the motor gave different results (Figure 2), and many times the team had to work with enthusiasm day and night to maintain or build up new test facilities. In the early days of the project the steering of the rocket had to be provided by nozzle deflection with no aerodynamic means (Figure 3). The exhaust nozzle of the rocket was suspended on a two-axis gimbal and driven by motors with collectors and brushes as used in vacuum cleaners.

The Swiss, known as good wood carvers all over the world, built the first fuselage completely out of wood (Figure 4). The first separation tests from a launcher were made in 1947 in parallel with the development of the propulsion unit. These were carried out at Walensee and at Lake Constance. Due to lack of the propulsion unit, the first models were launched by small 8 cm rockets with solid propellant. The launcher (Figure 5), trainable in azimuth and elevation, was built on a modified search-light undercarriage used by the Swiss Army during World War II. The rocket, visible in the launcher, was still completely made out of wood with a 5 sec propulsion unit attached to the aft section of the vehicle. Many disappointing but also some successful flights, first near lake shores and later in the Swiss Alps, were made in this configuration (Figure 6). The burning time of the rockets was increased step by step up to 15 sec. Initial tests with parachute recoveries were initiated in 1949.

Unfortunately, the engineering team was confronted with the same problems as on many of today's projects: overweight, low mass ratio and insufficient thrust. For this reason the missile had to be completely redesigned in 1949. A new propulsion unit with 1,000 kg thrust and a burning time of 30 sec had to be developed (Figure 7). Again nitric acid and kerosene were burned in a newly designed nozzle with regenerative cooling (Figure 8). The nitric acid served as a cooling fluid in the thin-walled steel jacket. The propellant for the motor was stored in three concentric cylinders. The outer ring cylinder was used as a nitric acid tank, the middle cylinder as a kerosene tank, and in the center nitrogen with a pressure of 300 atm was stored. After ignition the nitrogen pressurized the ring-shaped pistons for the propellant feed. A pressure regulator, located at the front side of the tanks, assured a constant pressure of 40 atm to the pistons and thus to the fuel. Flexible connections from the tanks to the combustion chamber allowed deflections of the motor for steering maneuvers.

The airframe was no longer built from wood but was designed in a lightweight construction to the farthest limit permitted by modern engineering practice at that time (Figure 9). The manufacturing of the wound fuselage section was made by an automatic winding process. A thin-walled aluminum tube was wound over a series of longitudinal stringers on a mandrel. When completed, the body was coated with liquid araldit resin. Subsequently the fuselage was slowly rotated in an oven with air circulation to cure the resin. In cooperation with the Swiss chemical industry, the first time setting resins derived from the epoxy line of resins, which have excellent adhesion to various materials and to metals in particular, were chosen for the bonding of the airframe shells. A smooth surface of the bonded fuselage was provided by means of an automatic grinding process. Figures 10 and 11 illustrate the fuselage consisting of wound tubing and longitudinal stringers. Bonding methods, such as riveting, welding and soldering, were not applied. The bonding procedure with resin, developed together with the chemical industry, was an initial step for today's applied technology in structural bonding for spacecraft structures.

A curious idea was the correction of aerodynamic stability during flight due to fuel consumption (Figure 12). The wing assembly, consisting of four delta wings fixed on a wing barrel, could be shifted forward during flight by approximately 200 mm to compensate for center of gravity and lift-force displacement. Thus, the stability of the missile was controlled according to a preset time program. Needle bearing mounted rollers, moving on the outermost tube of the tank system, enabled the displacement of the wing assembly in the longitudinal direction, which was actuated by hydraulic pistons. This wing-displacement idea represents a typical measure for aerodynamic perfection avoiding any value engineering methods. Such a solution is no longer understandable today where efficiency is one of the prime design objectives. In early 1950, much development effort was generated to realize a recovery system (Figure 13). A reliable parachute recovery unit was needed to compensate for the fact that the small size of the firing ranges in Europe had limited safety zones. Furthermore, limited funding of the project required the reuse of the flight hardware and immediate investigations of failures after flight. In addition, the tight test schedule did not allow for the manufacturing of sufficient new hardware.

Missiles were recovered in two parts due to weight problems, nose section and rear section. The missile was held together by means of a connecting ring which after flight was broken by a primer cord. Both nose and rear section parachutes were packaged in pot-shaped light-metal containers from which they were ejected as soon as the release mechanism was actuated. Ribbon parachutes were chosen since the opening shock of such a chute was less than on a standard model.

The first guided launches were made in the Swiss Alps and on a French firing range. Electronic guidance sections and autopilots with mechanically operated computers, which really merit the expression "transisterless", were developed.

Taking into account all the imponderables during the development phase at that time, the system nevertheless represented an advanced project. Therefore, an evaluation contract could be signed in 1951 with the U.S. Air Force. Twelve missiles and the necessary ground equipment were shipped across the Atlantic Ocean. An 18-month launch campaign started at Holloman Air Force Base at Alamogordo, New Mexico. It was a new feeling for all participants to be on a firing range with large safety areas without being limited by mountains, neighborhood villages and weather conditions.

A real disadvantage of liquid propulsion units was the extended preparation time (Figure 14). As a first operation, the center tank had to be pressurized with nitrogen by a mobile compressor. For loading the oxidizer, the crew had always to wear protective clothing and firing range safety regulations for handling nitric acid had to be strictly obeyed. A further disadvantage was the difficult procedure for fuel unloading if for any reason the missile firing had to be postponed. The vehicle could remain for only a limited time in the loaded condition.

The take-off weight of the missile was approximately 350 kg (Figure 15) and burnout altitude after 30 sec burning time was approximately 9 km. At a later development state, rudders were attached to the tail to control the missile by aerodynamic means. In such a way, controllable range was increased to 15 km. To compensate for the effect of the missing gas jet after burnout, the steering movements of the fins were amplified accordingly.

Figure 16 shows the missile ready for launch. With a thrust level of 1,000 kg and with a take-off weight of 350 kg the acceleration at launch was only about 3 g. Compared with today's rockets, this was a very low value, especially at a high launch elevation where nearly 1 g was consumed to overcome the force of gravity. For flight-stabilization purposes the missile travelled 3 m in a mobile sled before it was released. Even with such a procedure the first seconds of flight resembled more a balancing act on the gas jet than an aerodynamically stable flight.

As mentioned before, the shortcoming of the described rocket type was the complicated and difficult handling of the liquid propulsion unit, especially the loading procedure with nitric acid. Relating to continuous progress in propulsion technique in the mid-1950s, the first tests with solid propellants were made (Figure 17). The continuous development activity led to a solid propellant rocket motor with a total impulse of 90,000 kgsec and later to the Swiss-developed high-altitude research sounding rocket Zenit.

110

The highlight of the motor was the use of two different concentrically cast propellant types in one combustion chamber -- boost and sustain phase -- to achieve two different thrust levels during the rocket ascent phase. Both phases burn radially. Hence, two thrust levels are available and the thrust program could be optimized to suit the aerodynamic drag of the vehicle. The first phase has a higher thrust of 4,600 kg to reduce dispersion. The second phase has a lower thrust level of 2,200 kg. The total burning time is 31 sec. The cylindrical combustion chamber has a bonded laminate construction (Figure 18). It also serves as the body of the rocket.

This lightweight construction was made possible by the initial development of reliable metal-bonding techniques as shown before in the wound airframe made from aluminum tubes. The solid fuel combustion chamber is again manufactured on a winding machine. The axial forces are taken by longitudinal strips and the tangential forces by the high-strength wire windings. In order to stabilize this system against buckling the complete shell is coated with a thermosetting epoxy resin. First prototype flights with such a motor were made in 1961. The Swiss scientists, Prof. J. Geiss, from the University of Berne, who later became well-known for his solar wind experiment on the first Moon landings, and the Swiss astronomer Prof. Golay, prepared experiments for Zenit's maiden flight (Figure 19).

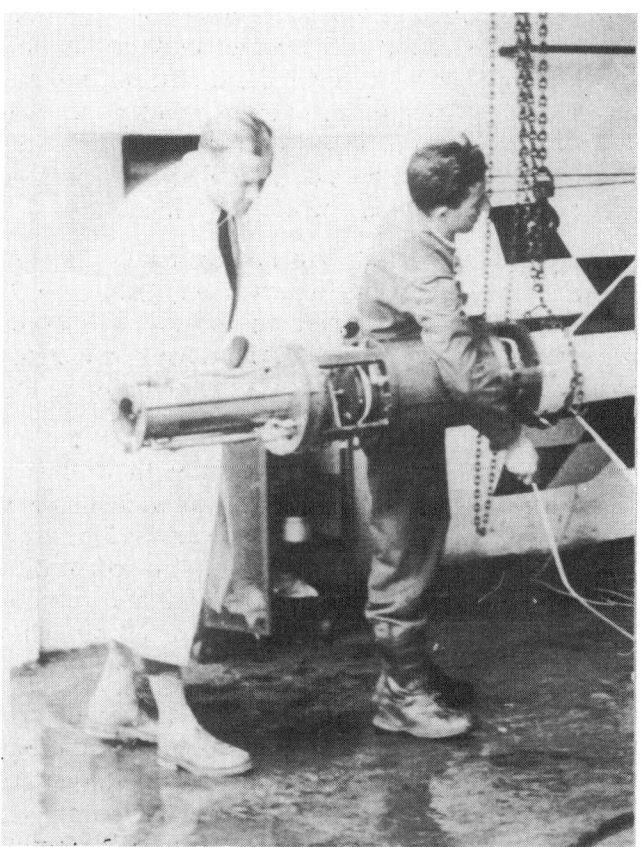

Figure 1 Experimental 600 kg thrust rocket motor for kerosene and nitric acid propellant

111

Figure 2   'Result' of a static test firing

Figure 3   Two-axis gimbaled rocket exhaust nozzle with drives

Figure 4   Short burn test firing of a wooden vehicle near a Swiss lake site

Figure 5   First trainable launcher in azimuth and elevation

Figure 6   Parachute recovery of an experimental missile in the Swiss Alps

Figure 7   Liquid propulsion unit ready for test firing

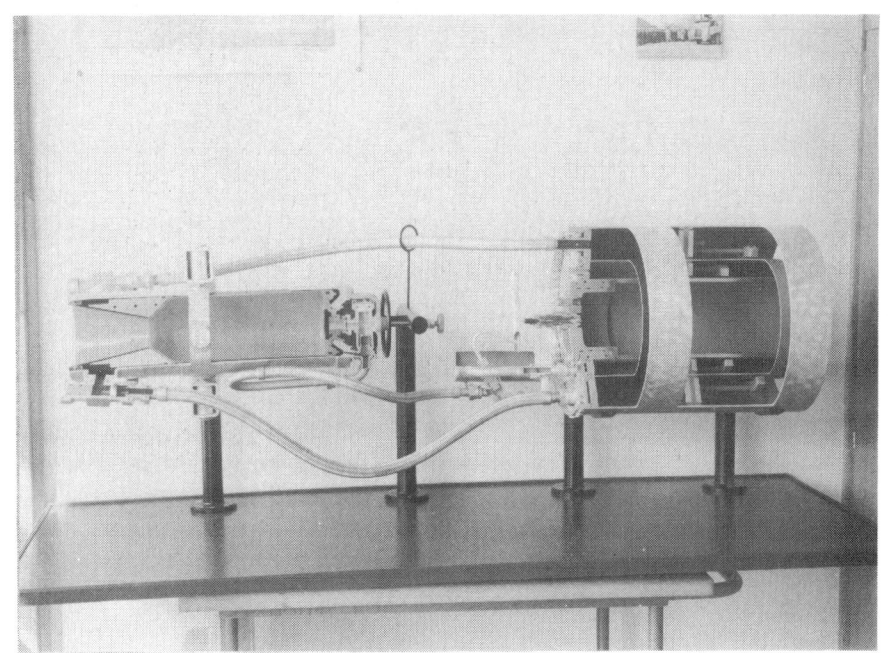

Figure 8 Propulsion unit consisting of combustion chamber, flexible feeding lines and concentric propellant cylinders

Figure 9 Winding process of a forward missile air-frame section

115

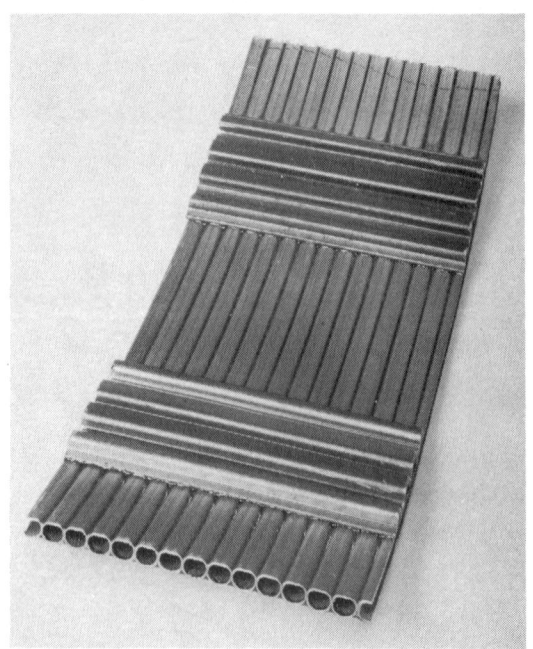

Figure 10 Air-frame construction in an epoxy bonding technique

Figure 11 Look through a cylindrical air-frame section; the wound tubes are bonded to 16 longitudinal stringers

116

Figure 12   Assembly of delta wings on the fuel tank

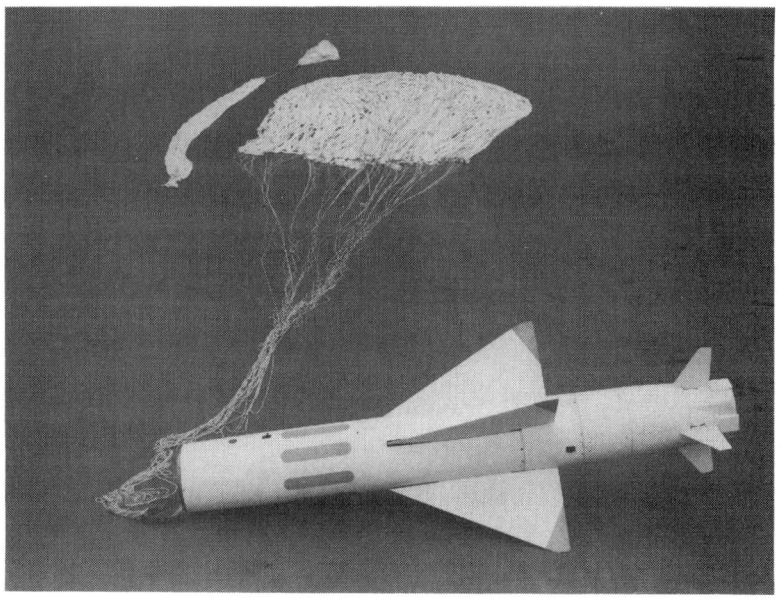

Figure 13   Recovery system with parachutes allows re-use of the missile after an
experimental launch

117

Figure 14 Filling procedure of the propulsion tank with liquid propellant

Figure 15 350 kg experimental missile with 1000 kg thrust motor

118

Figure 16   A defense missile ready for launching

Figure 17   First ballistic test vehicle with solid propellant in the early 1960s

119

Figure 18   Bonded laminated light-weight construction of a cylindrical combustion chamber (early 1960s)

Figure 19   Maiden flight of the first Swiss high altitude research rocket in Sardinia

120

Chapter 10

OPERATION BACKFIRE: ENGLAND LAUNCHES THE V2[*]

Mitchell R. Sharpe[†]

As World War II drew to an end in Europe, the British Army found itself in possession of a number of V2 rockets and ancillary support and launching equipment, as well as many of the technicians who developed the V2. Also in their hands were some of the German troops who had assembled, checked out, and launched these rockets against England and targets on the European continent. The Royal Army conceived a plan to gain experience in building and launching the rocket from a location in Germany, while carefully documenting all procedures. The British named the project Operation Backfire.

In Operation Backfire, the British sought further to recruit to England German scientists who had developed the V2. But as the project unfolded, other prominent Allied scientists and engineers who would later play major roles in the development of their national long-range missiles and launch vehicles also came to participate; from the United States: Theodore von Kármán, William Pickering, and Grayson Merrill; from the Soviet Union: Sergei Korolev, Yuri Pobedonostsev, and Valentin Glushko.

This paper considers Project Backfire and its implications for postwar rocket development among the Allied Powers.

World War II, in the European Theater of Operations, was for all practical purposes over by mid-March, 1945. Under increasing pressure from Marshall Bernard Montgomery, the German artillery units that had been firing V2 ballistic missiles from sites in northeastern Netherlands and the region northeast of Koblenz began withdrawing into the heartland of Germany. In doing so, they abandoned their rocket weapons and ancillary support and launching equipment. Also, the soldiers who manned the firing batteries began turning up in British prisoner of war camps.

With the growing accumulation of both materiel and the men skilled in preparing and launching the rocket, it occurred to the British that they had a unique opportunity to gain first-hand information and technology on the weapon of

---

[*]   Presented at The Tenth IAA History of Astronautics Symposium, Anaheim, California, U.S.A., October 1976.

[†]   Historian, Alabama Space and Rocket Center, Huntsville, Alabama, U.S.A.

future wars. The idea of a demonstration firing was proposed by Junior Commander Joan C.C. Bernard, Army Territorial Service, an aide to Major General Alexander M. Cameron, chief of the Air Defense Division (ADD), Supreme Headquarters, Allied Expeditionary Force (SHAEF) [1]. She suggested that the operations should be fully documented by technical reports, procedures, still pictures, and motion pictures.

On 1 May, she approached Cameron and briefed him. A special staff study, made on the following day, was submitted to the Assistant Chief of Staff, G-3, SHAEF, with the recommendation that the project be approved [1,3].

The remainder of the week saw two events take place that would have an important bearing on the proposed firings. On 4 May, SHAEF issued an order that no V2 materiel would be removed from the theater of operations pending further instructions [2]. On the day following, near Reutte, a small village in Austria near the Adolf Hitler Pass, a group of German civilians and army officers surrendered to agents of the Counter Intelligence Corps, of the U.S. 44th Infantry Division [4,5]. Among them were Dr. Wernher von Braun and Major General Walter Dornberger [6]. However, Second Lieutenant Charles L. Stewart was unimpressed by the two and grew increasingly irritated by their constant demands to be taken at once "to see Ike" [6,7].

With tactical intelligence matters more pressing, Stewart bundled the group off to a collection and holding center at Garmisch-Partenkirchen that had been established by the U.S. Army for such important military prisoners and detainees.

In the meantime, Colonel W.J.S. Carter, Assistant Chief of SHAEF's ADD, had been in London. Cameron had sent him there to convince the War Office of the importance of the proposed operation. Carter met with men such as Prof. Charles D. Ellis, Scientific Advisor to the Army Council; Dr. Alwyn Crowe, Comptroller of Projectile Development; and Lieutenant General Sir Ronald Meeks, Deputy Chief of the Imperial General Staff [1].

Carter very concisely told the group that such a demonstration then would save Britain countless man-hours of research and testing in weapon technology that was sure to dominate wars of the future. He was at once supported by Crowe, probably the only scientist in Britain who had been actively involved in rocket research prior to and during the early years of the war [1].

Not wanting to lose time, since they were certain that the project would be approved by SHAEF, Cameron's people moved out rapidly. By 19 May, all captured military personnel who had knowledge of launching the V2 had been identified and interrogated. A fortnight later, a select number of them were segregated into a special prisoner of war camp near Brussels [3].

Cameron's staff went on to compile a list of all materiel that would be required to assemble, check out, fuel, and launch the V2. In addition to the locations of such equipment revealed through questioning of prisoners and knowledgeable civilians, the British knew of sizable but unknown quantities of the weapon in two locations, both destined to be included in the Soviet Zone of Occupation. These were the huge underground manufacturing plants for the V2 at Niedersachswerfen (near Nordhausen), in Turingia, and the maintenance depot for the same weapon and its support equipment at nearby Klein Bodungen. Additionally, the names of manufacturers of components for the V2 system in Germany, France, Denmark, and Belgium also were known [9].

With the final approval obtained, Carter dubbed the project Operation Backfire, and the pace of activity, great as it was, increased further. On 26 May, the British 307th Infantry Brigade Headquarters, commanded by Brigadier L.K. Lockhart was assigned the mission of supporting Operation Backfire. Its primary function was to assist in finding a suitable location for the launchings and then providing the requisite administrative and logistical support to accomplish the mission [3].

Selection of the site by Cameron and Carter was not too difficult a problem. It had to be within the zone of the 21st Army Group. Furthermore, it had to be conducive to the siting of radars for tracking the V2s. The former Krupp Naval Gun Range, at Altenwalde, some 8 km south of Cuxhaven on the Schleswig Peninsula, was ideal. It was completely fenced in, had a good road and railway access and possessed several large buildings. From it the rockets could be launched along a northern azimuth to a target in the North Sea, while radars from the Elbe River to the Danish border tracked them [3].

With the good news of approval for Backfire, there also came some discouraging bad news. Practically every V2 under British control was lacking the critical guidance and control unit. The reasons why were various. It was the component first destroyed by the troops forced to abandon their weapons. Also, the unit was in short supply generally because of the effectiveness of Allied bombings of production plants. Additionally, as the war grew towards its end, raw materials for manufacture of the unit became increasingly scarce; thus, few were produced [19].

Nevertheless, Cameron put every man he could recruit to work on the problem of rounding up V2 materiel. Special teams were formed that included German-speaking English officers and, sometimes, German soldiers who knew where such equipment had been deserted. In all, these parties covered some 716,800 km in 6 weeks. The booty they found filled 200 trucks and 400 railway freight cars. To round out the initial logistical effort, 70 aircraft loads of special tools and equipment were flown in from England [3].

As the materiel accumulated, refurbishment of the range at Altenwalde grew apace. Ultimately, 2,500 British military troops and civilians were involved in Operation Backfire.

On 22 June, General Eisenhower issued Backfire Instruction No. 1:

The primary objective of this operation is to ascertain the German technique of launching long range rockets and to prove it by actual launch ... In addition to the primary objective, the operation will therefore provide opportunities to study such certain subsidiary matters as the preparation of the rocket and ancillary equipment, the handling of fuels, and controls in flight [3]. (One German engineer later suggested that the real purpose of the project was to familiarize the British with the originating end of a V2 trajectory.)

As the range preparation progressed, German scientists and engineers, including von Braun and Dornberger and many of their former colleagues from the rocket development center at Peenemünde, on the Baltic Sea, were interrogated by the British, with the consent of the Americans. The purpose of questioning these men at Garmisch-Partenkirchen was really two-fold. Primarily, it was to determine who among them would be of value at Operation Backfire. The other, and less successful one, was to identify personnel who for various reasons might prefer to work for the British rather than the Americans in pursuing their craft in rocketry. Dornberger, at the request of his interrogators, wrote an extremely helpful treatise on the safety aspects of handling rocket propellants associated with the V2 [9].

Curiously, the British were not interested in having von Braun participate in Operation Backfire. They knew quite a bit about him from their excellent intelligence services, as did the Soviets. Indeed, both countries knew far more about the man than did the Americans, who depended largely upon the British for strategic intelligence early in the war.

The reason why von Braun did not particularly interest the British is best explained by Carter, who years after the war, wrote:

"It may interest you to know that we always regarded von Braun as more of a visionary and front man than a scientist and technician. This may have been unfair because obviously he had great scientific and technical flair. I have in my notebook an extract from an intelligence report which was made in the very early days of the war, which reads as follows: 'This gentleman, despite his Nazi convictions and the fact that he often appeared in a uniform suggesting that he held some form of honorary SS rank, was not greatly enamoured of the operational possibilities of the A4 (i.e., the V2). He regarded it more as a medium for stratospheric and meteorological research and as a necessary stepping stone to bigger things' [10]."

To command the troops actually launching the missiles, the British already had in hand the one man in Germany best qualified to do so. He was Lieutenant Colonel Wolfgang Weber. At the end of the war, he had been commander of V2 Tactical Group, South; and he had learned his trade under the tutelage of Dornberger and von Braun at Peenemünde as the commander of the provisional firing unit established there in 1944. As the operation progressed, Weber found himself joined by 591 prisoners of war and German civilians, largely from Peenemünde, as well as 400 other Germans in a provisional labor unit.

By the beginning of July, the basic plan for Operation Backfire had to be modified. Despite the dedication of the search parties that had combed a good part of western Europe, there simply were not enough electric batteries, rate gyroscopes, and control amplifiers to outfit more than eight rockets. Originally the plan had been to have 30 V2s on hand in such condition that 9 could be fired [3]. Thus, the decision had to be made to launch the rockets in a purely ballistic mode; and there was no way to evaluate the performance of the all-important guidance and control unit.

On 14 July, SHAEF was formally dissolved; and Germany was divided into the various Allied occupation zones. Yet, the impact on Operation Backfire was minimal. The British War Office simply took over control of the project and redesignated Cameron's organization as Special Projectile Operations Group.

To work with Weber's former soldiers, the British selected 85 of the scientists and engineers being held at Garmisch-Partenkirchen [2]. They arrived in Altenwalde on 26 July and were divided into two groups. One group, under Dr. Kurt Debus, who would later become director of the Kennedy Space Center, was to provide technical assistance to Weber's men. The other group was sent to the nearby village of Brockeswalde. These two groups along with Weber's men denominated themselves the Versuchskommando, Altenwalde, and drew up an impressive organizational chart. (A year later, in the deserts of Texas and New Mexico, these same Germans found their names on a similar chart [11]. An American engineer assigned to work with them upon seeing it for the first time said, "My God! an organization with a president and 120 vice presidents!")

Not completely trusting the Germans under Debus, the British planned to use their colleagues at Brockeswalde as hostages in case something happened to the group at Altenwalde. The effort was futile, and though the British could not have known at the time, foolish. Neither group had any reason or motivation to dissemble or sabotage the project. They were, after all, once again working at their trade and happy to being so employed [13,14,15].

The former men of Peenemünde arrived at Altenwalde and Brockeswalde with inadequate clothing and a minimum of baggage allowed. For example, Karl Heimburg arrived literally without his shoes. Due to a mix-up, he had wound up at Schloss Kransberg, near Nauheim, a special camp for high-ranking German civilians. At once humble and puzzled to be in the company of men such as Albert Speer, Fritz Thyssen, Hjalmar Schacht, Alexander Porsche, and Hermann Oberth, he assumed that he was in for a long stay. Philosophically, he sent his shoes out to a cobbler. When the British located him at last, they sent him packing for Altenwalde barefooted [12,16,17].

To relieve the lack of clothing, the British quartermasters fell back upon the local economy. They found a warehouse filled with Nazi party uniforms and distributed them to the civilians at Altenwalde and Brockeswalde. The majority of the Germans, who had been party members, found the uniform a great joke. The nearby villagers did not. They assumed that their fellow citizens were former party members facing a British noose or firing squad. The good villagers were astounded by the refusals of the men behind the fence to offers of help in escape [1,12,15].

The hostage party at Brockeswalde did little other than sunbathe, swim in the nearby North Sea, play chess and skat, and meditate upon their future. Dieter Huzel, for example, was asked to write a lengthy memoir upon his days on Test Stand 7 at Peenemünde [4]. Lieutenant Colonel Wilhelm Zeppelius, Dornberger's officer in charge of propellants for the V2, was asked to write all he knew about such activities. He dawdled, asked for a typist, and generally proved that he was much more adapt at converting raw ethyl alcohol into schnapps.

Zeppelius had a roommate who was also of marginal value to the project. He was kept strictly segregated from his German colleagues, military and civilian. However, he cooperated in establishing the management of the German side of Operation Backfire, as the British requested him to do. Dornberger, for so he was, went

125

from Cuxhaven to the famed "London Cage" for high-ranking German prisoners in London. From it, he was subsequently sent to Wales, where he languished for two additional years [18,20]. Thus, Operation Backfire seemed to have provided the British with a means of insuring that Dornberger wound up in one of their prisons for some time at least. (He was told by Major Andrew P. Scotland, at the "London Cage" that he would be held for trial in place of SS Obergruppensfuerher Hans Kammler for the use of the V2 against England, a charge so flimsy that the British did not seriously press it.)

Liquid propellants for the V2 of Operation Backfire were no problem so far as ethyl alcohol was concerned. However, liquid oxygen was a more serious matter. Major C.W. Lloyd, Cameron's staff officer in charge of providing the propellants, had his difficulties. There were no storage facilities at the launching site for the highly volatile oxidizer. Additionally, very few liquid oxygen transport trailers from tactical firing units had been recovered. However, Lloyd found a plant at Fassberg, some 190 km away, that could produce about 4.4 metric tons of liquid oxygen per day and store about 62 tons of it. By 7 August, he had located another plant at Braunschweig, about the same distance away to the southeast. With the production facilities thus available and what limited means he had for transporting it, Operation Backfire was secured in that area [2].

On 11 August, the War Office issued Cameron a restated mission for Operation Backfire:

a. Information on testing, assembling, and filling of the German A4 rocket.

b. Detailed knowledge and experience of the German technique for launching long range rockets.

The intention is that you will collect this information by carrying out the operation of assembly and filling in Germany, using German disarmed personnel supervised by British technical experts, and that the successful completion of the operation will be proved by firing of a number of A4 rockets. Observations of the trajectory and photographic records will be aken as far as possible and the drill employed for firing the rockets will be recorded in detail [3].

By mid-August, Operation Backfire had resolved itself into two major efforts: the production of the V2 rockets and the recording of the process; and the preparation of launching procedures and means for tracking the missiles in flight. This latter phase was largely to be done by five SCR-584 radars loaned by the U.S. Army, the only tangible American contribution to the project [20].

On 21 August, Cameron received welcome news when a dozen V2s were found near Aachen and Hannover, one in almost mint condition. The discovery meant that eight rockets of high quality could be assembled for Backfire [21].

As the month continued the U.S. Army asked for 26 members of the von Braun team be returned to Garmisch-Partenkirchen in preparation for removal to America. The reason given was patently absurd: they were needed for use in the war against Japan. The British reply was only a little less absurd: their loss would jeopardize Operation Backfire. A compromise was reached when 14 of the men were returned [12].

In early autumn, the project was rapidly reaching culmination.

All items of ground support and launching equipment were on hand and in working condition. In some ways, the collection and assembly of such materiel was an even greater task than that of finding and rebuilding the V2s.

A target was selected in the North Sea some 75 km southwest of the village of Ringkoebing in Denmark. The firing azimuth was 365 degrees 51 min. true north. However, the range was set at only 240 km since a maximum range of 320 km would have sent the missiles out of radar tracking capability [22].

On 1 October, the first V2 was on its launcher awaiting the firing command from the concrete blockhouse that had been built near the launching pad. The safety-minded British had decided to employ it rather than the Feuerleitpanzer, a mobile launching control station built into a tank [23]. (Figures 1, 2, 3 and 4 depict various aspects of the preparations on that day.)

When the firing command was given, nothing happened. The British were disappointed and even suspicious of sabotage. The Germans, however, were quite used to such occurrences and merely shrugged. The ground-power connector had failed to eject. One of the German technicians donned a raincoat to protect himself from the drizzle of alcohol still in the combustion chamber of the rocket and stood up inside it to check its interior. Having found nothing amiss, he retired to the blockhouse, and the firing command was given. Again nothing happened. The pyrotechnic igniter had failed to operate. No further attempt was made to launch V2 on that day [22].

Figure 1 Pressure checkout of V2 propulsion system, Project Backfire, Krupp Proving Grounds, Cuxhaven, Germany on 22 September 1945.

Figure 2   Vertical checkout stand for the V2 rocket, 27 September 1945, Cuxhaven.

Figure 3   Electrical checkout of V2 prior to launch attempt on 1 October 1945, Cuxhaven.

Figure 4   Loading hydrogen peroxide form tanker into V2 at Cuxhaven, 1 October 1945.

On the following day, however, it was a different story. At 1443 hours, the V2 roared from its launcher and into a cloudless sky. In only 4 min. and 50 sec., it impacted just 80 meters to the left and 1.6 km short of the target [20]. Present in the blockhouse was Joan Bernard, whose idea it had been in the first place. (A German engineer also there stated that it was only the second time that a woman had been so present during a launch. The first was Eva Braun, later wife of Adolf Hitler [1].)

The second launch found the original, balky V2 up again. And again it demonstrated the inherent perversity of complex electromechanical things. While the rocket left the launcher, it traveled only 24 km because of an engine malfunction [20].

A decision was made to fire only one more missile and to invite Allied officers and members of the military press to observe the launching. The firing was called Operation Clitterhouse, and set for 14 October. The weather was ghastly. Beneath low-hanging clouds, there was a steady ground wind of some 12 meters per sec. [3].

Despite the weather, the launching went off spectacularly enough for the observers. The rumbling noise, flame, and smoke were very impressive to the men assembled. Most, who had any acquaintance with the V2, were used to a devastating explosion and wholesale destruction followed a few seconds later by the sound of a large missile headed for the area.

From the viewpoint of accuracy, the last V2 fired in Germany left something to be desired. It impacted 18 km short and 5.6 km to the right of the target [20,24].

Among the American and Soviet observers were men who had a vested interest in long-range rockets and were to varying degrees familiar with them, if more in theory than in first-hand experience.

From the U.S.A. there was Dr. Theodor von Kármán, in the crumpled uniform of an army colonel. A consultant to the U.S. Army Air Corps in rocketry, he was also a member of the National Advisory Committee on Aeronautics and Director of the Jet Propulsion Laboratory. Near him was Dr. William H. Pickering, Assistant Professor of Electrical Engineering at the California Institute of Technology and later Director of its Jet Propulsion Laboratory. Also close by was Dr. Howard S. Seifert, Chief of the Liquid Rocket Section of the Jet Propulsion Laboratory and later Director of Advanced Planning for the United Technology Corporation. Not far from those two men stood Lieutenant Commander Grayson P. Merrill, a naval officer later to become the Project Director for the Polaris missile.

Literally rubbing elbows with the three Americans were three Soviet officers, two of whom were very familiar with rockets. They were Colonel Yuri A. Pobedonostsev, leader of the Special Technical Commission (Rocket) in Berlin and later deeply involved in his nation's space program. With him was Colonel Valentin P. Glushko, currently in charge of refurbishing the engine test stands for the V2 at Lehesten and later chief designer of rocket engines for the first Soviet long-range missiles and space vehicles, and a General Sokolov [8].

Two additional Soviet observers showed up unannounced and uninvited. Cameron remained firm in not permitting them on the premises, and they had to be satisfied with watching the firing from beyond the pale.

The two were Lieutenant Colonel Sergei P. Korolev, in the uniform of a captain, and an unknown companion.

Korolev was perhaps the most interested of all the Soviets. He was currently the deputy of General Gaidukov, who was responsible for getting all V2 production and testing facilities in the Soviet Zone back into operation. Specifically, Korolev was in charge of refurbishing the underground plant at Niedersachswerfen, vacated by the Germans only six months earlier. He was particularly frustrated at not being able to see the assembly and checkout facilities at Altenwalde, as some other Allied officers were permitted to do.

Korolev had good reason to be frustrated. Within a fortnight to the day, two years later, he had to be ready to assemble and launch V2s in his own country from a proving ground near Kapustin Yar, some 190 km to the east of Stalingrad (now Volgagrad), the components of which were currently being produced in his plant at Niedersachswerfen and the engines of which were to be test-fired at Lehesten by Glushko, who stood inside the fence.

The friendly Pobedonostsev engaged a young American lieutenant in what at first appeared to be casual conversation. Later, First Lieutenant H.S. Hochmuth would recall:

> "He knew my name and that I had been there [Niedersachswerfen]. He told me the stuff [V2s removed from the plant by the Americans in July] was going to White Sands [Proving Ground in New Mexico]. This was supposed to be a secret. We began to discuss engineering. I asked him how things were at Nordhausen [i.e., Niedersachswerfen], and he said he was having a hell of a time because we had cleaned the place out. He was a very technical guy and said if they were able to see White Sands we could see Peenemünde [27]."

Hochmuth reported the offer to his superiors, but it was rejected out of hand. However, at the time, neither party would have seen much of interest. White Sands was an expanse of desert dotted with World War II radars and a few cinetheodolites and a collection of dilapidated wooden buildings, some relics of the Civilian Conservation Corps program of the mid-1930s. Peenemünde, of course, was a shambles wrought from Allied bombing and German demolition.

The Americans present were not upset as their Soviet counterparts. The cream of the von Braun team, including most of those involved in Backfire, were already under contract to the U.S. Army Ordnance Corps. In fact, the British were only able to recruit approximately 20 of the members taking part in the operation.

What, then, did accrue from Operation Backfire?

For the British, largely because of political decisions after the end of the war, little was gained. The nation was financially strapped and had nowhere near the funds needed to establish another Peenemünde. Indeed, one of the Germans, after being asked to consider working in Britain, declined with surprising candor: "We despise the French; we are mortally afraid of the Russians; we do not believe the British can afford us; so that leaves the Americans."

In order to have an arsenal of large rocket weapons, the British unwisely tied their limited funds and participation in such technology to American enterprises such as Skybolt and Blue Streak (a derivative of the Atlas intercontinental ballistic missile). Later, the nation would participate in the more successful Thor intermediate range ballistic missiles before bowing out of such expensive ventures for awhile.

Of the 20 Germans from Peenemünde who went to work for the British, including Dr. Walter Reidel, the highest ranking amongst them, little of real value was gained. They were simply too few in number and not employed as a team with specifically set goals. Additionally, they lacked the resources and facilities to pursue advanced work in the field of rocket technology.

For what it was worth, Operation Backfire did fulfill its primary mission. It produced the only complete set of documents for assembling, checking out, and launching the V2 rocket [3,20,22,23,28].

No such literature existed in German during the war. Military security simply forbade such a collection. Perhaps the most comprehensive book on the V2 was the *A4 Fibel*, a handbook for the soldiers who had to launch the missile. In many ways, it was an innovation in military training literature. Realizing that the soldiers would not be technically trained, instructions were kept to an absolute minimum. There was no theory of operation. The many cautions and warnings were graphically illustrated with cartoons, especially scantily clad girls who always draw attention [30].

Members of the British military, of course, received a good foundation in assembling, checking out, and launching V2s; however, such training, in hindsight, seemed of limited value.

Perhaps there was an indirect benefit, one the British present could have scarcely anticipated.

As Merrill watched the launching, he immediately wondered if such weapons could be launched from surface ships or submarines. Later he would write: "In looking back, I feel the Cuxhaven launchings had a definite bearing on the genesis of the now famous Polaris program. For example, it impelled me to work with Rear Admiral Calvin Bolster about 1951 to set up programs for adapting the Navy's Vikings to submarines [31]."

Since Britain later based her national defense on the use of the submarine-launched American missiles Polaris, Poseidon, and Trident, perhaps Operation Backfire did produce a tangible benefit for that country.

Obviously, the Soviets gained nothing of value in merely seeing the V2 launched, although it was their first such sight.

The immediate value to the Americans, except possibly for the inspiration given to Merrill, was minimal. They already had the components necessary to assemble 100 V2s in the Texas desert awaiting the skills of the German principals at Backfire. The documentation submitted by Cameron to the British War Office in January 1946, undoubtedly assisted in the preparation and launch of the V2s at White Sands Proving Ground between 1946 and 1950.

However, within the womb of the V2 that lifted off the launcher at Altenwalde on 14 October 1945, lay a technological fetus that would gestate for two decades before being born in both the U.S.A. and U.S.S.R.

Perhaps it is best described by Richard S. Lewis, a journalist for the U.S. Army newspaper *Stars & Stripes*, present at Operation Clitterhouse. Two and a half decades later after having watched the launching of the first men to the Moon, Lewis recalled what he had seen at Altenwalde: "That demonstration marked a transition point in the development of rocket technology in the West. That was the last V2 fired in Germany. The engineering science which the weapon represented was carried off by the victors as spoils of war. In the United States, it was to evolve into an interplanetary spaceship technology [32]."

REFERENCES

1. Letter to the author from W.S.J. Carter, Bristol, England, 5 September 1973.

2. Letter to the author from W.S.J. Carter, Bristol, England 1 November 1973.

3. *Report Operation Backfire, Vol. 1, Scope and Organization of the Operation*. London: The War Office, January 1946.

4. *Peenemünde to Canaveral*, Dieter K. Huzel. Englewood Cliffs, N.J.: Prentice-Hall, 1962, p. 187-190.

5. Interview by author of Magnus von Braun, London, 2 November 1972.

6. Letter to author from Charles L. Stewart, New York, 4 February 1974.

7. Interview by author of Charles L. Stewart, New York, 20 May 1971.

8. U.S. Military Attache Report, Great Britain, Subject: Evaluation of British Report on Operation Backfire, IG No. 0404.0700, from Military Attache London. December 13, 1945, signed by Howard S. Seifert. (National Air & Space Museum)

9. "Interrogation of Major General Walter Dornberger by Flight Lieutenant H.W. Stokes and Captain W.N. Ismay of CIOS Team 183 at Garmisch-Partenkirchen, Germany, 29 June 1945. (Library, Air War College, Maxwell Air Force Base, Alabama)

10. Letter to author from W.S.J. Carter, Bristol, England, 7 December 1973.

11. Copy in personal files of author.

12. Interview on tape of Karl Heimburg, Huntsville, Alabama, 26 June 1971. (author's files)

13. Interview on tape of Arthur Rudolph, Huntsville, Alabama, 7 April 1971. (author's files)

14. Interview on tape of Kurt Debus, Kennedy Space Center, Florida, 27 April 1972. (author's files)

15. Interview on tape of Albert Zeiler, Kennedy Space Center, Florida, 27 April 1972. (author's files)

16. *Crossbow and Overcast*, James McGovern. New York: William Morrow, 1964, pp. 200-201.

17. *Inside the Third Reich*, Albert Speer. New York: Avon Publishers, 1970, pp. 635-637.

18. *The London Cage*, Andrew P. Scotland. London: Evans Brothers, 1957, p. 130.

19. Interview on tape of Walter Dornberger, Huntsville, Alabama, 7 November 1971. (author's files)

20. *Report on Operation Backfire, Vol. 5, Recording and Analysis of Trajectory*, London: The War Office, January 1946.

21. Army Air Forces, Air Technical Service Command, Engineering Division Report, Serial TSEA-7-1225, Subject: Report on Travel in European Theater. November 9 1945, signed by Major C.W. Guy. (National Air & Space Museum)

22. *Report on Operation Backfire, Vol. 2, Technical Report*. London: The War Office, January 1946.

24. U.S. Military Attache Report, Great Britain, Subject: Operations "Backfire and Clitterhouse" (British). IG No. 0403.0700, from Military Attache London, 19 October 1945, signed by Major C.E. Martinson. (National Air & Space Museum)

25. Letter to author from W.S.J. Carter, Bristol, England, 10 July 1974.

26. Letter to author from W.S.J. Carter, Bristol, England, 31 July 1974.

27. Interview on tape of H.S. Hochmuth, Cambridge, MA, 27 October 1971. (author's files)

28. Film, *The German A4 Rocket*. London: The Ministry of Defence, December 1945. (U.S. Army Missile Command, Redstone Scientific Information Center, Huntsville, Alabama)

29. *Report on Operation Backfire, Vol. 3, Field Procedures*, London: The War Office, January 1946.

30. A photographic reproduction of this very rare document, as well as an English translation are in the archives of the Redstone Scientific Information Center, of the U.S. Army Missile Command, at Redstone Arsenal, Alabama.

31. Letter to the author from Grayson P. Merrill, Virgin Gordo, BVI, 17 September 1973.

32. Richard S. Lewis, *Appointment on the Moon*. New York: Viking Press, 1968, p. 4.

Chapter 11

EARLY UPPER ATMOSPHERIC RESEARCH WITH ROCKETS[*]

Thor Bergstralh and Ernst Krause[†]

In late 1945, the Naval Research Laboratory established the Rocket Sonde Research Section to "investigate the physical phenomena in, and the properties of, the upper atmosphere". While investigating sourses of rockets adaptable for high altitude research, it was found that U.S. Army Ordnance had obtained a considerable number of V2 rockets from Germany and was contemplating firing them in the near future. Since one of the purposes the Army Ordnance had in mind was to obtain data on the upper atmosphere, they invited interested service and university groups, including the Rocket Sonde Research Section, to join in this part of the program.

On 16 January 1946, a meeting was convened at the Naval Research Laboratory to discuss the proposed V2 upper atmosphere research program, and at this meeting a V2 Upper Atmosphere Research Panel was formed to coordinate activities and ensure the most efficient use of the limited number of boosters. Panel membership was limited to persons actually working on the program, and consisted of personnel from the U.S. Army Air Forces' Air Materiel Command, the Applied Physics Laboratory, the Army Signal Corps Engineering Laboratories, Harvard University, Princeton University, the University of Michigan, the National Bureau of Standards, General Electric Co., and the Naval Research Laboratory.

Assembly, firing, and tracking of the V2s were the responsibility of the White Sands Proving Ground of Army Ordnance, with General Electric Co. operating under Army Ordnance contract [1]. The Aberdeen Ballistic Laboratory and the Army Signal Corps were responsible for tracking the vehicle to provide an accurate knowledge of its position and velocity throughout the trajectory. Data were obtained through optical, radar with beacon, and doppler tracking to provide critical information such as fuel burnout time, maximum altitude, and range at impact during and immediately after each flight. Detailed trajectory information required considerable analysis of flight data and was available on a longer time scale.

---

[*]   Presented at The Ninth IAA History of Astronautics Symposium, Lisbon, Portugal, September 1975.

[†]   The Aerospace Corporation, El Segundo, California, U.S.A.

It was considered necessary to maintain the overall configuration and weight distribution of the missile essentially unchanged for aerodynamic and stability reasons. Therefore, the 2,200-lb. warhead had to be replaced by an equivalent-weight nosecone instrument chamber, instruments, electronics, and batteries. The first design [2] of a research warhead was constructed of 3/8-in. (0.95 cm) cast steel by the Naval Gun Factory and consisted of three sections: a nosetip, a forward conical section, and a main body, as shown in Figure 1. The nosetip section was used primarily for mounting atmospheric measurement devices, and the main body for housing equipment that required pressurization. The basic warhead was modified on some flights to accommodate special requirements [3].

Figure 1 Research "warhead" for peacetime V2, 1946.

Research instrumentation and related equipment were also installed in various parts of the missile body, and a typical arrangement is shown in Figure 2. The telemetry transmitter and storage batteries for primary power were individually pressurized and generally installed in the control chamber just aft of the nose section. Cameras for photographing the Earth were mounted in the mid-section between the oxidizer and fuel tanks in some rockets. Solar spectrographs, antennas for ionospheric transmission studies, and telemetry antennas were installed in the tail fins.

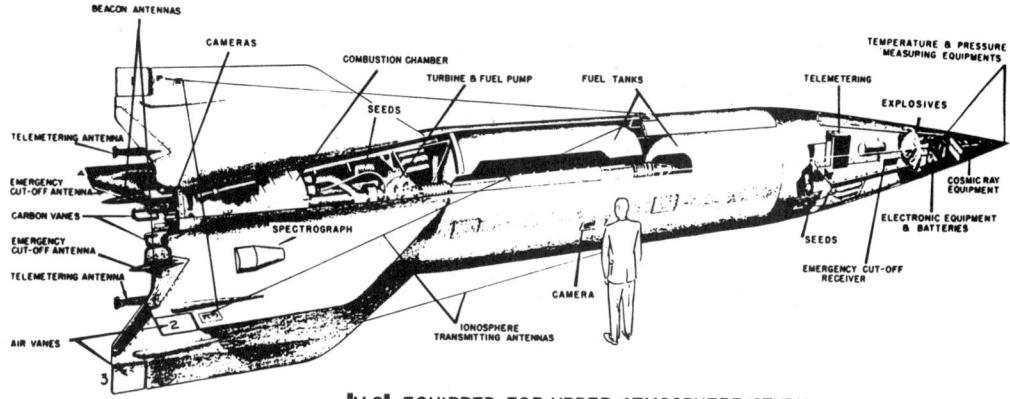

"V-2" EQUIPPED FOR UPPER ATMOSPHERE STUDY

Figure 2   V2 modified for upper atmosphere research, 1946.

Figure 3   NRL airborne transmitter removed from its pressurized container.

At the outset of the program, radio telemetry was selected as the prime method of data recovery. A group at the Naval Research Laboratory [4,5] developed a 23-channel pulse-time-modulated airborne transmitter having a peak rf power of 1,200 w at 1,000 MHz. A later version provided 30 channels with a peak power of 3 Kw at 1,000 MHz. Up to 15 channels were equipped with mechanical subcommutators for slowly varying data such as temperature and pressure, so that a total of 345 channels of data could be transmitted at a sampling rate of 1 cps. Figure 3 shows the transmitter removed from its pressurized container. The circuitry for each channel was contained on a plug-in unit for ease of servicing. The entire unit was about 14 X 14 X 22 in. (35.5 X 35.5 X 56 cm) and weighed less than 150 lb. (68 kg).

Two independent ground receiving and recording stations were operated for each flight to provide redundancy. Each consisted of a 1,000-MHz antenna, receiver, video amplifier, multichannel decoder, and recording equipment. A typical record is shown in Figure 4. The top and bottom channels provided timing signals. The subcommutated channels at the top represent pressure and temperature information, each individual deflection corresponding to a different gauge. The roll gyroscope channel shows no roll since the vehicle was stabilized at this time in the flight.

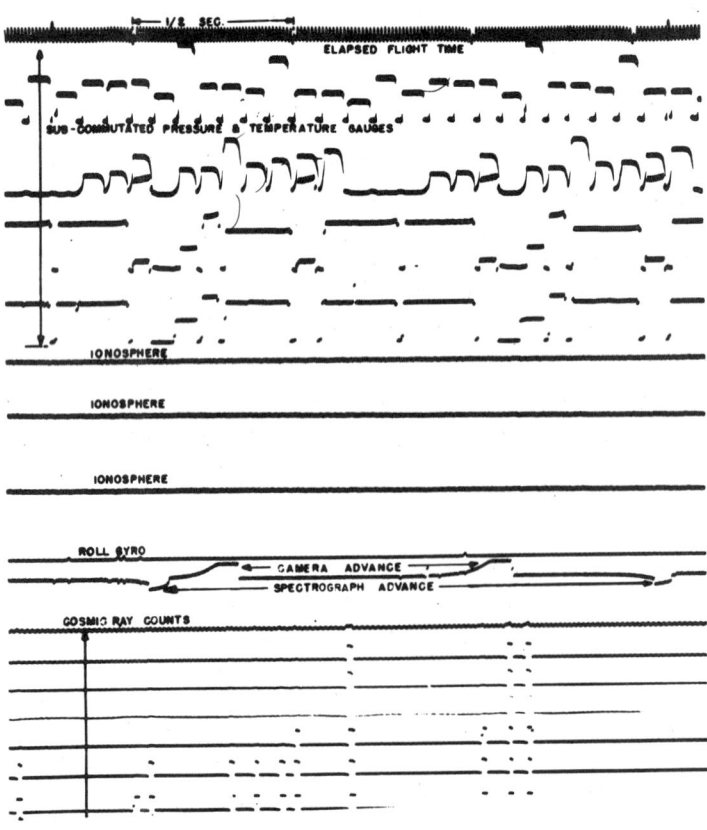

Figure 4 Typical radio telemetry record from V2 flight.

138

Preflight checkout was provided by a "relay" antenna system using a small dipole close to the transmitting antenna to pick up the radiated signal, which was then re-radiated from another dipole on a nearby 40-ft. pole. In this manner the telemetry flight configuration could be checked before launch. The Naval Research Laboratory provided telemetry services for all of the flights in the program.

The recovery of data by telemetering was not always completely satisfactory. Only limited spectrographic data could be transmitted, and films from cameras and biological specimens required physical recovery. Although efforts were made to provide ejection capsules provided with drag mechanisms by both the Army and the Naval Research Laboratory, these efforts were abandoned when physical recovery was successfully achieved by breaking up the missile prior to reentry into the denser atmosphere. TNT charges were attached to the four structural members of the control chamber and detonated by both a timer mechanism and a radio destruct signal at an altitude of about 60 km. After separation both the warhead and the afterbody exhibited high drag and poor stability, resulting in sufficiently low impact velocities so that equipment could be recovered in fair condition. Spectrographs, frame and motion picture cameras, and photographic data recorders were successfully recovered from flights that achieved altitudes of 170 km. In most cases the films were in excellent condition, including those taken by cameras for which no special precautions had been taken to protect the film. One solar spectrograph was recovered twice in such good condition that it only required recalibration before being flown.

The number of V2s was limited, and other boosters were added to the program. The Aerobee, which was first used in 1947, was a single-stage, liquid propellant rocket with a nominal payload of 68 kg and a corresponding peak altitude of about 110 km. Later versions were capable of higher altitudes. The Viking, designed and built under the technical direction of the Naval Research Laboratory, more closely resembled the V2, but employed a more efficient structural design and a gimbal-mounted motor for attitude control. Viking 11 carried a payload of 455 kg to an altitude of 254 km.

The Naval Research Laboratory program encompassed four fields of high altitude research: (1) atmospheric pressure, temperature, and composition measurements, (2) cosmic rays, (3) the ionosphere, and (4) solar physics, involving both the ultraviolet and x-ray spectra of the Sun.

ATMOSPHERIC PROPERTIES

Prior to the beginning of the V2 program, the physical properties of the atmosphere had been well explored over the first 30 km of altitude by balloon-borne instruments. Above that altitude the model of the thermosphere was based on ground-based observations of meteors, sound propagation, the ionosphere, and the aurora and airglow. The data from these observations were reflected in the National Advisory Committee for Aeronautics (NACA) tentative standard atmosphere. The advent of the sounding rocket offered an opportunity for direct measurements, and the early rocket results indicated a significant departure from the NACA standard atmosphere.

The Naval Research Laboratory undertook to measure the pressure at various locations on the rocket and reduce the measured pressures to ambient pressures and densities. Gauges were installed in the nose of the rocket to measure the stagnation pressure, which was reduced to ambient density by means of the Rayleigh formula

$$P = 0.92\rho v^2 + 0.46p + ...$$

for a diatomic gas, where p and ρ are the ambient pressure and density and v is the rocket velocity [6]. The relation holds for supersonic velocities and up to about 100 km, or more, even for angles of attack somewhat in excess of 10 deg. At higher altitudes the density measurements were obtained from the pressure changes as measured on the side of the rolling rocket. In this method, gauges were mounted in the side of the rocket and, at high altitudes and well after powered flight, the rocket axis was oriented perpendicular to the velocity vector and the rocket was caused to roll. Pressure readings were then modulated with a period equal to the roll period of the rocket. The ambient air density is related to the amplitude of the modulation [7]. A measurement of the density at an altitude of 219 km on a Viking flight on 7 August 1951, when corrected for an atmospheric wind, was determined to be 1 X 10^{-7} gm/m^3 with an accuracy of 20 percent.

To obtain the ambient pressure versus altitude, gauges were installed on the surface of the nosecone and on the rocket body just forward of the tail fins. The pressure readings from the nosecone gauges were reduced to ambient values by means of the Taylor Maccoll theory [8]. Theoretical studies and German wind tunnel data [9] had shown that the pressure at the surface of the rocket at points from 6 to 13 rocket diameters from the nose is equal to the ambient pressure within a few percent over a wide range of Mach and Reynolds numbers. The validity of this result was checked by comparing measurements made approximately simultaneously up to the balloon ceilings, and by comparing measurements made in different rockets with varying velocities.

The large dynamic range of pressures encountered in flight required a variety of pressure gauges: bellows-type gauges for 760 to 20 mmHg, Pirani-type gauges for 2 to 3 X 10^{-3} mmHg, and Philips ionization gauges for over 10^{-3} to 10^{-6} mmHg. A new type of gauge known as the Havens cycle gauge[10] was developed and used over a pressure range from 1 atm to about 10^{-3} mmHg. In this gauge a bellows containing a Pirani element is cyclically moved by a motor, causing a pressure modulation about the Pirani element. The modulation produces an ac signal that can be amplified. The average pressure in the bellows is equal to the outside pressure communicated into the chamber through a small hole if the pumping time is long compared to the cycling rate.

The motions of the rocket introduced measurement difficulties. To correct for the effects of small angles of attack, similar gauges were mounted on opposite sides of the rocket and their average value was used as the normal zero angle of attack pressure. When the rocket had a steady roll there would be a point in each revolution where equal pressures would occur in the two opposing gauges, and the reading at that point was taken to be the surface pressure for zero angle of attack. Obtaining ambient pressures near the peak of the trajectory was complicated by outgassing of both the rocket and the gauge surfaces, which was overcome by taking advantage of the rocket roll. The roll motion caused a modulation in the pressure reading, and, for a long mean free path, the modulation was directly proportional to the product of the ambient density and the component of the relative air velocity perpendicular to the gauge opening [11].

Typical results are shown in Figures 5 and 6, taken from [6]. Figure 5 presents the density versus altitude as determined from five flights over New Mexico and one Viking flight at the equator. Figure 6 shows pressure data from six New Mexico flights and the one flight at the equator. The difference between summer and winter pressures over New Mexico is indicated by the dashed line.

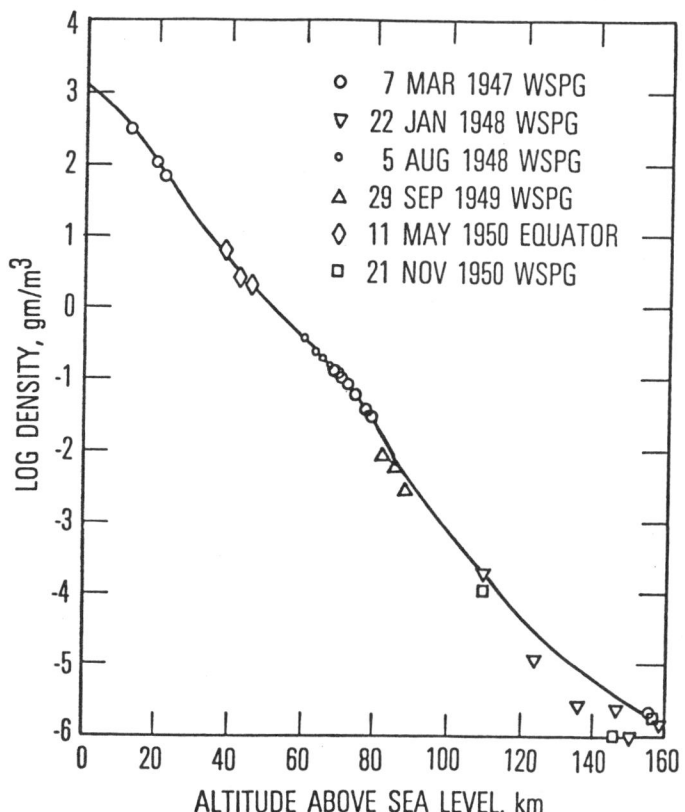

Figure 5 Log density versus altitude determined from five V2 flights from White Sands Proving Ground and one Viking flight at the equator.

The density data from Figure 5, plus the 219-km point obtained on a later Viking flight, are compared to the mean value of the Cospar International Reference Atmosphere 1972 [12] in Figure 7. A similar comparison is made for the pressure data [6] in Figure 8. The density points lie within the high and low values of the solar cycle up to the highest point shown. At altitudes of 90 km and below, the rocket pressure data agree with the CIRA mean within 10 percent, but above 100 km the variance becomes somewhat greater and the early rocket data tend to show somewhat higher values.

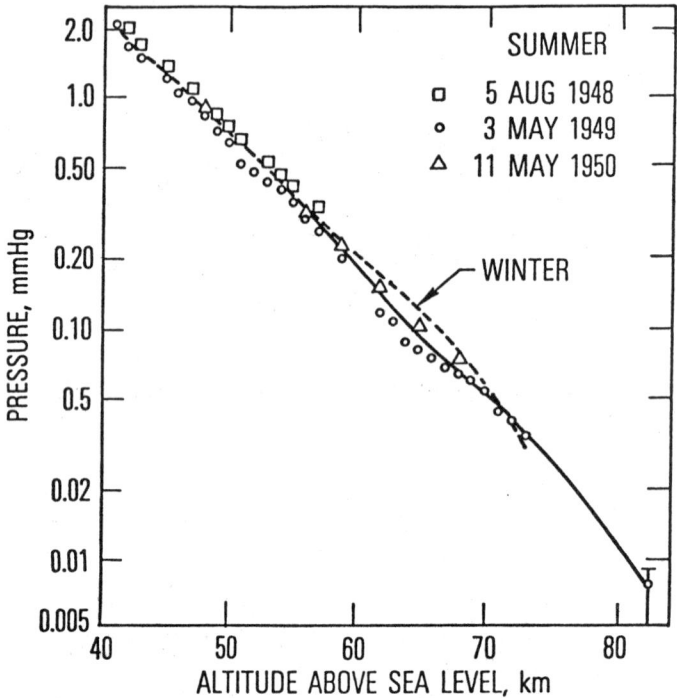

Figure 6   Pressure data from six White Sands and one Viking equator flights.

Atmospheric temperature was not measured directly, but was calculated from the pressure and temperature data. The average temperature versus altitude, as derived from the early rocket flights, is shown in Figure 9. The temperature calculation depends upon the average molecular mass in the atmosphere; and, in this figure, the composition was assumed to be molecular nitrogen and molecular oxygen with an average mass of 29. The altitude-temperature relationship below 100 km is in good agreement with the latest standard atmosphere. At higher altitudes, as shown by the CIRA points in the same figure, the temperature rises more rapidly with altitude than the values derived from the fairly limited rocket data from the first flights. The high-altitude variation could be expected, since the uncertainty in the pressure and density measurements increased with altitude.

Although early rocket measurements were geographically limited by launch facilities, and limited in number by the availability of rockets, they provided a good picture of atmospheric conditions at altitudes previously unexplored. In the following decades the data have been greatly extended by rockets and rockoons launched at a large number of sites, and more recently by satellites, to provide a greatly improved understanding of the upper atmosphere.

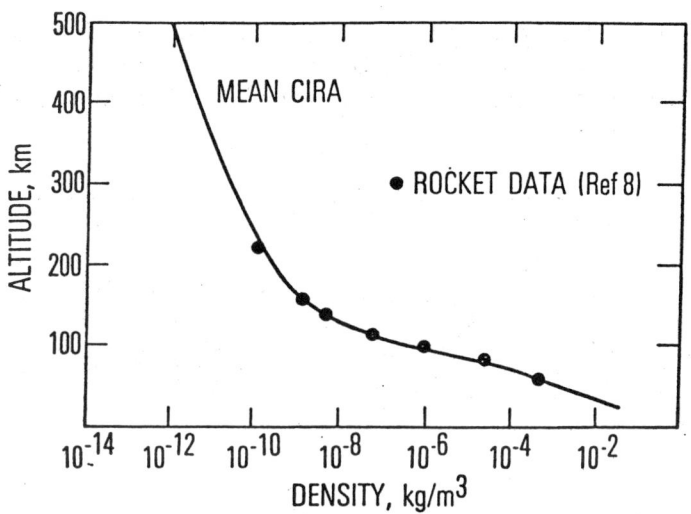

Figure 7   Density data from Figure 5 plus 219-km altitude Viking flight compared to Cospar International Reference Atmosphere (CIRA).

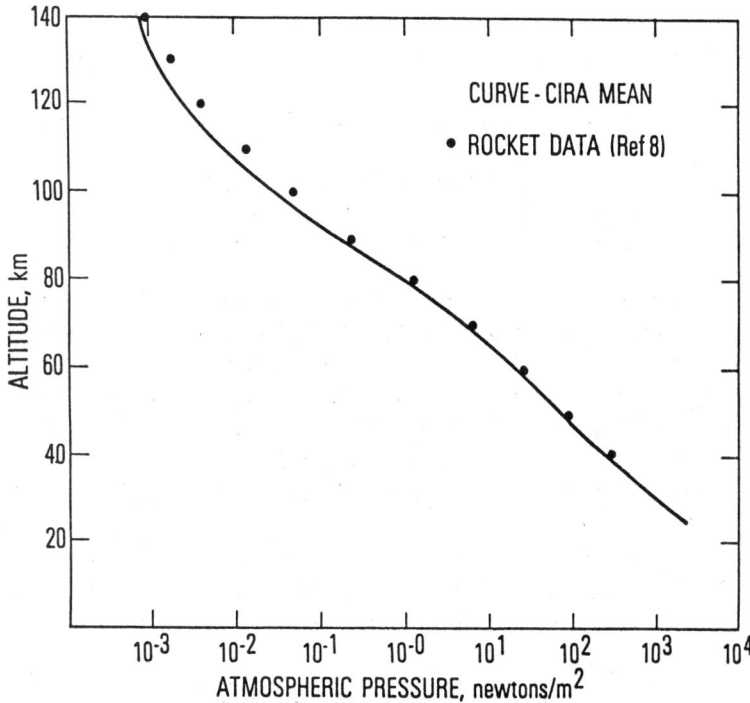

Figure 8   Pressure data from Figure 6 compared to mean Cospar International Reference Atmosphere (CIRA).

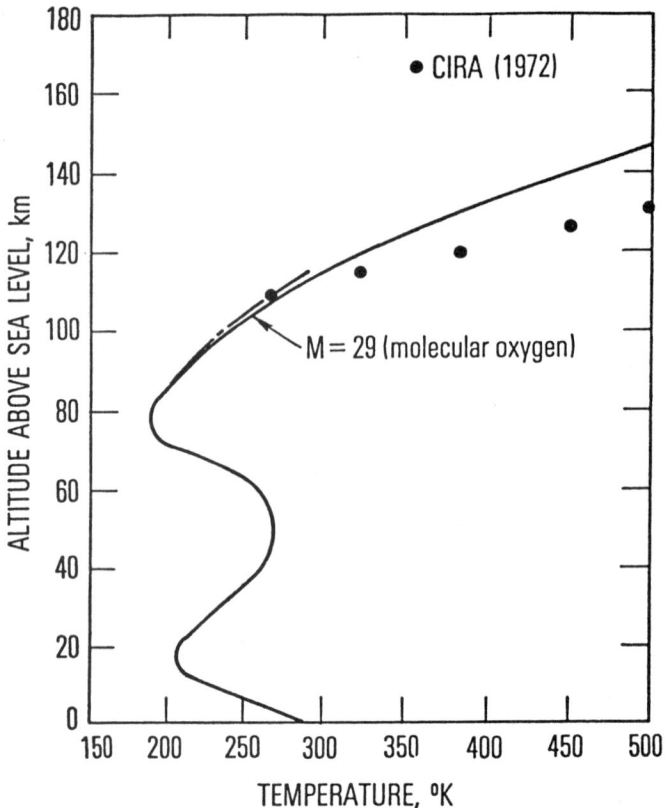

Figure 9 Average temperature versus altitude from early rocket flights compared to CIRA data.

COSMIC RADIATION

The availability of the V2 as a sounding rocket offered a new opportunity for a determination of the nature and intensity of the primary cosmic radiation. At that time, ground-based, mountain-top, and balloon-borne experiments had determined the distribution of both the total and the "hard" cosmic radiation throughout the lower atmosphere. These experiments indicated that at least the major portion of the primary radiation interacted with components of the atmosphere at altitudes where the pressure was as low as 2 cmHg, and identified the sea-level penetrating radiation as mesons produced in the interactions. Since only secondary and tertiary mesons, photons, and electrons penetrated to the altitudes then achievable with balloons, the fluence, composition, and energy distribution of the primary radiation had to be inferred from the secondaries. The nature and behavior of the secondaries had led most of the workers [13,14] in the field to the conclusion that the primary radiation consisted largely of very high energy protons, although the presence of gamma rays and electrons could not be ruled out.

Figure 10   NRL Geiger counter telescope.

Although the V2 could carry instruments to the region of the primaries, it was not an ideal platform for cosmic ray research for two reasons. First, the rocket spent only 2 to 3 minutes of its total flight time at the very high altitudes it could attain. Since the primary flux in terms of particles/cm^2-sec was known to be low, only about 100 primary events could be expected to be detected in each flight, with the size of the instrumentation carried. Secondly, the V2 had a large burnout mass and tended to replace the atmosphere as a source of secondaries. Early Naval Research Laboratory experiments used Geiger counter telescopes [15,16,17] such as shown in Figure 10, containing lead absorbers to obtain intensity and penetration measurements. Out-of-line counters were employed in an anti-coincidence arrangement to detect shower events. In these first flights the total intensity measured on ascent was in good agreement with balloon measurements up through the Pfotzer maximum at about 90 mmHg. At the highest altitude, however, about half of the events recorded by the rocket telescope were accompanied by the discharge of an anti-coincidence counter, indicating that these events were showers generated in the mass of the rocket itself. About 35 percent of the high altitude radiation was stopped in less than 4 cm of lead. This soft component was interpreted as being due to the albedo effect -- secondary particles ejected upward and returned to the Earth through the action of the Earth's magnetic field. Because of these effects it was not possible to obtain an accurate value for the primary intensity from the first rocket experiments, but they did indicate that the electron component was very small.

In 1950, Perlow and his co-workers [18,19] flew two sets of experiments to search for primary gamma radiation and to determine the composition and intensity of the charged primary radiation. The first experiment used counter arrays in coincidence and anti-coincidence, such that both the total charged-particle radiation and gamma radiation in the energy ranges of 3.4 to 90 MeV and 0.1 to 15 MeV could be detected. The total charged-particle intensity was essentially constant at 0.12 particle/cm^2/sr above 45 km altitude, which agreed with measurements by Van Allen, et al. [20], of the Applied Physics Laboratory and also with present values for the latitude of White Sands, New Mexico. Their measurements led to an upper limit of gamma-ray energy flow of less than 1 part in 1,000 of the total energy flow. The experiments were carried in both day and night flights and indicated that there was no appreciable diurnal effect in either the ionizing or gamma radiation. The absence of a diurnal effect was confirmed by the use of a similar apparatus in Skyhook balloon flights in which a statistical accuracy of about 3 percent was achieved. Both results agree with present data.

The second experiment employed a counter telescope incorporating proportional counters to determine the composition and intensity of the charged primary radiation. Lead absorbers were used to measure the range of the penetrating particles, and out-of-line counters were used to measure the range of the penetrating particles, and out-of-line counters were used to detect showers. A total of 263 events were detected in a period of 150 sec, during the time the rocket was at an atmospheric depth of 2.5 gm/cm^2, or less. Of the total, 148 events were discarded as being due to showers generated in the rocket, and 90 of the remaining events were associated with particles with a range in excess of 60 gm/cm^2. The ionization of the 90 events was measured in each of two proportional counters and plotted against the minimum ionization level as determined as sea level (Figure 11). Two peaks, centered about $I/I_0 = 1$ and $I/I_0 = 4$, were obtained and were interpreted as being due to protons and alpha particles. Using an I/I_0 value of 2.5 as the division between protons and alpha particles, Perlow obtained a proton-to-alpha particle ratio of 5.3, which is somewhat lower than the presently accepted value for that latitude. Although the histogram shows one particle with $Z = 6$, the statistics did not support any conclusions as to the presence of heavier particles in the spectrum. Perlow's value of 0.07 particle/cm^2-sec as the primary fluence agrees with later determinations for penetrating particles at the latitude of White Sands as well as the altitude achieved by the rocket.

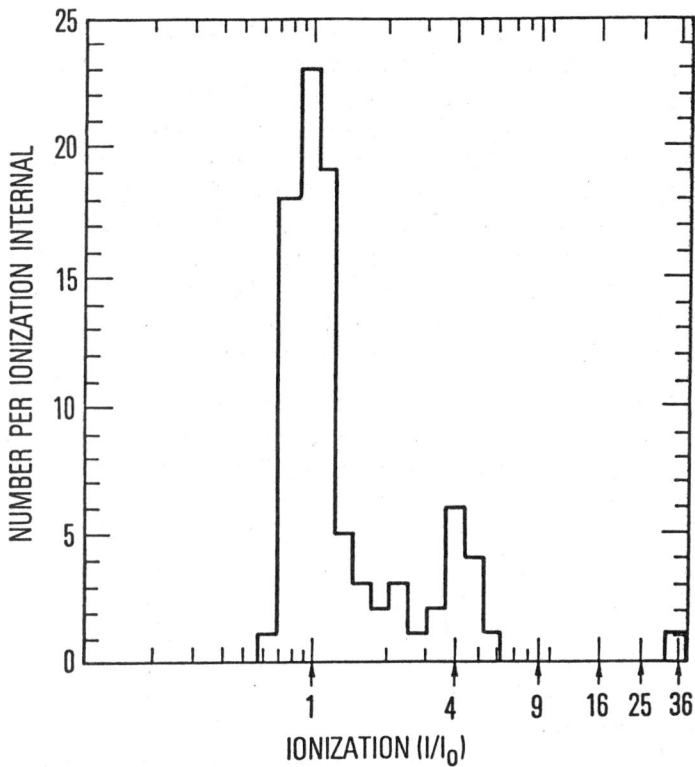

Figure 11 Charged primary radiation plotted against minimum ionization as determined at sea level. Peaks determined as due to protons and alpha particles.

In addition to the counter telescope experiments, a few cloud chambers were flown. A 6-in. chamber was flown in a V2 to an altitude of 159 km on 22 January 1948 [21]. Two lead plates, each 1 cm thick, crossed the chamber, and stereo photographs were taken at 25-sec intervals. As in the counter experiments, the major share of the events detected were associated with showers originating in the rocket. The most significant event detected in this flight was a single track contained in a photograph taken at 145-km altitude when the outside atmospheric pressure was about 10^{-5} mmHg. The track penetrated both plates and created heavy ionization. Since a proton with sufficient energy to penetrate the lead with very little scattering would have near minimum ionization, the possibility that the track was caused by a proton was ruled out. The event was interpreted as being due to an alpha particle of energy greater than 400 MeV, or to a more highly charged nucleus of correspondingly greater energy. In the same year, a group at the University of Minnesota [22] also found evidence for heavy primary cosmic ray nuclei in emulsions and with cloud chambers flown above 90,000 ft with Skyhook balloons.

IONOSPHERIC MEASUREMENTS

As in the other fields of high-altitude research, the ionosphere had been probed quite extensively with ground-based instrumentation. Both cw and pulsed-radio methods had been used with considerable success in obtaining information as to the layer heights and the variable nature of the ionospheric effects. Ground-based probing, however, was limited in several respects. Radio probing could only measure the index of refraction, or ion concentration at certain heights where reflection occurs at a critical frequency, but did not permit measurements on the details of the concentration above the regions of maximum density. The heights obtained were apparent heights, which were higher than the true heights, since the velocity of the radio waves in the ionized regions below the maxima could not be directly determined. Also, ground probing did not permit a determination of the ratio of free electrons to ions, since the latter do not respond to, or affect, the radio waves to any significant extent.

The high altitude rocket provided a potential for overcoming some of the limitations of ground-based ionospheric probing in several ways. Radio signals could be passed from high altitude to the ground through the ionized region without the need for meeting a reflection condition. As the rocket moved upward, the effects on the transmission over a specific region could be measured. Also, direct measurements of ion concentrations were possible with Langmuir probes mounted in the nose of the rocket, and with rf ion spectrometers. By using vertical incidence sounding during the rocket flight, the rocket and ground measurements could be combined to aid in interpretation of the data. However, the relatively infrequent launches were a considerable handicap in studying a region with such great and frequent temporal variations as characterize the ionosphere. Each flight could only provide a snapshot of the ionospheric conditions at the time and place of the launch.

The principal method undertaken at the Naval Research Laboratory [23,24] consisted of the transmission of two harmonically related crystal-controlled cw radio frequency signals from the rocket to ground-based receiving and recording equipment. The fundamental frequency was selected to be just slightly above the maximum critical frequency for the regions that the rocket would penetrate. The higher harmonic was selected so that the velocity of propagation would be essentially unaffected by the ionosphere, i.e., the frequency-dependent index of refraction was nearly unity for all points between the rocket and the ground. The two receiving stations on the ground were located 6 miles apart in the plane of the trajectory, and, with the short-range, high-altitude trajectory of the rocket, nearly vertical propagation was obtained.

Under these conditions, the phase velocity of the fundamental would be increased above the speed of light, whereas that of the harmonic, or reference, frequency was unchanged. After multiplying the received fundamental frequency of the harmonic factor, it was beat against the reference frequency to obtain a phase beat frequency that was a function of the radial velocity of the rocket and the effect of the ionosphere on the fundamental frequency. Since the velocity of the rocket could be determined by independent means, the beat frequency contained the information from which the index of refraction could be calculated. In this method there are actually two downcoming rays -- one ordinary and one extraordinary -- resulting from magneto-ionic splitting. The rays were separated at the receiving stations, so that both the ordinary and extraordinary indices of refraction could be calculated. Using the Goubau modification of the Appleton-Hartree equation, the values of electron density as a function of altitude were deduced.

The implementation of this technique on a vehicle such as the V2 required the solution of a number of difficult instrumentation problems. Although equipment was carried on the first V2s launched back in 1946, the first limited success was achieved on a midday flight on 7 March 1947 [25]. At that time the magneto-ionic components of the signal were not received separately and the data were very difficult to analyze. It was immediately noted that the fundamental signal was lost on ascent at an altitude of 111 km and reappeared on descent at the same altitude. The ground-based ionogram taken at the time of flight indicated the occurrence of a sudden ionospheric disturbance just before launch, and the signal dropout was attributed to the resultant sporadic E ionization. When the data were later successfully analyzed [26], the measurements showed a rapid and almost linear rise of electron density from about 85 km to the dropout altitude of 111 km, with a peak value of about 2×10^5 electrons/cm^3 at the 111-km point. The next attempt, on 22 January 1948, yielded similar results, with a signal dropout at 100 km.

On later flights on V2, Viking, and Aerobee-Hi rockets, measurements were made to an altitude of 260 km. The results obtained in four flights above White Sands are shown in Figure 12 [26-28]. These data show the same general rapid rise in electron density from 80 to 85 km to the 100-km region, followed by a slower and continuous increase to the maximum altitude obtained. The May 1954 and June 1956 profiles are similar, but the latter curve shows a denser ionosphere, which is consistent with the corresponding increase in solar activity. Both daytime and nighttime measurements into the E layer were made at Fort Churchill, Canada, later in the program [29]. The daytime profile was quite similar to that at White Sands, but very low densities (2×10^4 electrons/cm^3) were observed at night up to an altitude of 170 km.

The first measurement of the F-layer peak was made by W.W. Berning [30] of the Ballistics Research Laboratory on a Bumper-WAC firing on 24 February 1949, in which a WAC Corporal rocket was launched at altitude after being boosted by a V2. His data taken near a solar activity maximum showed a peak density of about 2×10^6 electrons/cm^3 at an altitude of about 32 km and a decrease in density to 400 km. Later NASA high-altitude rocket flights [31,32] indicated the F2 peak in the 300-km region, with slowly decreasing electron densities to very high altitudes. Soviet scientists, also using the Naval Research Laboratory (NRL) two-frequency techniques with sounding rockets, obtained electron density profiles in good agreement with the NRL results [33].

The program of rocket-borne measurements of ionospheric electron densities that was begun in 1946 with the V2 made significant contributions to the understanding of the ionosphere. The concept of the ionosphere as discrete layers of high charge density separated by regions of considerably lower density was altered by the measurements showing that the density remained high between the E and F regions. The steep electron density gradient in the bottom edge of the E region was established early in the program. In the following decade, as rockets capable of higher altitudes became available, the region of the F_2 maximum and beyond were explored, both in the U.S. and the USSR. The altitude of the F_2 maximum was found to remain fairly constant in the 300-km region, although the charge density varies by as much as an order of magnitude between sunspot minima and maxima.

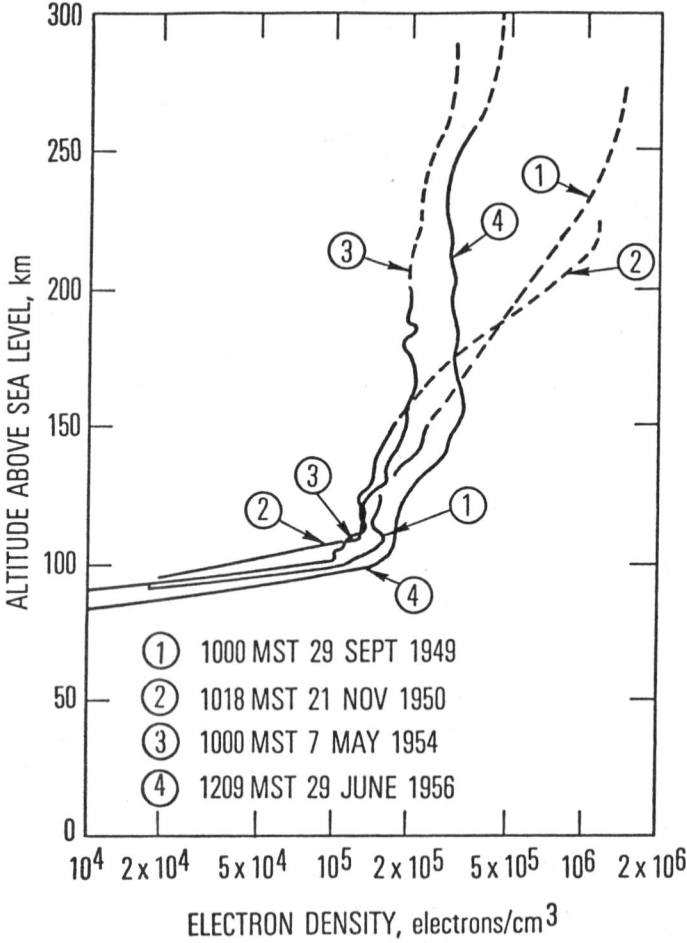

Figure 12 Electron density measurements to 260-km altitude obtained for White Sands flights using V2, Viking and Aerobee rockets.

SOLAR ASTRONOMY

The interest in rockets for solar astronomy is illustrated by Figure 13. The curve shows the altitude in the atmosphere at which the fluence of solar radiation is decreased to e^{-1} of its value at the top of the atmosphere when the Sun is immedi-

150

ately overhead. The atmosphere effectively absorbs all of the radiation at wavelengths shorter than 3,000 Å by a variety of processes. Between 300 and 2,000 Å the ozone layer is essentially opaque to the Sun's radiation. At shorter wavelengths the radiation is strongly absorbed by molecular oxygen, and the region of greatest interaction is at an altitude of about 100 km; however, narrow bands between 1,000 and 1,300 Å penetrate more deeply and interacts with all of the constituents of the atmosphere and is absorbed at even higher altitude. The wavelengths below 100 Å are x-rays with energies of 125 eV and greater and penetrate to altitudes of 100 to 120 km.

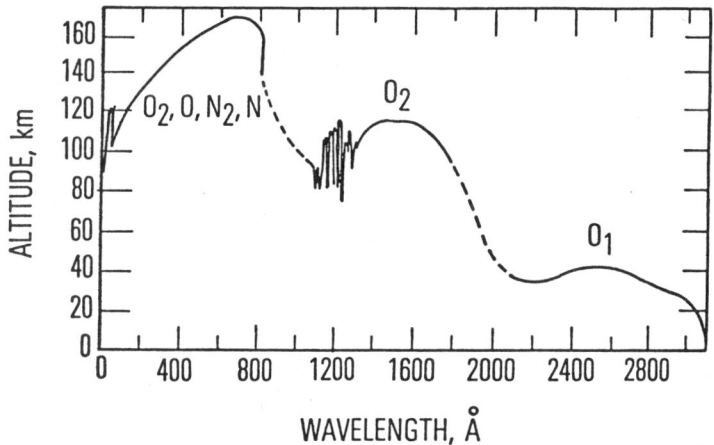

Figure 13   Earth's atmosphere: altitude and wavelength (see text).

The earliest investigations by the Naval Research Laboratory employed grating spectrographs to obtain solar spectra in the ultraviolet at frequent intervals during the rocket ascent [34,35]. By comparison of spectra obtained at different altitudes, the change in the ozone over the slant path between pairs of spectra was determined using known absorption coefficients of ozone from laboratory measurements. A curve of the total slant path ozone as a function of altitude was developed, and the vertical distribution was determined from the slope of the slant path curve. Spectra obtained at altitudes above the ozone layer provided data on the solar radiation to a lower wavelength limit set by the then unknown absorption by the atmosphere above the peak of the rocket trajectory.

A major problem for the operation of a spectrograph in a rocket was the need for an extremely wide useful field of view to compensate for the roll and yaw motions [34]. Instead of conventional slits, lithium fluoride beads 2 mm in diameter were used as the entrance apertures. The spheres, which were transparent down to 1,100 Å in the ultraviolet, acted as short-focused wide-angle lenses and provided a conical field of view 140 deg in diameter. Two entrance paths were provided on opposite sides of the grating normal, to double the probability that the Sun would be in the field of view of the instrument. Dispersion was provided by a 40-cm radius, 15,000-line-per-inch concave diffraction grating ruled on aluminum. Plane mirrors were used to fold the optical path to provide a compact spectrograph. the spectra were photographed on 35-mm film that was exposed frame by frame. The time of each exposure was telemetered so the altitude for each exposure could be determined from the rocket trajectory. Figure 14 shows one of the first spectrographs flown on the V2.

Figure 14   One of first spectrographs flown on the V2 rocket.

The first successful use of the instrument was on a V2 flight on 10 October 1946. Spectra were obtained from the ground to an altitude of 88 km, as shown in Figure 15, and the total slant range ozone between the spectrograph and the Sun for each altitude and the vertical distribution of ozone was determined. Ozone measurements were also successful on one flight in 1948 and two flights in 1949 [36]. An excellent determination of ozone was made on 14 June 1949 when the rocket was flown near sunset, resulting in a long slant path to the Sun. Two spectrographs were flown, one identical to the earlier instruments, and the second a dual device consisting of two spectrographs in a single housing. The ozone determinations from the three sets of spectra were in good agreement and showed a

152

peak concentration of ozone at about 27-km altitude, with the concentration decreasing approximately exponentially above 35 km. The concentration of ozone above New Mexico as determined in three flights is shown in Figure 16, based on the data given [34,35,36].

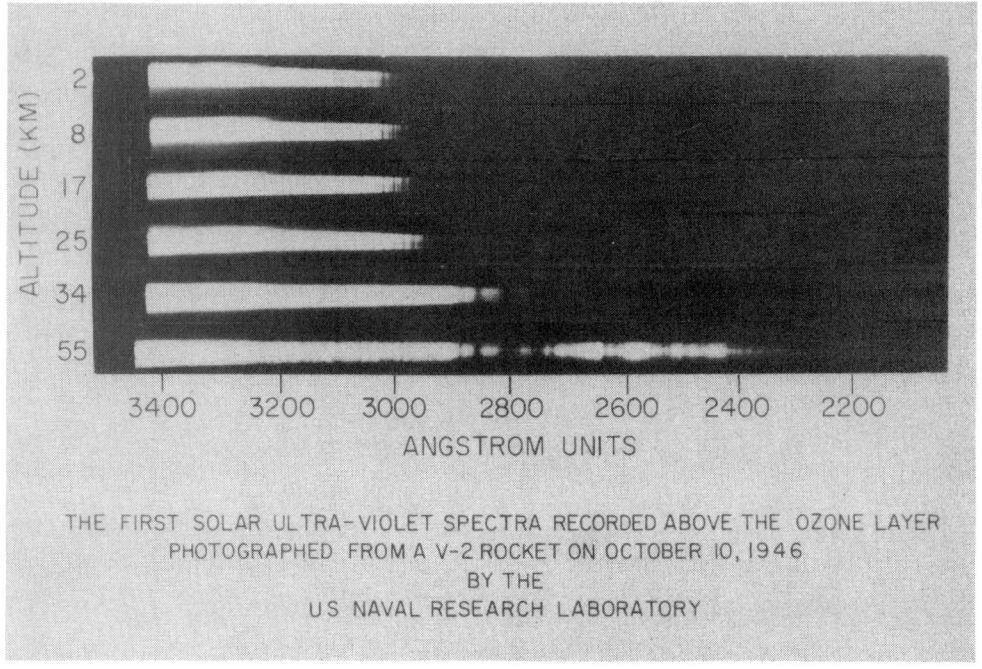

Figure 15   Spectra obtained from V2 flights between 1946 and 1949.

Additional composition measurements were obtained with a radio-frequency mass spectrometer developed for upper atmosphere research at the Naval Research Laboratory [37]. The spectrometer was designed to measure the ratio of argon to molecular nitrogen at altitudes above 95 km in order to obtain data on the diffusive separation of atmospheric gases. The first successful flight of the instrument was on an Aerobee rocket flown at night on 13 February 1953 [38]. Eighty-five samples were obtained on ascent between 96.8 and 137.3 km and eighty-seven samples on descent. In this early experiment the argon to molecular nitrogen ratio remained essentially constant with altitude, indicating that there was no diffusive separation of the atmospheric gases at this altitude. In later flights at Fort Churchill, Canada, a diffusive separation of argon relative to nitrogen was detected by the same group. Another version of the instrument was also used in Viking and Aerobee rockets to measure ion composition from 9 to 46 atomic mass units.

In addition to the measurements of ozone concentration, the data obtained at altitudes above the ozone layer extended the knowledge of the solar spectrum into the ultraviolet region. Considerable success was achieved early in the program. The spectra of Figure 15 obtained in October 1946 [39] showed a progressive extension into the ultraviolet above 25 km, and above 55 km the ozone absorption was sufficiently reduced to permit recording to about 2,100 Å. These spectra were the first measurements of the Sun's radiation at wavelengths below the 2,900-Å atmospheric cutoff, and represented the beginning of a new field of astronomy which, in the next two decades, contributed greatly to the knowledge of solar emissions and processes.

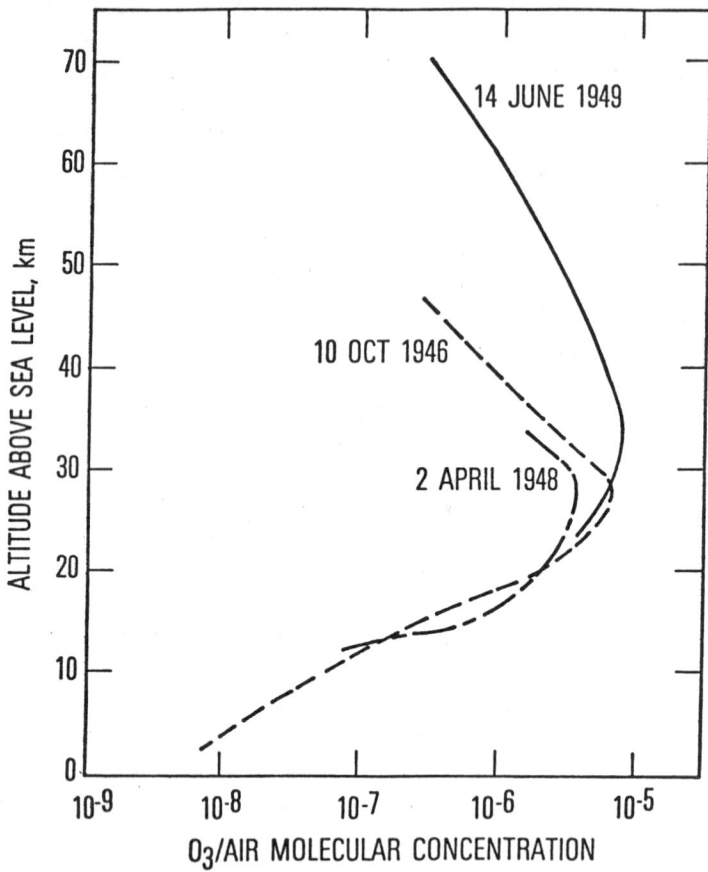

Figure 16   Concentration of ozone above New Mexico determined from three rocket flights.

Additional spectra covering the 2,900- to 2,100-Å region were obtained at altitudes up to 75 km in flights in March and October 1947 [40]. the curve of the average radiant energy of the Sun was extended from the previous 2,900-Å limit to about 2,200 Å and showed that the ultraviolet intensities were well below the values that had been predicted for a 6,000°-K blackbody [41].

The data made it possible to identify the principal contributors to many of the Fraunhofer absorption lines observed in the 2,950- to 2,300-Å region [42].

In the first 3 years of the program, the spectrographs were rigidly mounted in rockets that were unstabilized after fuel burnout. As a result of the roll, yaw and pitch motions, the Sun was generally well off the axis as the instrument at high altitudes. The lithium-bead entrance apertures provided a large field of view and partially overcame the difficulty. Nevertheless, it became evident that longer continuous exposures would be required to record the low-intensity ultraviolet radiation below 2,100 Å and that stabilization of the spectrograph would be required. In the interim, sets of thermoluminescent phosphor plates were flown in three V2s from 1948 to 1950 in an effort to obtain data on the far ultraviolet. The phosphors were manganese-activated calcium sulfate which absorbed energy at wavelengths below 1,340 Å and released the energy as visible luminescence when heated. Filters were used to limit the wavelength bands to which the phosphors were exposed. With the device the Lyman-α line of hydrogen at 1,216 Å was first detected in the solar radiation [44].

The first effort to overcome the problem of rocket motion was the use of a single-axis turntable on both Aerobee and Viking rockets in 1952. The photoelectrically activated turntable kept the entrance aperture pointed at the Sun, as the rocket rolled, but did not correct for yaw and pitch. In the Viking flight of 15 December 1952 using this device, the spectrum obtained at an altitude of 158 to 163 km extended to 1,850 Å. The principal gain was the increased density of exposure and improved resolution below 2,500 Å as compared to earlier results, which aided in the interpretation of the absorption lines in the 2,900- to 2,000-Å region. The next advance was the incorporation of a biaxial Sun follower, developed at the University of Colorado [46], with which Rense [47] first photographed the Lyman-α line in December 1952. The line was clearly visible; Tousey and his coworkers [48] shortly thereafter obtained several intense images of the line, as well as further extension of the ultraviolet spectrum. The roll of the rocket was counteracted by rotating the entire Aerobee nose section, and yaw and pitch were corrected by swinging the spectrograph in trunions driven by the biaxial servo system. With this system, and with a redesigned spectrograph [49], the NRL group achieved excellent results in a number of flights after 1954 and extended the data on the solar spectrum into the far ultraviolet. An excellent summary of the results of this work is presented in Tousey's Henry Norris Russell lecture of 1966 [50].

Another Naval Research Laboratory group, headed by Herbert Friedman, undertook intensity measurements in limited wavelength bands of the far ultraviolet by means of photon counters. Sets of detectors sensitive to portions of the solar x-ray and far ultraviolet radiation of the Sun were first flown in a V2 in September 1949 [51], the counter measurements marked the beginning of the new field of x-ray astronomy that has led to many important advances in astrophysics.

The detectors employed were basically Geiger counters in which the spectral response was controlled by the gaseous filling and the transmission characteristics of thin-film windows [53]. In the first experiment two sets of four counters were installed on opposite sides of the rocket warhead, with the exposed windows parallel to the warhead surface. The x-ray counters were most sensitive at about 2 Å, with decreasing sensitivity to 10 Å where the 0.005-in. beryllium window was essentially opaque. The ultraviolet photon counters were designed to be sensitive in three bands at 1,100 to 1,350 Å, 1,425 to 1,650 Å, and 1,725 to 2,100 Å, with the short wavelength cutoff set by the lithium fluoride, synthetic sapphire, and quartz windows. The counting rate was obtained by integrating the charge flow through the counter in an RC circuit and applying the resultant voltage to the telemetering system. As the rocket rolled at high altitude, the window aperture of each counter swept through one exposure to the Sun for each roll. The telemetered record was a series of spikes with about eight data points per exposure, showing that the detectors responded only when viewing the Sun.

A number of significant results were obtained from the data gathered in the first flight. The x-ray counters did not respond until an altitude of 87 km was reached, which indicated a high-energy cutoff at about 7 Å. Above that altitude the counting rate increased and the counters reached their maximum counting rate before the peak of the trajectory at 150 km. Based upon the data and the calibrated sensitivity of the counters, the total fluence at the top of the atmosphere was calculated to be about 10^{-4} erg cm^2 sec^1 for wavelengths shorter than 10 Å. Although the fluence was less than the 10^{-2} to 10^1 erg cm^{-2} sec^{-1} required for the E-layer ionization, this first experiment supported the theory [54] that solar x-rays were the major source for E-layer information on the basis that most of the energy was in x-rays at wavelengths between 10 to 100 Å. The data on x-ray threshold altitude and intensity variation with altitude were confirmed in other flights, [55,56], and in November and December of 1953 the x-ray measurements were extended to longer wavelengths, using counters sensitive in three bands; 8 to 20 Å, 44 to 60 Å, and 44 to 100 Å [57]. These first data on x-ray wavelengths longer than 10 Å showed an x-ray distribution approximated by a 700,000°-K grey body, and a total emission of about 10^{-1} erg cm^{-2} sec^{-1}, which was absorbed in the atmosphere between 110 and 130 km. The 1953 experiment confirmed the earlier tentative conclusions that the energy in the solar x-ray fluence was adequate to account for the ionospheric E-layer.

The counters sensitive to the 1,100- to 1,350-Å band showed that the radiation in this band penetrated the atmosphere to about 70-km altitude. Above that altitude the counting rate increased and a symptotically approached a maximum as the rocket approached the 150-km apogee of its trajectory. The increase in intensity followed the calculated absorption curve for the Lyman-α line of hydrogen, indicating that this line was the major contributor to the energy within the band. The experimental evidence that the Lyman-α radiation penetrated well below the E-layer also supported the suggestion [58] that it was the energy source for the D-layer ionization. Similar measurements in following flights confirmed the depth of penetration and showed that better than 90 percent of all of the radiation from the Sun in the 1,180- to 1,300-Å band was in the single 1,216-Å emission line of hydrogen and that the background radiation in the 1,200-Å region was inconsistent with a 6,000°K blackbody temperature for the Sun.

The 1,425- to 1,650-Å counters covered the wavelength band in which the absorption coefficient for oxygen is a maximum. The data obtained from these counters in the early flights also contributed significant results. The rise in counting rate in the 100-km region indicated transition of atmospheric oxygen from molecular to atomic. However, molecular oxygen was found to exist well above the

E region, and by 1955 [59,60] the complete departure of the molecular oxygen distribution from that predicted by photochemical equilibrium had been established. The relatively weak oxygen transition as shown by the counter experiments was consistent with the deduced solar intensities. The combination of the spectrographic and photon-counter intensity data in the ultraviolet then showed that the solar blackbody temperature dropped from 5,000°K at 1,200 Å to about 4,000°K at 1,200 Å.

SOLAR FLARE MEASUREMENTS

Although solar flares produce large changes in the solar output and sometimes spectacular effects in the atmosphere, they are generally short-lived. The possibility of obtaining information on flare radiation by means of rocket astronomy was a formidable challenge. In the summer of 1956 a series of small rockets instrumented with photon counters was launched from the U.S.S. *Colonial* in the Pacific Ocean about 350 miles southwest of San Diego [61]. The solid propellant rockets were carried aloft by large balloons early in the morning and permitted to drift throughout the day, while the Sun was monitored for signs of a flare. If no flare occurred, the rocket was launched near sunset and quiet Sun data were recorded. Solar monitoring was performed by the solar observatories at Sacramento Peak, New Mexico, and Climax, Colorado, U.S.A., which were in radio communication with the ship.

On 20 June 1956 a small flare occurred and the rocket was launched in time to reach peak altitude within 10 minutes of the time the flare was first visually observed. The flare was classified as being between class 1 and a subflare and did not create any radio fadeout.

The rocket was instrumented with an ion chamber to measure the Lyman-α radiation and a photon counter with a beryllium window sensitive to 1- to 8-Å x-rays. The Lyman-α radiation was essentially unchanged from that measured with a quiet Sun, but the x-ray intensities and wavelengths were quite different. The x-rays extended to wavelengths of 3 Å, as compared to a quiet-Sun short wavelength limit of 7- to 8-Å, and the intensity in this band was measured as about 5×10^{-3} erg-cm^{-2}sec^{-1}. In 1957, two-stage solid rockets capable of reaching an altitude of 400,000 ft. were launched on flare warning from San Nicolas Island, 60 miles off the coast of California [62]. Solar x-ray and Lyman-α were obtained during class 1^+, 2, and 3^+ flares. Again, there was no increase in the intensity of Lyman-α over quiet Sun conditions, but strong x-ray enhancement was measured for each flare, with the intensity and photon energy increasing with the flare magnitude.

The first decade of rocket astronomy provided experimental verification of a number of theories concerning the interaction of solar radiation with the Earth's atmosphere. It became clear that, under quiescent Sun conditions, the ionospheric D-layer was accounted for by the Lyman-α emission energy, and the E-layer by x-rays with wavelengths longer than 8 Å. The intensities of these radiations had been experimentally determined. It had also been established that the solar x-rays increase both in intensity and photon energy during flares, and that these higher energy x-rays penetrate deeper into the atmosphere to cause the enhanced ionization and lowering of the D-layer associated with the larger flares [63]. The distribution of the ozone and oxygen transition layers had been mapped and several thousand emission and absorption lines in the solar and coronal radiation had been identified. The later extension of rocket astronomy to the investigation of stellar x-ray sources [64] and night sky airglow [65,66] measurements is well-known.

The rocket-borne research investigations, begun with the V2 in 1946, provided a rich return in information on the upper atmosphere, cosmic rays, the ionosphere, and solar radiation. Some secondary experiments yielded unexpected results. Beginning in 1947, cameras were carried in V2s and Vikings to aid in defining the orientation of the rockets from photographs of the Earth. The photographs were useful for this purpose, but also provided information on large-scale cloud formations that could not be obtained from ground observations. Figure 17 is a composite of four photographs taken when the rocket was at an altitude above 160 km. These first high-altitude photographs cover an area of about 1.3 million km^2 of the southwestern United States and northern Mexico [67].

Figure 17   Composite of four photographs of southwestern U.S. and northern Mexico taken in 1947 by rocket-borne camera.

In addition to the experiments themselves, very valuable information and experience were gained with respect to operations in rocket and in space environments. The telemetry system developed for the V2 pioneered the recovery of data from space by electronic means. The problems of providing continuous communication with a gyrating vehicle were worked out, as were power-supply energy management and preflight checkout techniques. All of the lessons, sometimes painfully learned by the space pioneers, were of great value to the later space programs.

REFERENCES

1. C.F. Green, "Utilization of the V2 (A4) in Upper Atmosphere Research," *Rocket Exploration of the Upper Atmosphere*, (New York: Pergamon Press, Inc. 1953), p. 28.

2. J.T. Mengel, *Upper Atmosphere Research Report No. I*, Report R-2955, Naval Research Laboratory (1 October 1946).

3. T.A. Bergstralh, *Upper Atmosphere Research Report No. III*, Report R-3120, Naval Research Laboratory, (April 1947).

4. V.L. Heeren, et al., "Telemetering from V2 Rockets," *Electronics* 20, 100-105 (1947).

5. C.H. Smith, "Telemetering from Rockets," *Upper Atmosphere Research Report No. III*, Report R-3120, Naval Research Laboratory (April 1947).

6. R.J. Havens, R.T. Koll, and H.E. La Gow, *J. Geophys. Res.* 57, 59-72 (1952).

7. Homer E. Newell, *High Altitude Rocket Research* (New York: Academic Press, Inc., 1953).

8. G.D. Taylor and J.W. Maccoll, *Proc. Roy. Soc.* 139, 278 (1933).

9. N. Best, et al., *Phys. Rev.* 70, 985 (1946).

10. R.J. Havens, R. Koll, and H.E. La Gow, *Rev. Sci. Inst.* 21, 596-598 (1950).

11. H.E. La Gow, "Physical Properties of the Atmosphere Into the F_1-Layer," *Rocket Exploration of the Upper Atmosphere*, eds. R.L.F. Boyd and M.J. Seaton (New York: Pergamon Press, Inc., 1954).

12. D.A. Strickland, ed., *Cospar International Reference Atmosphere -- 1972* (Berlin: Akademie-Verlag, 1972).

13. Marcel Schein, W.P. Jesse, and E.D. Wallan, *Phys. Rev.* 56, 615 (1941).

14. T.E. Johnson, *Rev. Mod. Phys.* 11, 208 (1939).

15. S.E. Golian, E.H. Krause, and G.J. Perlow, *Phys. Rev.* 70, 223 (1946).

16. G.J. Perlow and J.D. Shipman, Jr., *Phys. Rev.* 71, 325 (1947).

17. S.E. Golian and E.H. Krause, *Phys. Rev.* 71, 918 (1947).

18. G.J. Perlow and C.W. Kissinger, *Phys. Rev.* 81, 552 (1951).

19. G.J. Perlow, et al., *Phys. Rev.* 88, 321 (1952).

20. A.V. Gangnes, J.F. Jenkins, and J.A. Van Allen, *Phys. Rev.* 75, 57 (1949).

21. S.E. Golian, et al., *Phys. Rev.* 75, 524 (1949).

22. Phyllis Frier, et al., *Phys. Rev.* 74, 231 (1948).

23. J.C. Seddon and J.W. Siry, *Upper Atmosphere Research Report No. I*, Report R-2955, Naval Research Laboratory (1 October 1946).

24. J.C. Seddon, "Propagation Measurements in the Ionosphere with the Aid of Rockets, *Rocket Exploration of the Upper Atmosphere*, eds. R.L.F. Boyd and M.J. Seaton (New York: Pergamon Press, Inc., 1954).

25. T.R. Burnight, J.F. Clark, Jr., and J.C. Seddon, *Upper Atmosphere Research Report No. IV*, Report R-3171, Naval Research Laboratory (1 October 1947).

26. J.C. Seddon, *J. Geophys. Res.* 58, 323 (1953).

27. J.E. Jackson and J.C. Seddon, *J. Geophys. Res.* 61, 749 (1956).

28. J.E. Jackson and J.C. Seddon, *J. Geophys. Res.* 63, 197 (1958).

29. J.E. Jackson and J.C. Seddon, V SCAG I (1958).

30. W.W. Berning, *J. Meteorol.* 8, 175 (1951).

31. J.E. Jackson, *J. Geophys. Res.* 66, 3055 (1961).

32. S.. Bauer and E.J. Jackson, *J. Geophys. Res.* 67, 1675 (1962).

33. V.I. Krasovsky, V SCAG I (1958).

34. F.S. Johnson, J.D. Purcell, and R. Tousey, *J. Geophys. Res.* 56, 583-594 (1951).

35. F.S. Johnson, J.D. Purcell, and R. Tousey, "The Ultraviolet Spectrum of the Sun," *Rocket Exploration of the Upper Atmosphere*, eds. R.L.F. Boyd and M.J. Seaton (New York: Pergamon Press, Inc., 1954).

36. F.S. Johnson, et al., *J. Geophys. Res.* 57, 157-176 (1952).

37. J.W. Townsend, Jr., *Rev. Sci. Inst.* 23, 538 (1952).

38. J.W. Townsend, Jr., E.B. Meadows, and E.C. Pressley, "A Mass Spectrometric Study of the Upper Atmosphere," *Rocket Exploration of the Upper Atmosphere*, eds. R.L.F. Boyd and M.J. Seaton (New York: Pergamon Press, Inc., 1954).

39. W.A. Baum, et al., *Phys. Rev.* 70, 781 (1946).

40. E. Durand, J.J. Oberly, and R. Tousey, *Upper Atmosphere Research Report III*, Report R-3120, Naval Research Laboratory (April 1947).

41. E. Durand, J.J. Oberly, and R. Tousey, *Upper Atmosphere Research Report III*, Report R-3171, Naval Research Laboratory (October 1947).

42. E. Durand, J.J. Oberly, and R. Tousey, *Phys. Rev.* 71, 827 (1947).

43. E. Durand, J.J. Oberly, and R. Tousey, *Astrophys. J.* 109 (1949).

44. R. Tousey, K. Watanabe, and J.D. Purcell, *Phys. Rev.* 83, 792 (1951).

45. N.R. Wilson, et al., *Astrophys. J.* 119, 590 (1954).

46. D.S. Stacey, et al., *Electronics* 27, 80 (1954).

47. W.A. Rense, *Phys. Rev.* 91, 299 (1953).

48. F.S. Johnson, J.D. Purcell, and R. Tousey, *Phys. Rev.* 95, 621 (1954).

49. F.S. Johnson, et al., *Astrophys. J.* 127, 80 (1958).

50. R. Tousey, *Astrophys. J.* 149, 239 (1967).

51. H. Friedman, S.W. Lichtman, and E.T. Byram, *Phys. Rev.* 83, 1025 (1951).

52. T.R. Burnight, *Phys. Rev.* 76, 175 (1949).

53. H. Friedman, *Proc. IRE* 37, 791 (1949).

54. E.O. Hulburt, *Phys. Rev.* 53, 344 (1938).

55. E.T. Byram, et al., *J. Opt. Soc. Am.* 42, 876 (1952).

56. E.T. Byram, et al., *Phys. Rev.* 91, 1278 (1953).

57. E.T. Byram, T.A. Chubb, and H. Friedman, *J. Geophys. Res.* 61, 251 (1956).

58. J.R. Bates and M.J. Seaton, *Proc. Roy. Soc. (London)*, B63, 129 (1958).

59. E.T. Byram, T.A. Chubb, and H. Friedman, *Phys. Rev.* 98, 1594 (1955).

60. H. Friedman, *Physics of the Upper Atmosphere*, ed. J.A. Ratcliffe (New York: Academic Press, Inc., 1960) p. 133 ff.

61. T.A. Chubb, et a., *J. Geophys. Res.* 62, 389 (1957).

62. H. Friedman, et al., *Ann. Géophysique*, 14, 232 (1958).

63. T.A. Chubb, H. Friedman, and W.R. Kreplin, *J. Geophys. Res.* 65, 1831 (1960).

64. E.T. Byram, T.A. Chubb, and H. Friedman, *Astrophys. J.* 139, 1135 (1964).

65. R. Tousey, *Ann. Géophysique*, 14, 186 (1958).

66. J.E. Kupperian, Jr., et al., *Ann. Géophysique*, 14, 329 (1958).

67. T.A. Bergstralh, Naval Research Laboratory Report R-3083 (April 1947).

Chapter 12

EARLY HISTORY OF THE SKYLARK ROCKET*

E. B. Dorling[†]

BEGINNINGS

The announcement by the British Government in 1955 that it proposed to commence a program of upper atmosphere rocket research in collaboration with the Gassiot Committee of the Royal Society of London came as a surprise to the general scientific community in the United Kingdom. Little of the research that had been in progress over the previous ten years in the United States of America, with modified V2 rockets and the newly designed Viking and Aerobee rockets, was known; and, so shrouded by security were missile developments in the U.K., there was then little to whet the appetites even of those who were aware of what might be done with the new research tool, the sounding rocket. Nevertheless a small group of university scientists with research interests directly connected with the upper atmosphere were following the U.S. developments with close interest.

Foremost amongst them was Professor Harrie S.W. Massey, head of the Department of Physics at University College London, and two of his staff, R.L.F. Boyd and M.J. Seaton. Massey, an authority on the theory of atomic collisions through his, by then, very well-known collaboration with N.F. Mott, was now studying the complex ion chemistry of the ionosphere and upper atmosphere. D.R. Bates [1] has recently described the history of this work to the present day. Boyd was working with Massey on the measurement of ionic recombination rates whilst Seaton's interests were turning away from processes in our own atmosphere to those in the atmosphere of the Sun, by then known to be a source of x-radiation. Elsewhere interest in ionospheric studies, for example by W.J.G. Beynon at the University of Swansea and J. Sayers at the University of Birmingham, was emphasizing the pressing need to find some alternative to the ionsonde as a tool for probing the E and F layers.

By 1952, it had become clear that the time was ripe for a conference at which to discuss the techniques of high altitude research using rockets, and the results

---

* Presented at The Ninth IAA History of Astronautics Symposium, Lisbon, Portugal, September 1975.

† Mullard Space Science Laboratory, University College London, Holmbury St. Mary, Dorking, England.

already obtained. Thanks very largely to the U.S. Office of Naval Research, in particular to the then Scientific Attache in London, S. Fred Singer, arrangements were made to bring to Oxford in August 1953 members of the Upper Atmosphere Rocket Research Panel of the United States for a conference arranged jointly with the Gassiot Committee of the Royal Society of London.

The conference was entirely successful in both its short and long term aims [2]. It was attended by men who were actively concerned in flying instruments on rockets, so giving U.K. scientists an opportunity to hear at first hand the details of what had been achieved in the United States and what was planned for the future. In addition, the conference began a dialogue between universities and Government laboratories about what might be done by the United Kingdom. Later, Boyd spent a summer at the Royal Aircraft Establishment (RAE), Farnborough, where King-Hele [3] was studying the performance of a possible upper atmosphere research vehicle powered by either a single motor or staged solid propellant motors that would serve the dual purpose of a test vehicle in the RAE's own research program.

The decision to eschew the lightness and high performance of a liquid propellant motor for the simplicity of a large and heavy solid propellant motor was based on this study, on the general conviction that such a motor would have very real advantages in cost and flexibility.

Dawton [4] made more detailed performance estimates for a single-stage vehicle, one capable of carrying 45 kg of instruments to heights in excess of 150 km. He based his calculations on a hypothetical motor giving a thrust of 54 KN for 30 sec, representing a total impulse of 1,590 KNs for a propellant weight of 909 kg. Though hypothetical, the motor was to be developed from an existing one, some 44 cm in diameter, but made three times as long and burning a rather different fuel more slowly. A long burning time was essential if the vehicle's speed were to be kept reasonably low until the worst effects of drag and aerodynamic heating had been left behind.

Rocket motor development was at that time concentrated in a separate department of RAE at Westcott; and, in June 1955, representatives from both departments concerned with the new project visited the United States [5] principally the Naval Research Laboratory at Anacosta, to discuss the performance and design of the Aerobee rocket in relation to the characteristics then envisaged for the British rocket. They visited the White Stands Missile Range in New Mexico, to see the launching tower and its three-finned Aerobee, and it was this visit that led to the 100 ft launching tower at Woomera in South Australia and a three-finned sounding rocket (for the very real reason that a launching from White Sands might then be possible). In fact, no U.K. Skylark rocket has been launched from White Sands although Skylarks have been used at many other ranges; and, if one is to be fired from White Sands in future, it may well be from a simple transportable single-rail launcher for the days of the launching tower are almost past.

With the main decisions on the size, weight and configuration of the rocket made in mid-1955, the detailed design of the vehicle structure, motor and launching tower was begun. It is interesting to look back on the financial arrangements given in the Government announcement, which became, in effect, the authority for this work. A sum of £100,000, spread over 4 years, had been authorized, one half to be made available through the Gassiot Committee to the university experimenters and the other half to cover the design and provision of rocket vehicles. Clearly, this was a very modest priming of the pump; but, nonetheless, effective in what it made possible. The detailed arrangements for the collaboration between the Royal Aircraft Establishment and the Gassiot Committee of the Royal Society were set out by F.E. Jones, then Deputy Director, RAE, and Massey in a letter to *Nature* in 1956 [6]. The rocket vehicle and its launching facility were described and an outline given of the first experiments to be carried out at the Woomera range.

Throughout this period a new event had appeared upon the international scientific scene: the International Geophysical Year (IGY), which in fact, extended over an 18-month period in 1957 and 1958. Though never specifically tied to the IGY, the new British rocket would clearly contribute to it and consequently was sometimes known in the United Kingdom as the IGY rocket. Its more common name, however, was the Gassiot rocket. The IGY connection initially stood it in good stead but later led to no little confusion. For why go on using the rocket once the IGY had ended? This misunderstanding competed, in what little attention was spared to the U.K. sounding rocket program in Britain, with a second, one widely conceived by scientists and non-scientists alike because of the esoteric nature of the subject. The upper atmosphere was to them a still and inactive region beyond the furthest reaches of aircraft or balloon, unchanging and therefore readily characterized by one or two key measurements to be made from one rocket flight. The IGY rocket became to many in Britain *the* IGY rocket, one single rocket that would measure all there was to be measured. What justification could there be for two, let alone 200? (At this writing, 247 Skylarks have been launched from Woomera.)

ROCKET DESIGN

The new rocket came into being at the RAE, not as the Skylark, nor as the Gassiot rocket, nor as the IGY rocket, but as the CTV5 Series III, the last of the so-called Control Test Vehicles. J.F. Hazell [7], who had been the physicist and aerodynamicist in charge of an earlier project in the series, was given overall responsibility for the Series III in September 1955 and much of the ultimate success of the new venture was due to him. The nominal characteristics of the motor were by then already decided, but the motor had still to be designed and made, as had the rocket head and the launcher. Steel was still in short supply 10 years after the end of World War II and finding the right material for motor case and launcher posed problems. Digital computers were still some months away and performance calculations were done slowly and laboriously by hand. Moreover, little was known about the dynamic behavior of fin-stabilized rockets at high speeds and low dynamic pressures; roll-yaw resonance was known to be plaguing the Aerobee program but no adequate theoretical treatment of the aerodynamics of fin-stabilized vehicles existed to give a guide to what might be expected with the CTV5 Series III. Best estimates had to be made for the actual weight of the motor case, propellant, unburned propellant (silver), structure and payload. Dispersion of the rocket's impact point was of primary concern and much of Hazell's time was taken up, together with that of his assistants, in assessing the likely behavior of the rocket once it left the launcher rails. Meanwhile, the design and engineering team got to work on the rocket head and launcher, whilst at Westcott work began on the motor.

The structural design of the rocket head and fins presented no great difficulties. This was in part due to the large overall weight of the vehicle, initially around 1,170 kg, with the motor around 1,020 kg full, 180 kg empty plus perhaps 35 kg of unburnt propellant. There was no need for a very sophisticated structure; nothing, for example, to compare with the spun aluminum ogive then used on Aerobee. The basis of the head design was the use of cylindrical instrumentation bays of cast magnesium alloy (DTD 748) bolted to strong rings housing standard equipment such as the tracking beacon. The bolts were soon replaced by manacle clamps, and the strong rings became part of the bay which themselves proliferated to meet the various new demands; time has shown the general approach to have been sound and of lasting benefit because of its great flexibility. The nose cone design was less well-defined, as it was clearly to depend upon the experimental requirements; as these were developed, the nose cone arrangements were changed. The manufacture of the fin assembly, three fins riveted to a Dural casting that was slipped over the rear of the motor case threatened to delay the project initially and so an existing fin from the CTV5 Series I rocket was used in the first few flights, heavier and bigger than was necessary, but one that could be relied upon not to be misaligned at launch nor to distort in flight.

Misalignments, whether due to the fins or the motor, were to be important factors in determining the rocket's dispersion. Jet misalignment was unmeasurable; only by taking great care in motor manufacture could bowing of the motor tube and uneven erosion of the venturi thrust be held to tolerable levels. Fin alignment could be measured, and individual fins chosen to have compensating imperfections.

Much work went into the calculation of wind corrections so that allowance could be made for the effects of all measured winds up to 30 km, not in displacing the rocket bodily -- a small effect -- but in turning it to a new heading. The dynamic behavior of the vehicle was first estimated in terms of its static stability and speed, so as to assess the degree to which it would respond to a step change in wind speed. Its slow response as it left the launcher caused it to turn only 60 percent as much as it would turn at 300 m; above this height its response was rapid, but the wind speed in relation to its own velocity diminished rapidly so that the net effect fell away equally fast.

Calculations were made of the wind effect at all levels to 30 km and a weighting factor was assigned to each. Then, for every different rocket configuration and trajectory to be flown, a unit wind effect was calculated, that effect produced by a constant unit wind at all heights. The summed weighted winds measured as close to launch as possible, multiplied by this unit wind, calculated well before the firing, gave the predicted offset of the impact point so that the launching tower could be trained to correct for it. Wind effects can be very large with simple fin-stabilized vehicles of this type and impact points can be displaced by very large distances, so that techniques such as these are an essential part of the operations. Even so, the uncertainties of wind measurement, particularly when low-level winds are variable, can produce displacements of tens of kilometers in the impact point. An interesting sidelight was the realization that a booster motor, used to kick the rocket more rapidly from the launching tower and so reduce its response to a wind step, also increases the initial dynamic response. The net result is that the booster may be a good deal less effective in reducing dispersion than first expected.

Studies such as these were aided immeasurably when, in 1956, the first digital computer, the Ferranti Pegasus, became available. Prior to Pegasus, calculations were laborious and slow; hair-raising extrapolations had to be made for want of calculated results. Analogue computers were already in use in other departments and it seemed sensible to enquire what help they might be. None, it was soon learned, but not before one enthusiastic analoguist asserted that in his opinion there was no question but that the analogue computer was the only choice for trajectory calculations. The prevailing ignorance of the potential of the digital computer was, seen in retrospect, remarkable.

Whilst the aerodynamics of the rocket were being explored, the problem of roll-yaw lock-in was much in the forefront of the aerodynamicists' thinking; but, with so much else to be done, the analysis proved intractable. The problem in a nutshell is that when the natural frequency of the rocket in yaw (or pitch) -- a property that varies with height -- becomes similar to the roll rate, the two may lock in and any forces resulting from an angle of attack, perhaps generated by a gust, wind step, thrust misalignment or other disturbance, may cause divergence and catastrophic break-up. One way of avoiding the problem is to postpone resonance until the effective atmosphere has been left behind. This is achieved by keeping the roll rate very low.

By early 1956, the clumsy nomenclature, CTV5 Series III, seemed hardly fitting for an upper atmosphere rocket and after some persuasion official agreement was given to the use of a nickname Skylark, first used in an article in the Royal Aircraft Establishment's house magazine in September 1956.

THE RAVEN MOTOR

The Raven motor in all its variants, even to being the progenitor of the Canadian Black Brant, is a product of the Rocket Propulsion Establishment, Westcott, formerly an RAE department. Their latest product the Raven XI is at this writing nearing its first launching, a big step forward from the Raven I of 1957. The steel motor case is a product of British-Aerojet Ltd., formerly British Aircraft (Weston) Ltd.

Initially, the main manufacturing and filling problems at Weston and Westcott sprang from the unusual length of the motor. The motor case, of wrapped and welded design, called for special steel sheet of the strength needed for such a pressure vessel, and in order to meet an early launching date Bristol Aerojet scoured Europe for supplies. New vertical heat treatment facilities were required to ensure that the tube remained straight and circular, instead of becoming bowed and oval. The propellant was to be burned radially along its length, and so had to be given a shaped charge and an igniter running along its length. A difficult balance had to be struck between achieving a slow burning, over 30 sec or so, yet an initial thrust high enough to meet the dispersion requirements, and an even consumption of fuel that left the minimum unburnt; above everything else was the need to achieve these objectives yet to pack in the maximum total impulse possible.

The first motor, Raven I, carried 840 kg of RD2332 propellant with 1,450 KNs total impulse, at sea level (about 1,579 KNs in vacuum); the fourth variant, puzzlingly still only Raven II, carried the same weight of RD2402 propellant giving 1,539 KNs, at sea level (about 1,675 KNs in vacuum), but with a new charge shape and changed propellant to improve the initial thrust. Today's Raven XI gives, by comparison, 2,415 KNs total vacuum impulse.

The propellant is a plastic formulation of ammonium perchlorate oxidizer and ammonium picrate coolant in a polyisobutylene binder. Five percent aluminum powder ensures combustion stability, and gives the beneficial side effect of reducing the unburnt propellant to a negligible amount. During manufacture, the propellant is injected into the case under vacuum and then compression-moulded to a star shaped section (slotted in the Raven XI). After proof tests the motor burning time is adjusted by machining the graphite throat of the steel expansion nozzle.

Lighting the Raven motor was initially something of a problem because of the occurrence of pressure peaks. During one early test a pressure pulse blew the nozzle clean out of the end forging into which it was screwed. Unbelievably, the thread in the forging was not only undamaged but was still accepted by the threat gauge as within tolerance. It was an igniter problem that held up the clearance of the first Raven motor to reach Australia; and, though all had been made ready at Woomera in November 1956, the firing had to be postponed. Range closures in the next 2 months caused the firing to be delayed until February 1957.

INSTRUMENTATION

The preparation of Skylark payloads was, from the inception of the project, carried out at the Royal Aircraft Establishment. Telemetry and tracking aids were made a standardized installation except in the first three flights. As compatibility with the Woomera range facilities was essential, it dictated the choice of instrumentation. Thus, the telemetry sender was, and at this writing often still is, the standard RAE sub-miniature 24 channel time-multiplexed FM//AM system with carrier frequency of 465 MHz. Twenty-three data channels were each sampled between eighty and one hundred times per second, the inputs being voltages in the range ±21/2 v into 3MΩ. The overall accuracy was 3 percent of full-scale. Two tracking facilities were provided, a standard Doppler transponder and a 5 GHz beacon that formed part of the range's Missile Tracking System (MTS). Tracking by radars and kinetheodolites supplemented these two, so that the final trajectory calculation was based upon a variety of data.

Every payload was further instrumented with accelerometers and rate gyroscopes, where possible on all three axes. This is an appropriate point at which to recall that the electronics installed in the first Skylark payloads both in the standard instrumentation and in the experimental equipment was wholly valve-based. There were no transistors of any kind. The valves were miniature and rugged, and were mounted in solid aluminum blocks which protected them and acted as heat sinks. Power consumption was necessarily high by today's standards, and the provision of individual supplies to avoid interaction by equipment when supplied from a common source put heavy demands on space and priming facilities. Reliability was generally good; but, by comparison with what can be done today, the circuits were simple.

LAUNCHER

The launching tower as first erected at Woomera was 25 m high; in October 1958 it was extended to 31 m. It is still in use there today.

The tower and three supporting legs, fabricated from Bailey bridge panels (normally used for temporary bridges), were made at the Royal Ordnance Factory, Woolwich. The tower is supported in gimbals and can be moved by remotely operated motors through $+15^{\circ}$ to -5° in elevation and $\pm10^{\circ}$ in azimuth. The Raven motor is brought to the launcher on a loading trolley. The payload is hoisted into the tower via the loading platform and lowered on to the motor. Three parallel rails guide the vehicle out of the tower.

AUSTRALIAN PARTICIPATION

Whilst the design of the Skylark rocket was underway at RAE Farnborough, discussions were being held with the Weapons Research Establishment (WRE) of the Australian Department of Supply about the arrangements for the Woomera firings. The agreement reached was that staff at WRE would become wholly responsible for the Australian end of the operations. Pre-launch checks, final preparation and firing were to become as much the Australians' concern, as the provision of standard range facilities. RAE staff were, where possible, to accompany payloads to the range for liaison reasons, but the Skylark rockets were in principle to be built by one group of people and checked-out and launched unaided by another. It was an arrangement that lasted for many years, during which time the Australian commitment expanded and became increasingly skillful.

In the early days the arrangement was not without its drawbacks. Sometimes the paper-work arrived late at WRE, with the result that the Australians would take delivery of an instrumented rocket payload without the corresponding explanation of its contents, and many misunderstandings followed. But these were minor matters set against the major success achieved at WRE in assuming full responsibility for payload preparation, experimenter support and range operations.

The general arrangements for the Skylark firings were agreed between the RAE and the WRE at meetings in Salisbury, South Australia, stretching over

169

several days and were embodied in a Planning Specification which then became the broad authority under which all work at WRE was carried out. This specification was re-negotiated from time to time as the program developed and as new requirements came along. Individual firings were covered by WRE's own Trials Specifications. These were negotiated on behalf of the RAE by the WRE trials teams, who had to show a great deal of insight and perspicacity in interpreting the written words of engineers and physicists 8,000 miles away, and somehow formulating the requirements in precise enough terms to bring into effective operation the large and complex organization of the Woomera range.

SCIENTIFIC PROGRAM

Whilst the design and development of the Skylark vehicle got underway work began in five British university departments and in the RAE on the development of flight instrumentation. Seven investigations were proposed, three concerned with the ionosphere, two with the airglow and two with the neutral atmosphere. In 1955, the mean daytime and nighttime profiles of the ionosphere were still unknown because the standard ground-based instrument, the ionsonde, was unable to see what lay between the E and F layers; the heights that it gave for these layers were virtual, not real. The rocket, as the U.S. experimenters were already demonstrating, could fly instruments through these regions and send back hopefully unambiguous measurements that would resolve the uncertainties.

There were two quite distinct experimental methods of ionospheric sounding being proposed, the *in situ* measurement and the wave propagation measurement. Boyd and Sayers were proponents of the direct method, whilst Beynon preferred the indirect. A key point at issue was whether the rocket vehicle would so disturb the ambient conditions that the measurements would be unrepresentative however carefully the experimental conditions were arranged and corrections were made. Clearly, only a comparison of the results from both techniques with ionsonde measurements would finally decide how successfully each technique would be developed. Boyd initially proposed a mass spectrometer to be carried well ahead of the rocket on an extending probe, and later went on to develop the Langmuir probe in a variety of forms to measure ion and electron densities and temperatures. Sayers built a large ionization chamber to be thrown clear of the rocket on a length of cable for the detection of negative ions; he also devised a means of using the rocket's nosecone itself as a probe to measure electron densities. Beynon, with the cooperation of Admiralty and RAE scientists, set about assembling the equipment for two ambitious propagation measurements. These required the use of large ground transmitters, one sending continuous wave signals, the other pulses, to corresponding receivers carried in the rocket. In each case the signals at frequencies low enough to be affected by the ionosphere were to be paralleled by signals at a much higher frequency, so that the two could be compared either in the rocket or on the ground and the required ionospheric data then extracted. Beynon's experiments were ultimately carried through very successfully but only after many years of work during which time his original objective, that of calibrating the ionsonde and searching behind the E and F layer peaks, had been overtaken by the swift progress of space research elsewhere.

The airglow experiments were proposed by Bates and his colleague, E. B. Armstrong, in order to learn more about the chemistry of the ionosphere, using photomultiplier and filter combinations to study various line emissions from the nighttime ionosphere. They also constructed burners to release quantities of sodium vapor at high altitudes so that the resulting emissions could be recorded with ground-based spectrographs.

The neutral atmosphere was to be explored by the now very familiar grenade experiment, a technique which yields neutral atmosphere wind and temperature measurements to 90 km. It relies upon the accurate timing of the flashes and the sound waves at a number of ground sites as explosive charges are released one by one from the rocket at night, and on the equally accurate location of the bursts by the use of ballistic cameras.

Murgatroyd had experimented with the technique many years earlier by ranging on the explosions of anti-aircraft shells, and in the mid-50's in the United States the technique was being developed as a standard method of neutral wind measurement from the Aerobee and other rockets. One attraction is the limited amount of instrumentation required in the rocket; at a minimum it need be only the grenades and a timing mechanism. The main instrumentation, ballistic cameras, microphones and flash detectors, are deployed about the range, with good communications the main additional requirement.

Boyd proposed the experiment and was joined by G.V. Groves, who has since made a distinguished contribution to neutral atmosphere studies. They had built for them a number of small ballistic cameras and flash detectors, with the unusual feature that the camera shutters could be triggered by the grenade flashes (provided that they were long enough), in order to extend the measurements to the daylight hours. The grenades were obtained through Ministry of Supply channels after what turned out to be a good deal of needless experimentation with alternatives to Boyd's original choice, the 1.75 in. RAF photoflash cartridge. This cartridge, used for aerial photography, had an explosive core and so made the requisite bang and flash at low altitudes; the question was whether it would function as satisfactorily higher up, in the low ambient air densities. The experts thought not and set about providing two alternative fillings. Low-altitude tests of these alternatives were not encouraging, and when the opportunity was taken to compare all three during a rocket flight, the photoflash won hands down at all heights. The main failings of the grenade were in the igniter that initiated the gun powder expulsion charge and the fuse that allowed the grenade to be thrown clear of the rocket before the explosion. These were sensitive to the change in air density and new components had to be designed to maintain pressurization.

The microphone and recorder array was obtained through WRE and Army channels. Ten microphones were deployed around the rangehead, not to any pre-arranged pattern but at sites determined largely by existing facilities, the area covered being approximately 36 km along range by 18 km across range. Much of the success

171

of the experiment depended on how well the wind noise at the microphones and electrical pick-up on the lines could be reduced. Three ballistic cameras were sited at distances of up to 60 km from the rangehead, success here depending to a large extent on how closely the rocket followed its expected trajectory, since the grenade bursts could all too easily occur outside a camera's field of view, and a last minute change of pointing direction required an operator with a very cool head.

All camera and microphone positions were established by careful surveying. Groves had developed a sophisticated technique for the analysis of the data which, there being twelve microphones, contained a degree of redundancy, and after the first trials he was able to discern from the residuals of his analysis that one microphone was not sited where it was reported to be. Its position was resurveyed and the error was confirmed, so providing convincing proof of the validity of the technique. Much effort went into the planning of the grenade experiment, even to the extent of full-scale trials on a gunnery range in England, observing the bursts of anti-aircraft shells. This epitomized the wide interest and support that was given to this new and exciting field of research in the 1950's. The whole system was ready for action at Woomera by November 1957.

The sixth and last experiment of those initially proposed was an adjunct to the grenade experiment. P.A. Sheppard of the Department of Meteorology at Imperial College proposed the release of aluminum dipoles (chaff) at various heights so that neutral wind speeds could be obtained by radar tracking. It was a convenient arrangement to release photoflash cartridges and chaff cartridges from the same specially constructed bay in a Skylark payload, and the two experiments were performed simultaneously.

This, then, was the line-up for the commencement of the British upper atmosphere research program in 1957. It is worth noting the complete absence of the research topic that today dominates rocket programs everywhere: the search for and study of x-rays from cosmic sources. The Sun was known to emit x-rays but there was as yet no evidence for the existence of processes elsewhere in our Galaxy and beyond so powerful as to be detected at x-ray wavelengths. There was speculation in plenty but hunches were not then enough to justify the expense of developing and flying x-ray detectors.

Solar studies, in the ultraviolet and x-ray regions, were being considered, but without some means of pointing an instrument, little effective work could be done. A bi-axial pointing control had been developed at the University of Colorado as early as 1953, and in 1957 we were generously offered one to help us move into this very rewarding field of rocket research. The Air Force Cambridge Research Laboratories even loaned one to the RAE in May 1957. But RAE's problem was to see the way to flying not one instrument but a series, and this meant developing and building our own pointing system in the U.K. With all available effort and money devoted to the initial development of Skylark, work on the pointing control was not to begin for many years. Another notable absentee was, of course, high-energy radiation-belt particle studies. The first discoveries of these particles were still to be made.

The planning of the research program was initially under the general supervision of the Royal Society's Gassiot Committee. The actual meetings were held in the office of its chairman, Sir Harrie Massey, at University College London (UCL) where the first meeting took place on 27 September 1955. Later, with the formation of the British National Committee for Space Research (BNCSR), again under Massey's chairmanship, the meetings moved to the Royal Society's apartments at Burlington House. Still later, in May 1965, the newly formed Science Research Council took over the management of the program from the BNCSR and Massey therefore ceased to be directly involved. He remains chairman of the BNCSR, but on 30 September 1975, 20 years almost to the day from the first gathering at University College London, he retired from the Quain Chair of Physics there, so ending a period of distinguished service to space research at UCL.

TEST FIRINGS

Six test flights of the Skylark rocket were to precede the commencement of the high-altitude research program, with the fourth and fifth flights providing opportunities to test several UCL experiments. Each payload was built at the RAE and was then sent by air to WRE at Salisbury, South Australia for final preparation. Figure 1 shows a typical Skylark leaving the launch tower at Woomera, Australia.

Figure 1   Boosted Skylark research rocket launched at the Woomera range in Australia. Courtesy British Aircraft Corporation.

173

Though giving a sea level total impulse of 1,450 KNs, the Raven I motor had shown in ground tests an initial thrust of 22.3 KN. This was far too low to be acceptable for general use, and a re-design of the charge shape was put in hand. Indeed, there were two re-designs, because the introduction of an improved propellant again affected the initial thrust. The Raven IIA, with the first re-designed charge and the same propellant, followed the Raven I. The Raven IA was, perversely, the IIA but with a new propellant, giving 1,538 KNs total impulse. The Raven II used the new propellant and a third charge shape, giving an initial thrust of 53.5 KN. All four motors were used in the six test firings. For some years the Raven II remained the standard motor with various improvements being added along the way.

Skylark 01

Skylark 01 was launched on the morning of 13 February 1957, the firing having been postponed from the previous November because of a motor ignition problem encountered during proof tests at Westcott. The launcher was depressed to its maximum of 15 deg and the surface winds were light. The combination of low initial thrust and low launcher setting gave, as expected, a very low trajectory, the peak height being only 12 km. But the launch phase and flight were uneventful. Range coverage was less than perfect. Telemetry reception was continuous, as was tracking of the 6 cm MTS beacon and the kine-theodolites, but radar follow was soon lost and Doppler too. Of course, for so low a trajectory, this was in no sense a fair test, but it reflected a pattern that was to continue as trajectories were raised and the performance of airborne and ground installations were improved. Telemetry reception would be continuous -- the most essential requirement. Doppler, radar and optical follow would be sufficient to establish the trajectory in the lower atmosphere, and MTS follow would be more continuous but with decreasing absolute accuracy as the range increased.

A computer calculation, based upon all available measurements and using a ballistic trajectory above the height at which drag becomes small enough to be ignored, then gave the final trajectory. The accuracy with which a rocket's position may be measured at, say, 200 km altitude is now a matter of how much instrumentation is deployed and how much refinement is put into the computer calculations; the effort has to be matched to the experimenter's requirements.

The flight instrumentation in Skylark 01, accelerometers, rate gyros, nosecone and aerial thermocouples, showed nothing to cause concern. The flight trajectory was very close to that predicted by WRE, so preparations for the second flight went ahead without delay. The rocket was located 43 km downrange, buried in the ground to its motor nozzle, and no attempt was made to recover it. Finding a rocket, which may be a hundred miles away down the Woomera range, has since those days become a highly skilled business. Today, with the all-essential helicopter, experimenters are carried out to the predicted impact point as quickly as possible after a firing to recover instruments or photographic film. The skill of the regular crews in spotting the almost invisible remains amongst the scrub of the Australian outback is quite uncanny.

Skylark 02

Skylark 02 was fired in the afternoon of 22 May 1957, using a Raven IA motor and carrying much the same set of instruments as those on 01, but with the addition of six barium titanate vibration sensors and a second telemetry system. The establishment of a vibration specification for Skylark to which experimental equipment could be tested was the objective, although the difficulties and complexities of vibration measurements gave little hope that one flight alone would yield much usable information. As it turned out none were obtained, for the vibration amplifier itself failed in flight. This, seen in retrospect, was ironic as the vibration environment in Skylark has proved to be, by missile standards, not at all severe and in-flight electronics failures have never been a big problem.

The rocket was ready to be fired two hours after beginning its assembly in the launcher, and it was then a matter of awaiting suitable wind conditions. The launcher was depressed again 15 deg but was also swung 10 deg to the right; it was not appreciated at the time that this resulted in an effective depression of 72 deg and a lateral offset of 31 deg to the right. The motor was fired with a wind of almost 7 m/s at the launcher, which turned the rocket upwards, to an effective 77 deg, and as a consequence of the misunderstanding still further to the right, to a 42 deg offset.

Thus Skylark 02 flew away, cleanly and stably but very much in the wrong direction, reaching a peak height of 75 km and falling to the ground 178 km downrange without ever being found. "I shot an arrow in the air, it fell to Earth I know not where" wrote the launching officer later that day, convinced that Hazell's carefully devised technique of wind correction was quite ineffective. Later, when it was realized what the true training angles were, he was able to show that the rocket had responded as predicted.

The dynamical behavior of this rocket during flight, as recorded by accelerometers and gyroscopes, was unexceptional. In the light of subsequent flights we were to view rather differently the small lateral oscillations that the accelerometers recorded, but even so there were apparently no problems arising from this second flight and preparations for the third flight were continued.

Skylark 03

Skylark 03, using the higher performance Raven IA, was instrumented much like 02 for a third test of rocket performance. In addition, it was to flight-test blind a pair of photometers of the type to be used by Armstrong of the Queen's University, Belfast for airglow measurements, and three Pirani type pressure gauges made at the RAE to be used for routine measurements of air density. The rocket was fired just after midday on 23 July 195, after three earlier attempts, again with a 15 deg depression but into a wind calculated to increase the elevation by 5 deg. The launching itself would have been uneventful but for a failure to switch correctly to internal power at the release of umbilicals. As a result, none of the flight instruments were powered and there was a total loss of information, including for a second time the much needed vibration information. The kinetheodolite records were used to deduce a peak height of 85 km and a range of 218 km. Again, the impact point was never found.

Skylark 04

The Skylark 04 firing was made the occasion for a full-scale test of the grenade and chaff experiments. In addition, Sayer's electron density probe and three more Pirani gauges were carried. The normal flight instrumentation was shifted to the nosecone position so that the instrumentation bay could be replaced by the grenade bay carrying 18 grenades and 10 chaff cartridges. An airborne flash detector was installed in a strong ring. The nosecone was specially modified for the electron density experiment with a forward portion one meter long insulated from the remainder to form a 115 pf capacity, part of a resonant circuit oscillating at about 1.2 MHz. The Raven IA motor was again used.

The firing took place on 13 November 1957 for the first time at night. The rocket flew well, reaching a height of 127 km with an effective elevation at launch, allowing for the effect of quite a strong wind, of 84 deg. Eleven of the 18 grenades exploded at heights between 40 km and 97 km, poor pressurization of the fuses and igniters causing the loss of the remainder. The wreckage of the rocket was found 171 km downrange with evidence of some grenade explosions on impact.

The flashes were recorded on three ballistic cameras, good star background calibrations were obtained and eight burst coordinates wre ultimately computed. All flashes were recorded on the ground, most were detected in flight, and eight bursts were recorded by the sound-ranging microphones. The grenade experiment had thus begun extremely well, the data yielding in due course good measurements of neutral gas temperatures and wind velocities.

The chaff was released in two salvos at 38 km and 52 km, the radar operators having instructions to range on the extremities of the clouds of dipoles as they fell in order to measure the dispersion rate. In the event the dipoles were found to fall at only 5 m/s at 52 km and had dispersed after falling only 3 km, so the hoped-for wind profiles were not forthcoming. As a result of this trial it became necessary to look for a much heavier dipole to replace the aluminum chaff. The tests of the electron density probe and of the pressure gauges were satisfactory, and this fourth firing was therefore altogether most successful.

Indeed, it was now clear that completion of the test series need not hold up the start of the research program proper. Four more grenade experiments were planned for Skylarks 07, 08, 09 and 18, together with the electron density probe as on 04, and the first of these, Skylark 07, was launched on 17 April 1958. It flew to a height of 152 km with a payload of 59 kg in a total head weight of about 105 kg, it impacted 101 km downrange, and the grenade experiment was again successful. The British high altitude rocket program therefore began formals in April 1958, although to all those participating in it, November 1957 and the Skylark 04 firing marked the real beginning.

Skylark 05

The fifth test vehicle, Skylark 05, made use of the first Raven II motor, which became the standard propulsion unit for some years. The new and lighter fins, again in use for the first time, gave the rocket a new look. The rocket instrumentation was by now approaching the standard form for all future firings, with a combined telemetry, Doppler transponder and MTS beacon package, accelerometers and rate gyroscopes.

Two new pieces of instrumentation were being flight-tested for the first time: a three-axis fluxgate magnetometer and a group of Sun cells. The objective was to develop an aspect measuring system. The major piece of instrumentation was a pair of photometers, again provided by Armstrong, for the measurement of the night airglow at 5,577Å. They were carried under a forwards jettisoned nosecone and were specially modified as this was to be a day firing. A cine camera viewed the inside of the nosecone to record its release and ejection by springs.

As Skylark 05 was representative of many of the early rockets, its weight breakdown is of interest. The figures in Table 1 are compared with those for the first American Aerobee-Hi.

Table 1
COMPARISON OF SKYLARK AND AEROBEE-HI SOUNDING ROCKETS

SKYLARK			AEROBEE-HI		
Element	Weight,Kg	Percent	Element	Weight,Kg	Percent
Motor case and nozzle	177	15	Tank, tailcone, thrust chamber	120	20
Propellant	839	72	Propellants	385	63
Fin assembly	40	3	Fins	9	1.5
Payload structure	56	5	Nose cone & extension	14	2
Parachute	none		Parachute	10	1.5
Payload	60	5	Payload and ballast	75	12
Gross weight	1,172		Gross Weight	613	

The rocket was taken to Woomera for a December 1957 firing. Unfortunately, it was set about by many vicissitudes, including an electrical fault that burned out its cable loom, and was eventually overtaken by 06 and 07. Finally, it flew on the afternoon of 20 May 1958.

Again the launching was good. The tower was set at a depression of only 3.6 deg in fairly light winds, and the rocket reached a peak height of 150 km, rather lower than expected. The head was severed from the motor on the descent to aid recovery, and motor case and head were found 1½ km apart, 122 km downrange. Even the ejected nosecone was discovered. The flight yielded little in the way of positive measurements: the camera failed to run, the shutter in front of the one photometer designed to view the sky failed to open, and the flight tests of the magnetometers and Sun cells showed that they would require much development before becoming reliable aspect measuring devices. Despite these shortcomings, the vehicle had performed well and the main objectives were reached.

Skylark 06

The objective of Skylark 06 firing on 2 April 1958 was the flight test of a motor interrupter unit, an explosive device opening the head of the motor so as to terminate the powered flight on command. It was a generally successful test, operation of the interrupter unit bringing the flight to an early end.

The opportunity was taken to try, for a third time, to obtain vibration data, and this time there was more success. One last point of interest was that the nosecone carried a 1.5 m-long, 2.5 cm-diameter probe of a type to be used in later flights to carry a proton procession magnetometer. This marked the entry into the research program of a sixth university group, this one from Imperial College, which was planning to detect current systems in the ionosphere by observing magnetic field discontinuities.

This firing concluded the series of Skylark flight tests, which were described in detail by Dorling [8].

On the propulsion and structural side all had gone well, so much so that the main research program had already been started. The Raven II motor, though a little down on its expected performance in terms of peak height, had shown the required high initial thrust, and there was general confidence that as its development continued it would fully meet all expectations. What was still rather uncertain was the rocket's dispersion -- the amount by which its actual impact point differed from the aiming point for reasons of structural and jet misalignments; inaccurate knowledge of motor performance, drag, air density; and inaccurate measurement of the ballistic wind and the required launcher corrections. The evidence so far was quite encouraging.

Otherwise, attention was turning away from the questions of structural and aerodynamic stability, of motor performance and dispersion, to what is known in the aerospace industry as product improvement. Although the modular design of the rocket head was preserved, the detailed design was revised progressively over the following years. The forward ejecting nosecone, first used on Skylark 05, was replaced by a pneumatically operated split nosecone, divided along its length and separating sideways. Additional bays were introduced, of varying lengths, the coupling being by way of manacle clamps. Electrical inter-connections between bays were modified to ease assembly and disassembly. Also, an inspection service was introduced to ensure that each payload was built up correctly so as to eliminate time wasting delays at the range.

Priming arrangements, that is the arrangements for monitoring and powering the payload through the umbilicals, were reengineered for greater versatility. Vibration testing of sub-units was introduced, although it was to be some time before vibration tests on complete payloads became a practical possibility. One can see in retrospect that these steady improvements in the quality of engineering were necessary, not to speed up the preparation of payloads, which they probably never did, nor to reduce overall cost, which they certainly could not, but to make possible the very considerable increase in complexity that is seen in the rocket payloads of today.

BOOST MOTORS AND PARACHUTE RECOVERY

Apart from the detailed improvements in the Skylark rocket that have been mentioned, two new facilities were under development at the end of flight testing. One of these was a parachute for payload recovery, and the other a tandem boost motor to reduce dispersion and increase peak height. Both came into use during the first half of 1959. The boost motor, the Cuckoo, is ignited first, burns for four seconds and then, as the main motor is initiated by a timer, is separated. Its introduction was not complicated by any but minor difficulties, and it was quickly adopted as a standard accessory. Later, the larger and more powerful Goldfinch booster was developed and is now a standard facility.

The parachute system proved that nothing is simple. Though quite satisfactory when tested in aircraft drops, it frequently misbehaved in rocket use -- usually because of premature deployment. The recovery procedure begins with the head separation from the rocket on re-entry (unless separation had been initiated earlier for experimental reasons), followed by drogue release by a cartridge initiated by a pressure switch to stabilize the head, and then by main canopy deployment at about 3 km height.

Initially, it was thought that abnormally high dynamic pressures were being generated at an early stage of re-entry, this triggering the initiation too early; but, palliatives based on this hypothesis were never successful. Several pressure measuring points were installed, manifolded first directly then electrically, but still failures occurred. It is only comparatively recently that the true cause has been established. As a rocket head re-enters, it is driven, whether spinning or not, into a propelling motion that becomes so fast that the main parachute may be torn from its bay by centrifugal force unless powerfully restrained. Now that the failure mechanism has been identified and shown to be controllable by the use of strong wire restraints that are later freed by explosive cutters, the parachute system is being re-designed to accommodate this unexpected phenomenon. It is also being strengthened to handle the very much heavier payloads now being carried.

RAVEN MOTOR DEVELOPMENT

By the end of the vehicle proving trials in 1958, four motors had been tested: Ravens I, IA, II and IIA. Of these, Raven II became the motor on which the research program was to rely for the next few years. However, motor developments were continuing with many aims, including those of lightening the case, increasing the total impulse, improving the nozzle to eliminate uneven erosion, eliminating uneven burning and reducing the unburnt propellant.

Not every experimenter needed an increased apogee, and for some D- and E-region ionospheric experiments a low-performance motor is beneficial. Solar and astrophysical studies, however, put a premium on rocket improvements, and in recent years the very viability of Skylark as a research tool has rested on the production of ever better motors.

Raven V followed closely on the heels of the II version, using a new propellant at higher density giving 1,780 kNs sea level total impulse (over 1,900 kNs in vacuum); it was cleared for use in June 1958. Later, it was modified as the VA and was first flown, with a Cuckoo boost as SL35B on 6 February 1962. There were then two motors available for general use, the II and the VA. Minor structural changes caused these to be re-classified as the VII and the VIA, respectively. When the erratic burning of the propellant resulted in two in-flight tube bursts the less troublesome Raven VI propellant was used with the Raven VII to result in the Raven VIII. Thus, over the course of the years the lower performance II gave way to the VIII with 1,750 kNs vacuum total impose, and the higher performance VA to the VI with 2,100 kNs.

These motors are substantially unchanged today. They are boosted by one of three motors, Cuckoo IA, Goldfinch IIA, a longer and more powerful version of the Cuckoo, and Cuckoo III, a faster burning Cuckoo for short-rail launches. The main characteristics of these sustainer motors and boosters are given below in Tables 2 and 3.

The performance of any motor/booster combination is measured in terms of headweight and peak height. Some typical heights for a standard headweight of 200 kg are given in Table 4.

Table 2
RAVEN SUSTAINER MOTORS

Function	Raven V1	Raven V111	Raven X1
Propellant mass, kg	977	837	945
Total mass, kg	1160	1018	1130
Total impulse, kNs	1800	1500	2415
Specific impulse, Ns/kg	2105	2055	2556
Nominal thrust, kN	53.4	44.5	80
Nominal burning time, sec*	30	30	30

*burning times vary by up to ± 10%, specific impulse by 2% rms

Table 3
BOOSTERS

Function	Cuckoo IA	Goldfinch IIA	Cuckoo III
Propellant mass, kg	182	316	180
Total mass, kg	243	405	238
Total impulse, kNs	364	699	407
Specific impulse, Ns/kg	2000	2210	2610
Nominal thrust, kN	91	189	192
Nominal burning time, sec	4.0s	3.7s	2.45s

Table 4
TYPICAL ALTITUDES ATTAINED BY MOTOR/BOOSTER COMBINATIONS

Performance Summary (in kilometer)*

Motor	Unboosted	Cuckoo IA	Goldfinch IIA
Raven VIII	112	170	230
Raven VI	-	212	290
Raven X1	262	-	415

*for standard headweight of 200 kg.

ROLL-YAW LOCK-IN

The six development firings of 1957-58 appeared to show that the Skylark rocket had no vices aerodynamically, and the following six consolidated this feeling of confidence. However, the 13th flight of Skylark 21 on 5 March 1959, *was* unlucky; the rocket broke up during the powered phase of the flight and high-speed film records showed a fin to have been torn away.

This was the first overt signs of roll-yaw lock-in, already known to be afflicting other sounding rockets. There appeared to be two ways to meet the difficulty: to speed up the spin rate and to fly through resonance early or to reduce the rate to as near to zero as possible and so postpone resonance until aerodynamic forces became insignificant. The decision at RAE was to take the latter course as more certain to be effective and requiring no design changes, only greater care in the manufacture, inspection and selection of fins. Some anxiety that the actual cause of failure was bending of the forebody at the clamped joints of the various body sections was dismissed when loading tests showed that the stiffness was entirely adequate. Once the resonance effect was identified more careful study of the records of earlier flights showed that resonance and lock-in had occurred on a number of occasions, notably during the Skylark 05 flight when the peak height was lower than had been expected and dispersion rather higher.

The low spin-rate remedy was put into practice and it generally proved to be effective. A second in-flight failure, of Skylark 50 in December 1960, showed that a structural failure had again occurred in a fin as a result of distortion. Subsequent flights with more carefully aligned fins of stronger build were free of any serious manifestations of resonance. Although lock-in occurred many times during these flights, its effect at the worst was to reduce vehicle performance. From that time the pattern of flights became established; the rocket could be expected to spin only slowly, if at all, whilst developing as it left the atmosphere an almost flat propelling motion, a motion actually brought on by the postponed lock-in. It was not in every experimenter's eyes an ideal environment, and it made the aspect analysis problem difficult.

Ionospheric experiments would certainly have benefited (as later they did) from the rocket being spun whilst maintaining a constant heading. Astronomical experiments could in principal benefit from a slow roll rate, but only if chance brought the source under study into the instrument's field of view; a stable if rather uncertain pointing direction with spin was generally thought preferable. Whatever, the pros and cons, no change was made in the RAE practice until the mid-1960's when the European Space Research Organisation (ESRO) began a rocket program using, amongst other vehicles, the Skylark rocket. They chose to cant the three fins on their Skylarks to build up a spin rate of about 3 Hz at all-burnt which, they believed, would time resonance to occur when disturbance would be nominal. Flight tests showed that their analysis was correct, resonance being minimized to the point where it ceased to be troublesome. The U.K. then adopted the procedure and in 1968 rockets became available in the British national program in which experimenters could for the first time build into their experiments the rocket's spinning motion.

The dividing line between the mild and the extreme forms of the lock-in phenomenon is difficult either to define or to predict. The indications are that resonance between spin rate and yaw frequency can safely be advanced in the flight by the use of a larger fin angle, bringing the final spin rate as high as 5 Hz. Still higher rates would risk inducing resonance at a much earlier point -- in the first few seconds of flight -- with disastrous results; but, as higher spin rates bring with them new structural and motor burning problems, 3 Hz has come to be the accepted vacuum spin rate. Resonance is passed through at about 1.5 Hz around 30 sec after launch. These rather general statements about the lock-in problem apply only to Skylark and are based largely on flight experience.

It is clear that the dynamic behavior of a sounding rocket is very sensitive to changes in geometry. Thus, what might be true about the Skylark geometry may very well be quite misleading for another comparable vehicle. Besides the two failures attributed to roll-yaw lock-in a number of others occurred during the course of the program. Five happened between 1961 and 1963 when structural failures occurred in the head, the most likely cause being distortion of the nosecones under heating. The nose structures were subsequently strengthened and materials were improved. The tubes of two Raven motors (on a II and a VII) burst because of erratic burning. Three motors failed to ignite at Woomera and four elsewhere; positive explanations of these failures have been the exception rather than the rule, but it seems likely that the faults lay in the ignition circuits. Two motors suffered head-end failures, in one case because the thrust termination unit was badly fitted. Two early motors suffered rear-end failures and failed to leave the launcher; rather surprisingly the ends were refitted and the motors were fired successfully. Lastly, two expansion nozzles of an experimental type failed.

DISPERSION

The dispersion of the point of impact of a sounding rocket comes to be the most decisive factor when considering whether or not it may be launched at a firing range. Experience since the early days of the Skylark program has shown that of the many contributory causes of dispersion the dominant one is motor thrust misalignment, particularly in the first few hundred feet above the launcher.

For a typical Skylark, a thrust misalignment of 0.001 radian will produce a dispersion of about 20 km; and, in 1972, the accumulated data for past firings showed that a misalignment of 0.002 radian was representative of a Raven VIII -- Cuckoo combination. With no spin, the rms dispersion was 25 percent of the apogee height, which is equivalent to a launcher tilt of 1.6 deg. The most effective way of reducing the consequences of thrust misalignment is to spin the rocket as it leaves the launcher. Provided the vehicle rotates once or twice during the time taken to describe the first complete oscillation in yaw, a large proportion of the dispersive effects of thrust and structural misalignments is eliminated. With typical Cuckoo-boosted Skylarks this time is some 4 seconds, whilst the vehicle covers 350 m, and canted fins alone are not enough to ensure at least one full rotation.

Such a consideration led some years ago to the fitting of small spin motors on the boost adapter. Six IMP IV spin motors are now used, burning for 1/2 sec and raising the spin rate momentarily above 0.5 Hz, from which point it decays to the aerodynamic value provided by the canted fins. In this way, the effect of thrust misalignment is reduced by 60 percent, and the overall dispersion by 40 percent. For the Raven VIII -- Cuckoo combination quoted above the rms dispersion drops from 25 percent of apogee to 11 percent. The use of spin-up together with the more powerful Goldfinch booster (or the Cuckoo III, an alternative to the Goldfinch) has made possible the operation of Skylark from much shorter launchers. Thus, the Raven VIII/Cuckoo III combination launched from a 12.5 m beam has an rms dispersion which is 13 percent of the apogee height, compared with the 11 percent (above) from the 100-ft. tower.

ATTITUDE CONTROL

Probably the most important of the new facilities developed for Skylark is the attitude control unit (ACU). This much-needed facility was first worked on at RAE and in November 1961 a gas-jet system was flight tested on Skylark 34. However, it had become clear that the considerable development work needed to perfect so complex a device would require the resources of an industrial firm, and contractual arrangements were completed in 1962 with Elliott Brothers (now part of Marconi Space and Defence Systems) of Frimley, England.

A key question had first to be answered concerning the reference directions against which the rocket payload was to be stabilized, whether these were to be inertial, astrophysical or geophysical. The decision was based on an analysis in 1961 of experimenters' requirements, which showed that the great majority of them were initially for solar pointing, with stellar pointing still a minority interest. The British National Committee for Space Research, the body then responsible for all planning matters, chose a stage-by-stage development beginning with a Sun-pointing gas-jet control system (Stage 1), moving on to a low accuracy Moon-pointing system (Stage 2), a higher accuracy Sun- or Moon-pointing system (Stage 3), a zenith-pointing system (Stage 4) and, finally, a high accuracy star-pointing system (Stage 5).

Work began on Stage 1 in 1962, the requirement being coarse Sun-pointing to an accuracy of 1 or 2 deg. The first prototype system, tested on Skylark 301 at Woomera on 11 August 1964, carried a normal-incidence grating spectrograph provided by the Culham Laboratory for studies of the solar spectrum between 50 nm and 300 nm. A fine optical alignment system in the instrument maintained the limb of the solar image tangentially to the spectrograph slit to an accuracy of 10 arc sec. The flight was very successful. The rocket payload, already separated from the motor, was pointed towards the Sun for 226 sec with an accuracy better than 10 arc min. Although the parachute failed to deploy correctly, the film cassette was recovered from the wreckage and a successful solar spectrogram was obtained. So began this important new phase in the Skylark research program.

Two further proving flights followed, SL 302 on 17 December 1964 and SL 303 on 9 April 1965. Both were successful and the instruments were recovered correctly thereby providing the Culham Laboratory group with the ultra-violet spectrograms of outstanding quality. Meanwhile, plans for ACU development were changed as the Moon-pointing requirement of Stage 2 appeared to be no longer pressing and was omitted. Instead, Stage 3 development was begun eventually culminating in a first launching on SL 403 in July 1968. However, continuing work on the Stage 1 system, which had bettered its declared pointing accuracy so emphatically even in the first flight, was making it clear that the Stage 3 accuracy could be achieved without the greater complexity of the Stage 3 system. Consequently, this latter development was terminated after four units had been produced. The last of these was flown in its Moon-pointing role on SL 402 in October 1972.

A valuable engineering change to the Stage 1 system began in 1969 when the pneumatic section was separated from the attitude control bay so that the latter could be included in the recoverable portion of the payload for re-use; the new version was first flown in August 1971. Table 5 shows how the build-up of the program of stabilized rockets proceeded, reaching a peak of nine launchings in 1969. The program had begun with solar physics as the major objective but almost at once the new and exciting field of cosmic x-ray astronomy came swiftly to the fore. Early experiments were conducted from spin-stabilized Skylarks, the first pointed experiment being a high-resolution scan of the M-87 galaxy from SL 403 with the instrument looking sideways from the payload and the Sun providing the main pointing reference.

Table 5

SUMMARY OF U.K. SKYLARK LAUNCHINGS AT WOOMERA

Year	Space research Flights		RAE (R & D) Flights		Total Flights
	unstabilized	stabilized	unstabilized	stabilized	Flights
1957			4		4
1958	5		3		8
1959	9		2		11
1960	7		2		9
1961	8		5		13
1962	14		4		18
1963	14		5		19
1964	9		6	2	17
1965	19	1	2	1	23
1966	9	2	5	2	18
1967	8	3	1	2	14
1968	6	4	2	0	12
1969	9	8	2	0	19
1970	6	8	0	0	14
1971	3	6	0	0	9
1972	2	5	0	2	9
1973	0	7	1	0	8
1974	0	6	1	0	7
1975*	0	2	0	2	4
Totals	128	52	45	11	236

*to 3 July 1975

185

Clearly the Stage 5 system was now a priority development and once again a stage was omitted. In mid-1967, a contract was let with Elliott Brothers for the Stage 5 development. The objective was a system that would acquire a number of stars during one flight, the limiting stellar brightness to be 5th magnitude, lateral pointing accuracy to be about 2 arc min, roll accuracy 1 deg. Two prototype models were to be produced. the principal system change was that lunar acquisition would result from coning the payload around the local magnetic vector at the appropriate angle. This reliance upon the Moon as the secondary reference implied inevitable limitations on firing times.

The two prototypes were flown on SL811 on 16 July 1970 and on SL812 on 10 May 1971; and, though both failed to acquire their target stars, the star search and lock sequences were good.

Two further prototypes were built and flown on SL1011 17 April 1973 and on SL1111 16 June 1973, and both found and locked-on their target stars successfully. The Leicester University group had the distinction of being the first experimenters on both Stage 3 and Stage 5. Since that time, a further two more star-pointing payloads have been launched.

The overall star acquisition of the Stage 5 system is a lengthy process. Magnetic coning before moonlock may take 30 sec, moonlock itself another 30 sec, twisting and slewing to a guide star yet a further 30 sec. Scanning the guide star area and locking-on may take 15 sec, and the final twist to point the observing instrument at the target (often invisible) another few seconds. A typical Skylark may well have reached apogee before acquisition has been completed and measurements begun.

There can be little doubt that the attitude control unit, an outstanding success for all concerned in its development, manufacture and preparation, at MSDS Frimley, RAE Farnborough and BAC Filton, transformed the Skylark program when it came on the scene in 1964. Indeed, for a while the United Kingdom was in the lead in solar astronomy; now, in its more advanced Stage 1 and Stage 5 guises, the attitude control unit is enabling us to make yet more valuable advances in astronomy. Up to the end of 1974, a total of 57 stabilized Skylarks had been flown; 47, Stage 1; 4, Stage 3; and 6, Stage 5. Today much interest is centered on the development of an attitude control unit based on a commercially available inertial navigation system. The first flight is expected to be in 1977, and it should bring the benefits of lower weight, freedom from launch constraints, short acquisition times and simpler payload integration procedures.

PREPARATION AND FIRING ARRANGEMENTS FOR SKYLARK

The preparation of the early Skylark payloads was carried out, as has been described, at the Royal Aircraft Establishment, whilst the final preparation and launching was wholly the responsibility of the Australian Weapons Research Establishment. When in 1961 the contract was prepared for the attitude control unit development, the associated payload preparation task at RAE was seen to be of

186

such a magnitude that additional resources would have to be employed to keep up the momentum of the remainder of the rocket program. A contract was awarded in that year to the Guided Weapons Division of the British Aircraft Corporation (Filton) for the preparation and testing of payloads. By 1964, the program had so expanded that BAC became Skylark managers, coordinating design authority and industrial agent, whilst the RAE remained the research and development authority and continued to assemble certain payloads. Since that time BAC have assumed an increasingly responsible role in the running of the overall program, becoming contractors for the preparation and launching of Skylarks from Woomera through the British Aircraft Corporation (Australia) Pty. Ltd. On 1 April 1974, the Appleton Laboratory of the Science Research Council became responsible for Skylark procurement, accountancy, contracts, etc., with its Sounding Rockets Division taking over the role of range user at the Woomera range in place of the Royal Aircraft Establishment's Space Department. Trials at Woomera are now planned jointly by the Australian Weapons Research Establishment Trials Wing and by the Appleton Laboratory. BAC (Filton) prepare the specification and BAC (Australia) check the pre-flight performance estimates and other information requirements before passing them to the WRE Planning and Data Analysis Group who prepare the trials instruction, detailing the required range instrumentation and services.

Skylark payloads are today assembled and the experiments integrated at Filton; they are then accompanied to Woomera by the payload engineers and experimenters. Travel to and from Adelaide, Australia, was made possible from the outset of the research program by an extension of the existing arrangements for manning trials at Woomera. For many years, the Royal Air Force Transport Command provided a passenger and freight service; and the journeys, first by the piston-engined Hastings, later by Comet II aircraft, were a memorable experience. Eventually, the military aircraft gave way to chartered flights, and today commercial airlines are used. Travel to Woomera from Adelaide is by WRE air charter.

SUMMARY OF FIRINGS AT WOOMERA

The magnitude of the U.K. Skylark rocket program at Woomera from 1957 to the present date is shown in Table 5, the data from 1963 being taken from Royal Society's reports prepared on behalf of the British National Committee for Space Research as well as from information provided by BAC (Filton).

U.K. Skylark rockets have been launched from ranges other than Woomera, from Andoya, Arenosillo, Kiruna and Aberporth. Still other Skylarks have been used in ESRO and national research programs. The total numbers of such launchings are summarized in Table 6.

Table 6
SKYLARK LAUNCHING SUMMARY[*]

Range	Country	Skylark Rocket Launchings					
		NASA	UK	ESRO	Germany	Argentina UK	Total
Andoya	Norway		5				5
Arenosillo	Spain		1		4		5
Kiruna	Sweden		1	22			23
Mercedes	Argentina					2	2
Woomera	Australia	4	236	6	1		247
Perdas de Fogu	Italy			54	2		56
Aberporth	United Kingdom		2				2
Totals		4	245	82	7	2	340

*Includes all launchings up to 3 July 1975.

In simple terms of rocket numbers, the United Kingdom's program based on Skylark reached its peak in the period 1965-1970, then fell to a level of about 7 firings a year as new opportunities for satellite and rocket flights became available to U.K. experimenters. The ESRO rocket program began in 1965 and in its 8 years (1965-1972), U.K. instruments were flown on 53 Skylarks, 23 Centaurs and 15 smaller rockets. In 1967, the smaller Petrel rocket (23 cm dia) and the Skua rocket (14 cm dia) were brought into increasing use as part of the U.K. national rocket program, first at the South Uist range in the Outer Hebrides and later at Kiruna and Andoya. Between 1967 and 1973, 87 Petrels were flown from South Uist, 32 from Kiruna or Andoya and 10 from Thumba; in the same period 36 Skuas were flown from South Uist, 18 from Kiruna and 3 from Thumba.

Cooperative projects with other countries were also being carried out, all of which are mentioned in the BNCS reports. As a consequence of all this activity it became possible to concentrate the Skylark program at Woomera on meeting the growing demand for pointing control, as provided by the various stages of the ACU. The rocket numbers in Table 5 reveal this change.

Throughout the 18 years at Woomera engineering development payloads were flown by the RAE and new motors and boosters were tested. Of the 56 firings listed in Table 5 two-thirds were in support of such activity, the remainder having been flown in separate research programs.

CONCLUSION

The purpose of this paper has been to provide an historical record of the events from 1952 onwards leading to the commencement in 1958 of the British Skylark sounding rocket program. For completeness, technological innovations since 1958, in motors, pointing control and recovery, have been reviewed; they emphasize the remarkable capacity for growth and development that was built into the original rocket design.

A review of the scientific achievements made possible by the Skylark rocket has not been attempted, and must await another opportunity and another pen. It will be a more difficult task because of the diversity of the investigations, because these investigations have usually formed part of wider studies embracing ground and satellite based observations, and above all because it is impossible to quantify the fresh interest and new drive brought to an existing scientific discipline by so radically new a technique.

Space research in the early 1950's was truly exploration into the unknown with the sounding rocket affording the only direct means of involvement. Today, the very existence of the sounding rocket is challenged by rival techniques, principally the use of orbiting spacecraft and -- increasingly -- of high altitude balloons as well as by ever more elegant ground-based measuring techniques. There *is* a niche for small rockets in studying the aeronomy of the lower atmosphere below the direct reach of satellites; whether for this reason we in the United Kingdom will see the smaller Petrel and Skua rockets gradually ousting Skylark, only time will tell.

REFERENCES

1. D.R. Bates, 1974, Radiative and collision processes in the ionosphere, J. Atoms. Terr. Phys., 36, 2287.

2. R.L.F. Boyd and M.J. Seaton, 1954, *Rocket Exploration of the Upper Atmosphere*, Pergamon Press Ltd., London.

3. D.G. King-Hele, 1954, The performance of an upper atmosphere research vehicle powered by solid fuel rocket motors. RAE Technical Note GW 315.

4. D.I. Dawton, 1955, Performance estimates for a single stage upper atmosphere research vehicle powered by a solid fuel rocket motor. RAE Technical Note GW 387.

5. T.L. Smith and W.E. Parker, 1955, RAE Technical Note RPD 134, on a visit to the United States in June 1955 to discuss rocket vehicles suitable for upper atmosphere research.

6. F.E. Jones and H.S.W. Massey, 1956, Rocket explorations of the upper atmosphere. *Nature*, Lond., *177*, 643.

7. J.F. Hazell and E.B. Dorling, 1959, *Sounding Rockets*, McGraw-Hill Book Company Ltd.

8. E.B. Dorling, 1959, The first six Skylark firings. RAE Technical Note GW 530.

Chapter 13

FIRST ROCKET EXPERIMENTS FOR RESEARCH
ON SOLAR SHORTWAVE RADIATION[*]

G. S. Ivanov-Kholodnyy and L. A. Vedeshin[†]

On 15 August 1951, for the first time in the Soviet Union, scientific equipment was lifted on board a rocket to an altitude of around 100 km in order to study the spectral composition of solar shortwave radiation.

The opportunities for spectroscopic research on celestial bodies on the ground are substantially limited by the absorbing action of the terrestrial atmosphere. Located on the Earth, we can observe the universe surrounding us only via two relatively narrow spectral ranges of atmospheric transmittance. The first encompasses the so-called visible range and the nearby sections of the ultraviolet [UV] and infrared [IR] ranges and the nearby sections of approximately 3,000 Å to 14 μ (with a non-transmittance range of from 2.5 to 8 μ). Astronomers conduct their observations through this "window". The second "window" lies in the range of from several centimeters to several meters. Radio astronomers use this band of electromagnetic radiation. Thanks to the electromagnetic radiation coming to the Earth, scientists have available basic data about the composition and structure, temperature, pressure and other parameters of the external envelopes of the Sun and the stars, of a planet's atmosphere, of the nebulae and other celestial bodies, as well as of the upper layers of the Earth's atmosphere.

The fact of absorption of the UV section of the spectrum with long waves shorter than 3,000 Å was even noted by scientists nearly 100 years ago and, in 1880 Hartry ascribed it in accordance with the coincidence of the absorption bands to the ozone. Subsequent research on board rockets and satellites confirmed this and indicated that the absorption of the UV section of the solar spectrum shorter than 3,000 Å is basically associated with the ozone which forms a quite narrow layer in the atmosphere, the maximum of which is located at an altitude of around 30 km.

In the range of long waves shorter than 1,800 Å and right down to 800 Å, the absorption is determined by molecular oxygen and in the even shorter-wave range of the spectrum -- by atomic oxygen and molecular nitrogen. Water vapor intensive-

* Presented at The Eleventh IAA History of Astronautics Symposium, Prague, Czechoslovakia, September 1977.

† Committee of the Soviet National Association of Natural Science and Technology Historians, USSR Academy of Sciences, Moscow, USSR.

ly absorbs UV radiation; however, its content quickly diminishes with the altitude, becoming dissipatingly small at altitudes exceeding 30 km. In the IR range of the spectrum, the absorption is produced first of all by water vapor, then by carbon dioxide and only after this by molecular oxygen. Finally, in the radiowave range, the absorption is associated with the ionosphere, which usually makes the long-wave range greater than 30 m inaccessible for observation. In the submillimetric band, the molecular absorption becomes substantial, particularly that associated with water vapor and carbon dioxide gas.

Beginning in the middle of the 1930's, scientists made attempts to expand the observation range and in particular to investigate the solar shortwave radiation from high mountains and aerostats. However, these attempts were unsuccessful, inasmuch as the shortwave radiation does not descend to the heights attainable using stratostats and aircraft [1]. The first attempts at experimental detection of solar shortwave radiation using the new technical means -- rockets -- date back to 1943. In Germany, Kiepenhäuer and Regener prepared a spectrograph to be sent up on the V2 rockets; however, the experiment was not carried out.

In the Soviet Union, on the initiative of Academician S.I. Vavilov in 1947-48, in the State Optics Institute (SOI), A.V. Yakovleva and in 1950-51, in the USSR Academy of Sciences' Physics Institute P.N. Lebedev and S.L. Mandelshtam began work on developing equipment for research on board rockets of the spectral composition of the UV and x-ray sections of the solar radiation and the absorption capabilities of the ozone at altitudes of 55-60 km [2]. Similar research was begun in the U.S.A. in 1946-47. At the end of the 1940's, American scientists, using captured V2 rockets, obtained the first spectrograms of the solar shortwave radiation. In the first operation of the USSR and U.S.A., they used spectrographs with photographic recording of the spectrum and small resolution (in the USSR with quartz optics, in the U.S.A. with a diffractional lattice). In the American spectrograph, R. Tousey and his associates, instead of a slit, used the image of the Sun with a diameter of 0.03 mm, obtained from the ball from the LiF, and in the experiments by Hopfield and Clearman, a spectrograph was used with two slits, and in order to increase the field of vision, opaque plates, illuminated by lighting, were placed in front of the slits [2].

The first research in the USSR was carried out on the V1B geophysical rocket. It was developed based on the R1 ballistic missile with certain changes in the design of its tail and nose sections, as well as a guidance system for ensuring the vertical trajectory of the flight. In addition, for the first time, a system for recovery of the nose section was developed. The latter consisted of an instrument compartment with the spectrographs for investigation of the solar UV radiation (2,170-3,000 Å), a sealed compartment for experimental animals and a compartment for the recovery system with a parachute container and braking shields [3].

The first launch of the V1B rocket (with the SOI spectrographs) took place on 15 August 1951. The rocket soared upwards carrying with it a nose container with scientific equipment and experimental animals weighing on the order of 590 kg. The flight trajectory was nearly vertical. In the ascending section of the trajectory after the engine ceased operating, when the rocket was moving by inertia, for 188

192

sec, which corresponded to an altitude of 100 to 110 km, on command from the program device, the nose section separated from the body of the rocket.

Upon the transmission of the current impulse to the explosive bolts, the bonding links connecting the nose section with the body of the rocket separated. The separation was accomplished using six spring pushers which imparted to it an additional velocity -- of 0.6 m/s, in order to preclude the nose section colliding with the rocket body during the descending branch of the trajectory. Then there was a subsequent catapulting of the first (at an altitude of 75-90 km) and second (at an altitude of 75-85 km) carts containing the animals. At the same time, the braking shields were deployed with the aid of springs at a 60 deg angle and in accordance with the degree of entry into the dense layers of the atmosphere, first stabilized the nose section and then slowed it down to a speed of 140 m/s. At an altitude of 6-8 km, the lid of the parachute container shot off. The pilot parachute activated the drag parachute (with an area of 3.5 m^2) and the main parachute (with an area of 400 m^2) [4].

The spectrographs prepared for flight photographed the Sun on the ascending branch of the trajectory until the ceiling was reached. The main experimental difficulty was ensuring that the Sun would fall into the field of vision of the spectrograph for an adequate amount of time during the rotation and tip-over of the rocket in the passive section of the trajectory. In connection with this, the SOI spectrographs were equipped with an illuminator with an angle of vision of 120 deg and three instruments were installed in the nose section, which covered the entire field of vision.

The recovery system operated so well that it was possible to use the instruments for a number of flights. Three launches were made on the V1B and 56 spectrograms were obtained which were suitable for processing, of which 22 were beyond the limits of the ozone absorption layer. A recording was made of the section of the spectrum from 4,000 Å to 2,300 Å. Using the quartz spectrograph, a series of spectrograms were obtained, according to which the displacement of the boundary with the altitude, caused by the absorption of the ozone, which extends in the atmosphere right up to 55 km, is traceable. In the entire range of the spectrum obtained on these photos, its nature remained the same as that of the intensive continuous spectrum with numerous lines of absorption in the $\lambda \sim 3,000$ Å range previously observed from the Earth. Particularly intensive and broad were the lines Mg II $\lambda \sim 2,802.7$ and $\lambda \sim 2,795.5$ Å (corresponding H and K to the lines of Ca II), observed from the Earth. The obtained spectrograms had a resolution of up to 1 Å. In the section of 2,250-2,881 Å, nearly 300 Fraunhofer lines were recorded [5].

In order to investigate the upper layers of the terrestrial atmosphere and basically the ozone layer, scientific equipment was sent up on the MR-1 meteorological rockets in the USSR. In the SOI, special spectrographs had been developed with circular coverage illuminators, for the spectrum range from 4,000 to 2,000 Å. The use of fluorite optics in them in combination with a mirror-like objective made it possible to obtain a plane focal surface and to place the spectrum on the generated cylinder using a drum-type cassette. At the same time, the amount of time required to change the exposure was all of 0.1 sec. The photographing was done with a set of exposures ranging from 0.07 to 4 sec.

All the equipment was tested on CAO [Central Aerological Observatory] stratostats, sent up to altitudes of 20 km, before being launched on the V1B and MR-1 rockets. These tests made it possible to discover and eliminate certain design shortcomings in the instruments, but the altitude was inadequate for observation of the ozone layer. The first launch on an MR-1 rocket was accomplished on 19 July 1955, with the Sun at an altitude of 14 deg 15 min. Thirty result-yielding spectrograms with an exposure of 4 sec were obtained using a second version of the illuminator. The last spectrum was obtained at an altitude of 75 km. In order to calculate the ozone concentration, the method of the relative intensity of two long waves was used. At the same time, on the day the spectrograph was launched and during the very same hours, ground observations were made of the ozone layer according to the scattered radiation from the zenith [6].

During this same period, an evaluation was made of the solar radiation stream in the UV range without spectral analysis using the thermoluminescent phosphors $SaSO_4(M4)$ developed in the SOI by V.A. Arkhangelskaya and photon counters.

The phosphor $CaSO_4(Mn)$ possesses extremely valuable qualities, making it possible to use it to produce absolute radiation measurements in the shortwave range of the spectrum of 1-1,300 Å. The described instrument was used during the total solar eclipse of 15 February 1961 to measure the solar x-ray radiation. The instrument was installed on an R2A rocket and it operated at altitudes of from 60 to 96 km. During the measurements, the instrument was aimed at the Sun with an accuracy of ±1 deg. After every 22 seconds there was a change of the plates with the phosphor. In all, six measurements (of the total amount of light) were obtained, five of which were related to the moment of totality of the eclipse. The results of the measurements indicated that the recorded light sum decreases with the decrease in the altitude of exposure of the phosphor and the maximum light sum corresponds to the trajectory peak [7].

Further successes in the investigation of the solar UV radiation were due to the use of the servo systems in the rocket experiments, which ensured control of the spectrographs and other instruments over the course of a significant section of the rocket's flight.

The original design of the rocket spectrometer with photoelectric recording of the spectrum in the 20-1,300 Å range was developed by the SOI and FIAN [The Academy of Sciences' Physics Institute], in 1956. In this instrument, in order to increase the aperture ratio, a plane diffraction lattice and (Soller) collimators for collimation of the incoming and outgoing beams were used. An open-type VEU [Reiterative Electron Multiplier] was used as the receiver. The instrument was combined with the servo system [2].

In 1955-56, a new model solar spectrograph with a diffraction lattice with a 1-meter curvature radius was installed on an updated V1Ye rocket. The spectrograph was placed on the very tip of the nose of the rocket and was equipped with a homing head. Azimuth tracking was accomplished by rotation of the entire head, and altitude tracking by oscillation of the plane mirror, with a 60 deg angle of view. The modification of the V1Ye distinguished it from the preceding V1B by the presence of special powder accelerators, with whose aid the nose section moved away from the rocket at the trajectory peak. This solar spectrograph, the spectrum from 3,000 to 2,470 Å with an inverse dispersion of 16.7 Å/mm and a resolution of 0.3 Å was recorded.

In 1957, the new V2A geophysical rocket was developed for research up to 200 km. The rocket had a separable and recoverable nose section weighing 2,200 kg. On 13 August 1957, the first experiment on the investigation of the solar UV radiation took place on the V2A rocket using the SOI spectrograph. Later there followed launches in 1958, 1959 and 1960. In these experiments, solar spectrograms from 3,000 to 2,080 Å with an inverse dispersion of 16.7 Å/mm were obtained for the individual sections, and in 1959, ones were obtained with an inverse dispersion of 8.3 Å/mm and a resolution of 0.15 Å. As a result of this research, bismuth with an abundance corresponding to its prevalence in space was discovered on the Sun. A detailed study of the resonance lines of Mg II at 2,800 Å indicated that, on the broad absorption lines with wings encompassing nearly 200 Å, sharp emission lines were superimposed, which in turn were self-inverted. The intensities of the lines of the components of the doublet were as indicated in Table 1 and, apparently, do not depend on the activity of the Sun [8].

Table 1
INTENSITIES OF LINES OF COMPONENTS OF THE DOUBLET

Date of Photographs	Time	(Units of microwatts)/cm^2 2,975	2,802	Spectral Resolution	
31 May, 1956	2 h 57 m	1.05	0.76	0.3	2,016
10 July, 1959	4 h 47 m	1.06	0.72	0.15	1,570
15 June, 1960	3 h 22 m	1.02	0.79	0.4	1,513

The distribution of energy on the solar UV radiation for the range of 3,000-2,470 Å was measured by comparison with the radiation of a crater of a carbon arc and a krypton lamp. The data obtained according to the spectrograms with a resolution of 0.3 and 0.4 Å agree with the photometric curves obtained by the American authors. The results of the measurements according to the spectrograms with a resolution of 0.15 Å agree with them only in the sections up to 2,870 Å, and for the shorter-wave range there is a notable divergence, amounting to 60 percent at 2,700 Å. This divergence, evidently, must be attributed to the discrepancy between the programmed exposure and the actual exposure, which resulted from the fact that they still remained exposed while radiation that fell through the slit of the spectrograph did not illuminate the lattice but could cause flashes within the instrument that distorted the density of the film.

Although the brightness of the continuous spectrum in the UV range, because of the abundance of absorption lines, was lower than in the visible range and corresponded to the effective brightness temperature ~4,800°K, within the spectrum, several sections were discovered with a brightness temperature exceeding 6,000°K, for example, for sections $\lambda = 2,913$ and $\lambda = 2,917$ Å T≈6, 200°K.

Beginning with 1958, this research was continued on even more powerful V5A rockets with a lift altitude of more than 500 km and stabilized in the passive section on all 3 axes with an accuracy of ±3 deg using gas jet nozzles. The new type of geophysical rocket made it possible to substantially increase the duration of the measurements. An attempt was made on these rockets to record the solar radiation in the range of the hydrogen line 1,215.68 Å, using the same spectrographs with a metric diffraction lattice, however, the exposure turned out to be inadequate and the spectrum was obtained with a strong underexposure and broke off at 2,080 Å [6,8].

At an altitude of nearly 200 km on the descending section of the trajectory, the nose section of the V5A rocket separated, turned at an angle of 90 deg relative to the direction of the flight and moved away in order to avoid the possibility of a collision with the rocket body. At an altitude of 4-5 km, the recovery system worked perfectly and the nose section landed by parachute [3].

In 1958, in order to investigate the composition of the atmosphere and the solar UV and x-ray radiation, the small R2A geophysical rocket was developed with a high-altitude automatic geophysical station (HAAGS) with a diameter of 1 m and weighting 400 kg [3].

In 1959, FIAN equipment was sent up twice on these rockets to an altitude of around 100 km. In the experiments, for the first time, the equipment was homed in on the Sun. The counters were placed outside the instrument container, which, after the passage through the dense layers of the atmosphere, separated from the rocket and oriented itself in space according to three axes, aiming the instruments at the Sun and maintaining its orientation in the ascending and descending sections of the trajectory with an accuracy of ±0.5 deg.

On 21 July 1959, the intensity of the x-ray radiation in the range of 2-10 Å was measured on an R2A rocket during a launch to an altitude of around 105 km. The Sun was located close to the horizon; therefore, the x-ray radiation passed through a large layer of the atmosphere and began to be recorded only at an altitude of around 90 km. Right next to the operational counter was a control counter turned away from the direction towards the Sun by 15 deg. The counting speed of this counter was on the level of the cosmic background and this indicated that the radiation recorded by the operational counter actually did come from the Sun. These measurements indicated for the first time that it was possible to have on the Sun an active region with a temperature of $\sim 4.10^6$ °K [2].

The close connection uncovered between the solar x-ray radiation stream and the active regions on the Sun led to the setting up of special experiments to investigate the regions of primary x-ray radiation generation in the solar corona. The direct experiments were performed during the total solar eclipse of 15 February

1961. In order to do this, a rocket with photon counters was launched in the zone of the total eclipse during the time of its development.

At the same time, radiation ≤ 10 Å was measured coming from the "hottest" regions of the corona. The time of the launch and the trajectory were chosen so that the highest point of the trajectory (around 96 km) would be approximately on the axis of the shadow cone. At this moment, the entire transition region between the chromosphere and the corona and the innermost part of the corona were covered by the Moon and the only exposed areas were two active regions on the western and eastern edges of the disc. The radiation stream decreased in comparison to the average value of the stream for the completely exposed Sun, however, maintaining a notable value of 8.10^{-5} ergs/cm^3 sec. This was proof of the fact that the x-ray radiation generation occurs in the solar corona and primarily in the regions of the corona located above the active regions in the chromosphere. This yields an immediate interpretation of numerous ionospheric observations during an eclipse, from which the primary role of the corona's active regions in the formation of the E layer becomes apparent [2].

In 1962, in order to have more qualitative research on the upper atmosphere and the shortwave solar radiation, a new nose section was developed for the V5B rocket -- the HAAGS; and on 6 and 18 June 1963, on the HAAGS, I.V. Katyushina carried out the first experiments on measuring the intensity of the direct solar radiation at altitudes of 80-500 km using the ionization chamber to measure the solar radiation in the Lyman-alpha hydrogen line. On 6 June, 25 October, and 25 December 1963, using counters for UV scattered radiation, measurements were made of the intensity in the lines of the atomic oxygen triplet $\lambda \sim 1{,}300$ Å at altitudes of 100-500 km.

The instruments were installed in the spherical container of the HAAGS, equipped with a stabilization and attitude determination system; thus during the stabilized flight of the container, the instruments were aimed at the Sun.

As a result of these experiments, a measurement was made of the distribution of the intensity of Lα radiation with altitude; and, as consequence, there was a determination of the absorption coefficient of Lα radiation at altitudes of 80-90 km and the concentration of molecular oxygen. The experiments indicated that the intensity of solar Lα radiation beyond the limits of the atmosphere amounted to 4.5-8.9 ergs/cm^3 sec, and the intensity of the scattered radiation at the maximum amounted to 0.62; 0.91 and 0.05 kR for the experiments of 6 June, 25 October, and 24 December, respectively.

The experiments conducted on the V5B rockets made it possible to draw the conclusions that the maximum intensity of the scattered radiation in the 01 triplet line increases at the zenith angle of the Sun decreases and the maximum of the intensity is shifted at the same time into the region of the lesser altitudes [9].

Later, in several experiments on the rockets, the direct photographing of the solar disc was accomplished in the soft x-ray region of the spectrum. In particular, on 1 October 1965, a photograph of the Sun was obtained in the 170-200 Å range.

In this and in other experiments, the Sun was photographed using several cameras obscured with apertures covered by filters made of beryllium and aluminum foil and organic film, separating the individual sections of the spectrum. The cameras were located in the recoverable instrument compartments of the geophysical rockets, which climbed to an altitude of 500 km. During the flight, the cameras were aimed at the Sun using the servo system with an accuracy of ±30 min. in the ascending and descending sections. The equipment descended to the ground by parachute. An analysis of the obtained photographs indicated that the x-ray radiation was generated primarily in the corona's active regions, located above the calcium floccules and with angular dimensions on the order of 1-3 min, possibly having a thin structure. These regions are regions of increased radio radiation in centimeter and decimeter waves; in comparison with the rest of the corona, their electron temperature and electron density are higher. The regions of increased temperature and density begin in the lower layers of the solar atmosphere and penetrate it completely, up to the corona, stretching to an altitude of 50-100,000 km. These regions can be maintained on the Sun for a relatively long time -- on the order of solar days and longer. Evidently, the corona's regions with increased density and temperature are retained and isolated from the rest of the corona by magnetic fields on the Sun similar to the way hot plasma created in laboratory settings for research on thermonuclear reactions is retained and isolated from the walls of the chamber.

An important characteristic of coronal x-ray radiation is its spectrum. Using a spectrograph with a diffraction lattice during launches of V5V rockets on 21 June 1959, 20 September, and on 1 October 1965, in the USSR, experimental data were obtained on the investigation of the solar spectrum in the x-ray region.

On this photograph, for the first time, they captured the x-ray flash, which occurs, as recently explained, on the Sun in one of the so-called "evident spots" of activity [2].

In the period from 1965 through 1971, in the Byurakan Astrophysics Observatory, a set of instruments (K-2 and K-4) was developed for investigation of the Sun and stars on the V5V astrophysical rockets.

The rocket observatory for investigation of the Sun (K-2) is a set of various scientific instruments gathered on a special platform. They include several x-ray chambers built to receive radiation from various bands of long waves, an (externally darkened) coronograph for photographing the corona at large distances from the edge of the solar disc, a shortwave spectrograph, a camera for photographing the chromosphere and others.

In the period from 1970 through 1971, within the framework of the "Intercosmos" program, two international experiments took place on investigating the solar UV radiation on the Vertical-1 (28 November 1970) and Vertical-2 (20 August 1971) rockets with participation by specialists from the GDR, Poland, and the USSR. Using equipment developed by Polish specialists, the solar corona was photographed in several spectral ranges of the soft x-ray region of the spectrum of 8-60 Å, and in addition, spectrograms were obtained of the Sun in individual lines in the far UV band of long waves of 250-400 Å. Soviet scientists used spectrometers to record the solar corona spectrum in the long wave range of 5-20 Å. The Soviet and Polish instruments were installed on one platform which made it possible to track the Sun with an accuracy of ±1 min. The GDR specialists developed and prepared a Lyman-alpha photometer for these experiments in order to measure the intensity of the solar UV radiation in the Lα hydrogen line (1,215.6 Å) and its absorption by the terrestrial atmosphere [10].

The importance of the research begun in 1951 on the solar shortwave radiation is in no way exhausted by the results listed by us. The development of this research preceeded along identical paths in the USSR and the U.S.A. and the results of the Soviet and American rocket research, and more recently, of the research conducted in England and France, to a significant degree complement each other. On the whole, the accumulated material quite completely characterizes the solar shortwave radiation and, at the present time, it is possible to expect the use of the data obtained to solve important questions in the prediction of solar activity and geophysics.

What is the mechanism of the solar x-ray radiation? Based on all the data obtained up to the present time, it is possible to say that in the case of the quiet Sun, this radiation is of a heat nature, i.e., that it is caused by interaction of electrons having a Maxwellian velocity distribution and ions of hydrogen, helium and the heavier chemical elements which makeup the corona's plasma.

BIBLIOGRAPHY

1. S.L. Mandelshtam, "Survey of Works on Research on Solar Shortwave Ultraviolet Radiation," UFN, Vol 46, Issue 2, 1952, p 145.

2. S.L. Mandelshtam, "Research on Solar Shortwave Radiation," "Uspekhi SSSR v issledovanii kosmicheskogo prostranstva" [The USSR's Successes in the Investigation of Outer Space], Moscow, 1963, pp 296-297, 299.

3. L.A. Vedeshin, "The Development in the USSR of Rocket Research on Near-Earth Space," in the collection "Iz istorii aviatsii i kosmonavtiki" [From the History of Aviation and Cosmonautics], Issue 15, Moscow, 1972, pp 5, 19.

4. A.A. Blagonravov, "Research on the Upper Layers of the Atmosphere using High-Altitude Rockets," Vestnik an SSSR, 1957, No 6, p 29.

5. V.P. Kachalov, N.A. Pavlenko, and A.V. Yakovleva, "Ultraviolet Spectrum of the Sun in the 2,636-2,937 Å and 2,471-2,635 Å Regions," Izvestiya an SSSR, Seriya Geofizika, No 99, 1959, p 1,099 and No 9, 1959, p 1,177.

6. A.V. Yakovleva, and L.A. Kudryavtsev, et alia, "Spectrometric Research on the Ozone Layer up to an Altitude of 60 km," in the collection "Iskusstvennyye sputniki Zemli" [Artificial Earth Satellites], Issue 14, Moscow, 1962, p 61.

7. T.V. Kazachevskaya, V.A. Arkhangelskaya, and G.S. Ivanov-Kholodnyy, et alia, "Measuring the X-ray and Ultraviolet Radiation using the Thermoluminescent Phosphor $CaSO_4(Mn)$," in the collection "Iskusstvennyye sputniki Zemli," Issue 15, p 173.

8. V.P. Kachalov, and A.V. Yakovleva, "Solar Ultraviolet Spectrum in the 2,470-3,100 Å Region," Izvestiya Krymskoy Astrofizicheskoy Observatorii, Vol 27, 1962, p 44.

9. V.V. Katyushina and V.G. Kurt, "Measurements of the Scattered L Radiation in the Upper Atmosphere at Altitudes up to 500 km," Kosmicheskiye Issledovaniya, Vol 3, Issue 2, 1965, pp 243, 248.

10. L.A. Vedeshin and M.G. Kroshkin, "The 'Vertikal-1' Geophysical Rocket," Vestnik an SSSR, Vol 3, 1971, pp 86-87.

Chapter 14

STRUCTURE OF NEUTRAL UPPER ATMOSPHERE AIR SAMPLES AND FALLING SPHERES[*]

Leslie M. Jones[†]

In 1946, when rockets became available for sounding the upper atmosphere, the principal features of the distribution of its structural parameters were known. A temperature profile to the lower thermosphere had been deduced from balloon, sound propagation and meteor drag observations combined with adiabatic cooling considerations. Then, by straightforward theory, the density and temperature were deduced. Less certainty attached to the composition and, consequently, the molecular weight. The leading question then was the altitude at which diffusive separation becomes significant.

The role of rockets was to verify the leading model of the atmosphere, rejecting radical departures, and to provide average and extreme magnitudes for the parameters. Many ingenious schemes were devised by many investigators for rocket instruments to probe the neutral atmosphere. By virtue of performance, reliability and cost perhaps five or six have survived and over the years have contributed to models as well as to our knowledge of the details of solar control of atmospheric structure.

At the University of Michigan's Department of Aerospace Engineering an early experiment was devised to collect samples of the upper atmosphere in steel vacuum bottles and to analyze the contents for nitrogen and the noble gases. The goal was to measure r, the separation ratio which indicates the extent to which diffusion has overcome mixing to produce a partial or complete Daltonian atmosphere. Samples were collected from 55 to 106 km over a period of 10 years with analyses being made at the Universities of Durham and Michigan. Separation starting variably between 60 and 93 km was detected. An exhaustive search for non-geophysical causes was carried out with negative result. The investigators concluded that separated air can exist as low as 60 km but probably must be convected there by an as-yet-undescribed circulation process.

---

[*]   Presented at The Ninth IAA History of Astronautics Symposium, Lisbon, Portugal, September 1975.

[†]   High Altitude Engineering Laboratory, Department of Aerospace Engineering, University of Michigan, Ann Arbor, Michigan, U.S.A.

As an engineering alternative to various complex aerodynamic techniques for air density, the Michigan group developed the falling sphere drag experiment. First flights with a DOVAP-tracked inflatable sphere took place in 1952. Other versions using accelerometers or radar tracking were developed and used. The sphere experiment has generated a large amount of upper air data including specific phenomenological studies. During the 2-year International Quiet Sun Year, 170 sphere flights were carried out by various groups. A limited number of flights, none at Michigan, continue at this writing.

INTRODUCTION

The principal features of the thermal profile of the Earth's atmosphere up to the lower thermosphere result from the cooling of adiabatic expansion working against warming due to absorption of solar UV below 2,900 Å by ozone near 50 km and absorption in the Schumann-Runge continuum by molecular oxygen above 100 km. The temperature profile is the framework upon which our understanding of the phenomenology of the neutral atmosphere is built and upon which the nomenclature of important regions is based. Calculations of density and pressure from temperature are quite straightforward and the analysis of the time of diffusion in the homosphere and of diffusive equilibrium composition in the heterosphere proceed from temperature profiles.

In tracing the history of neutral structure measurements, then, our point of departure will be the thermal profile. Paradoxically, the majority of structure measurements up to the thermosphere are of density from which temperatures are derived quite successfully but with rather more smoothing being required than with temperature data. The use of density-measuring instruments results from engineering trade-offs rather than a desire to have density data in preference to temperature. The measurement of temperature itself in an altitude interval is, of course, possible with the grenade method, a major contributor of upper air data. On one occasion, independent temperatures at single altitudes were made with shock angle probes.

Figure 1 shows a group of temperature profiles to 120 km which are of interest in discussing the role of rocket measurements in upper air history. As early as the turn of the century it was known from the anomalous propagation of gunfire sound that the atmosphere must warm up to about sea level temperature in the 50 km region and again at a higher altitude.

An early model atmosphere by Maris [1] shows a warm and nearly isothermal "stratosphere" extending well into the present thermosphere. There is no hint of the mesopause although it might have been inferred from an early suggestion that noctilucent clouds near 80 km consist of ice crystals. Maris's isotherm results in a Daltonian stratification and the concept of an extensive and true stratosphere persisted for some time. In spite of an overly simple atmosphere, Maris's work was an important attempt to deal with diffusion and the absorption of solar radiation.

In 1932, Epstein made his well-known calculations of times to reach 50 percent of diffusive equilibrium after complete mixing. His settling times of years at even so great an altitude as 100 km greatly increased the height at which Daltonian conditions could be accepted. Epstein used an isothermal profile at 273°K for his calculations (this does not necessarily represent his acceptance of an extended stratosphere). Mitra and Rakshit [2], in an analysis of constituent distribution, took 100 km as the lower limit for significant separation.

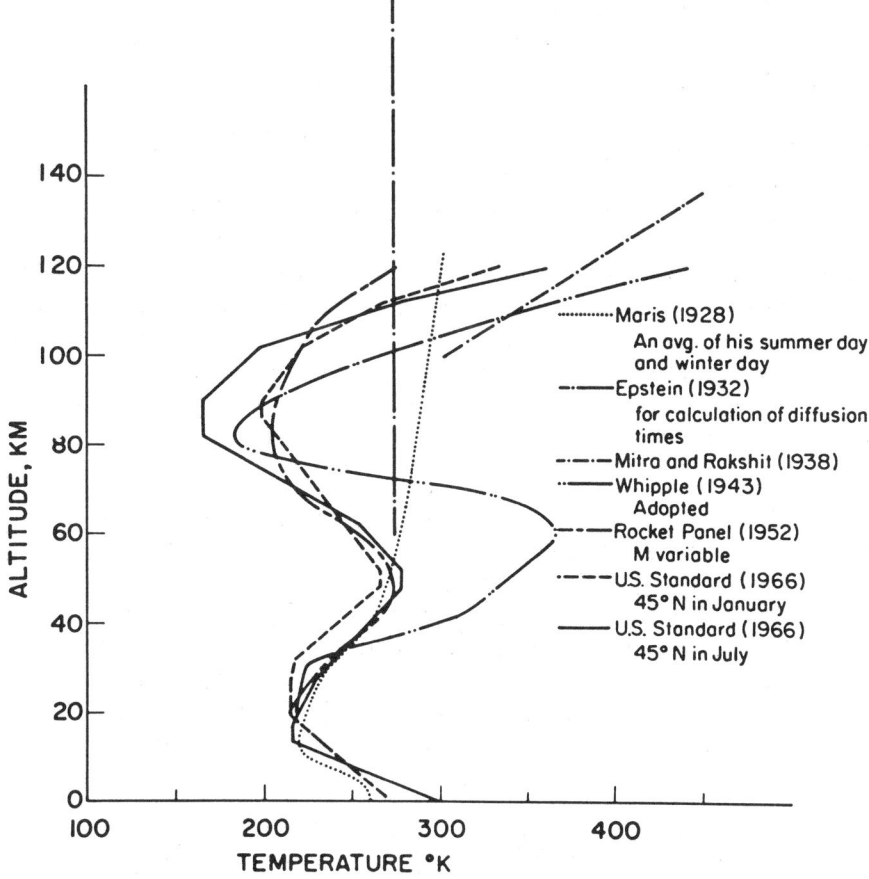

Figure 1   Curves showing temperature profiles vs. altitude from 0 to 120 km

In 1943 Whipple [3], reporting on a brilliant extension of the meteor drag technique of Lindemann and Dobson [4], adopted a temperature profile that has the essential features that we know today. The meteor observations result in density profiles and the evaluation of the adopted temperature profile was made by calculating from it a density profile to compare with the meteor points. (This method is used now in deriving thermospheric parameters from satellite drag.) The meteor data ranged from 45 to 110 km so that, taken with what was already known from balloons, anomalous sound propagation and the requirement of a mesodecline to account for atmospheric oscillation (Taylor, [5]), Whipple was able to propose temperatures from the ground to 130 km.

In 1952 The Upper Atmosphere Rocket Research Panel, a group of representatives from U.S. government and university laboratories, published the so-called Panel Atmosphere that included results from the U.S. sounding rocket program which started in 1946. This model evolved into what is now the U.S. Standard Atmosphere (published in 1962) and U.S. Standard Atmosphere Supplements (published in 1966). Other important models based on rocket results but not represented in Figure 1 are the Air Force ARDC models (Minzner and Ripley [6]; Minzner, et al. [7]) and the COSPAR International Reference Atmosphere, CIRA 1965 [8].

The advent of sounding rockets in 1946 brought the possibility of confirming the fairly complete structural picture which had emerged: an atmosphere with two major warming trends in the interval up to 120 (or so) km and an atmosphere in which Dalton's law must assert itself at some altitude but probably not much below 100 km. We must credit hindsight to some extent for the strength that the models discussed above have shown. There were, after all, other models and when instrumentation was proposed and prepared for the early flights it was anticipated that they might lead to new discoveries and radical concepts. That the measurements supplied magnitudes for existing profiles is of great importance but less exciting than new concepts. The discoveries in atmospheric structure are in the dynamic responses to solar control, the meteorology, if you will, of the high atmosphere. Much has been done and much remains to be done in this field.

DIFFUSIVE SEPARATION

The complete diffusion equation for a binary mixture given by Chapman and Cowling [9] has terms for the effect of a pressure gradient, a thermal gradient and external forces (ignored in the neutral atmosphere) in addition to the classical term for concentration gradients as given in Fick's Law. By assuming one component to be scarce and light with respect to the other and by assuming equilibrium to have been reached, a distribution law for individual species can be derived:

$$n_1 = n_{o_1} \left(\frac{T_o}{T} \right)^{1+\alpha} \exp \frac{-m_1}{k} \int_{z_o}^{z} \frac{g dz}{T} ,$$

where

n_1 = conc. of species (1) at altitude z

n_{o_1} = conc. of species (1) at ref. alt. z_o

T_o = temp at ref. alt.

T = temp at alt.

α = thermal diff. factor

m_1 = molecular mass

k = Boltzman's constant

g = accel. of gravity

Under quiescent conditions, such as obtained in the stratosphere and thermosphere, the species tend to distribute themselves according to Dalton's Law, that is, independently of each other according to the temperature, gravitational field and their own masses, as shown in the equation. The rate of the diffusion process is a function of the density and the density gradient and will therefore be exponentially faster with increasing altitude. Mange [10] has examined various criteria of the time of diffusion, but Epstein's, which was available at the beginning of the rocket program, is still useful. Starting with complete mixing, Epstein [11] calculated the time for various constituents diffusing in air with the temperature constant with altitude at $273^{\circ}K$ to reach 50 percent of diffusive equilibrium:

Altitude	Helium	Argon
120 km	34 days	180 days
100 km	1.2 years	6.4 years
80 km	14 years	73 years

With these times the effect of mixing due to motion is difficult to overcome and the experimental problem of determining at what altitude separation is measurable presented itself. The phenomenon is usually expressed in the form of a separation ratio:

$$r = \frac{n_1/n}{n_{10}/n_0} = \frac{\text{Concentration ratio with respect to ref. gas n at alt.}}{\text{Concentration ratio with respect to ref. gas n. at ref. alt}}$$

The separation ratio can be stated for any two gases and a given temperature profile. The usual practice, however, is to use N_2 (or $N_2 + A$) as the reference gas and an isothermal profile. In the case of an isotherm:

$$r = e^{-\frac{zg}{RT}(M_1 - M_2)}$$

where

Δz = altitude interval above mictopause (level of cessation of mixing)

g = accel. of gravity

R = Universal gas constant

T = absolute temperature

M = gram molecular mass.

UPPER AIR SAMPLING

Various features of upper air composition can be examined by absorption and emission spectrocopy, by mass spectrometry and by sampling with subsequent analysis. Only the latter two have small enough errors to examine the onset of separation. Mass spectrometry has come into its own in recent years and has shown separation in the thermosphere. See, for example, Schaefer and Nichols [12]. In 1946, spectrometers were an established laboratory device but not developed sufficiently for successful use on rockets. Also, below 100 km spectrometers require input pumping. The collection of samples appeared to be a useful and feasible technique and in the Department of Aeronautical (now Aerospace) Engineering at Michigan a program of sampling and analysis was initiated in 1946 and continued until 1956. A similar program but with somewhat different technique was carried out in the Soviet Union [13].

The Michigan sampling container[*] was an 8,200 cc steel aviation oxygen breathing bottle fitted with copper inlet and withdrawal tubes and automatic openers and closers. The metal system permitted survival without parachutes but precluded any work with oxygen.

The plan was to analyze for helium, neon, argon and nitrogen and, using nitrogen as the reference gas, investigate the separation ratio r as a function of altitude. The first design used a pyrotechnic bellows fitted with an opener knife which pierced a copper "roof-top" diaphragm. The sealer squeezed a flattened portion of the intake tube, which was tinned on the inside and heated, by the sealer, after squeezing. The roof-top diaphragm was centered in a flushing chamber through which upper air passed as the rocket ascended. The chamber communicated with the ambient air outside the rocket through copper pipes the ends of which were fitted with inflow and outflow aerodynamic nozzles.

Between October 1947 and November 1948, five samples were collected on four V2 rockets in the altitude interval 49 to 72 km over White Sands, New Mexico. Laboratory analyses (described below) showed no significant separation. The samples were thought then (and now), however, to be highly suspect because the bottles were mounted in the mid-section of the rocket between the propellant tanks and were probably contaminated with rocket-borne ground air leaking out through the many openings in the V2.

A significant advance was made in 1949 when the V2-type bottles were mounted in Aerobees on which the nose cone was sealed against leakage ahead of the intake scoops. In addition, on some of these flights (as well as some of the final design), radioactive $C^{14}O_2$ was released inside the nose cone just before the bottles were opened in order that it might be ascertained whether or not nose cone air was entering the bottles. In all instances where this technique was used the result was that negligible contamination occurred.

Each Aerobee carried three bottles and the entire bottle assembly was detached from the rocket and lowered by FIST-type silicone and fiber glass parachutes obtained from the Aerojet General Corp. This was one of the earliest successful uses of parachute recovery from rockets. Between June and December 1949, six samples were obtained in six rocket flights and again the analyses showed

---

[*] For more complete details of the Michigan sampling and analysis apparatus see Jones [14] and Wenzel, et al [15].

206

no appreciable separation (Table 1). These samples are considered to be representative of the atmosphere up to about 60 km.

Table 1

UPPER AIR SAMPLING, JUNE - DECEMBER 1949

Sample Bottle	Aerobee Rocket Number	Altitude (km M.S.L.)	Date of Sampling	Analysis			Calc. Pitot Pressure (closing) (mm Hg)	Bottle Pressure (mm Hg)	P_b/P_p
				He Ratio	Ne Ratio	A Ratio			
63	SC-4	54.7-58.3	21-07-1949	1.01	1.45*	1.01	1.22	0.19	0.16
63	SC-4	54.7-58.3	21-07-1949	1.01m	1.07m	-	1.22	0.19	0.16
61	SC-2	53.6-57.7	2-06-1949	1.00	1.00	1.01	1.60	1.00	0.63
61	SC-2	53.6-57.7	2-06-1949	1.00m	1.02m	-	1.60	1.00	0.63
77	SC-3	50.4-53.3	6-12-1949	0.98	1.00	1.00	1.32	0.80	0.60
60	SC-2	49.6-53.6	2-06-1949	0.96	0.98	1.00	3.14	3.05	0.97
68	SC-5	42.0-45.0	20-09-1949	1.01m	1.01m	-	4.75	3.60	0.76
74	SC-7	41.4-44.9	6-12-1949	1.00m	1.02m	-	5.22	3.40	0.65

* Unreliable because of contamination by H_2, confirmed by mass spectrometry.

Final Design

All of the samples collected after December 1950 benefited from several significant improvements in the sampling technique. The inlet tubes were made of 2.5 cm diameter copper tubes about 25 cm long protruding through a vacuum-tight bulkhead. The automatic openers, shown in Figure 2, removed the entire assembly at the front of the tube leaving an unobstructed input path free of outgassing. The closer was a pyrotechnically operated cold welding device which produced vacuum-tight seals without solder or flux, see Figure 3. The opener-closer assemblage was covered in the early part of the flight with a nose cone containing a small rocket that removed the cone just before sampling. In these flights, as in earlier ones, the bottles were open for about 6 sec, which is the calculated dynamic filling time. All things considered, it is reasonable to conclude that the samples in the bottles consisted exclusively of atmospheric air at the altitude of the open interval which was about 4 km. Figures 4 and 5 show the Aerobee nose cone assembly. Figure 4 illustrates a knife opener, the predecessor to the more satisfactory opener of Figure 2.

In the interval from December 1950 to May 1952, 11 samples were collected on three rockets. One rocket was V2 No. 59, which was fitted with three of the Aerobee-type assemblies in one of which there was a single 34,000 cc steel bottle instead of the usual three 8,200 cc bottles. The large bottle collected a sample between 102.7 and 105.8 kilometers. The results, which are shown in Table 2, clearly indicate changes in the separation ratio.

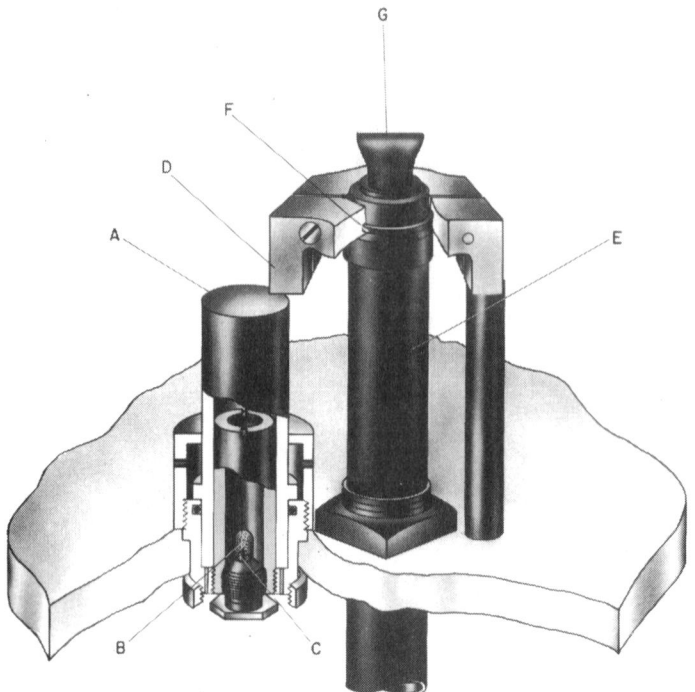

Figure 2 Pyrotechnic bottle opener: (A) piston, (B) black powder, (C) squib, (D) yoke, (E) copper intake tube, (F) weakend section, (G) pumping seal-off.

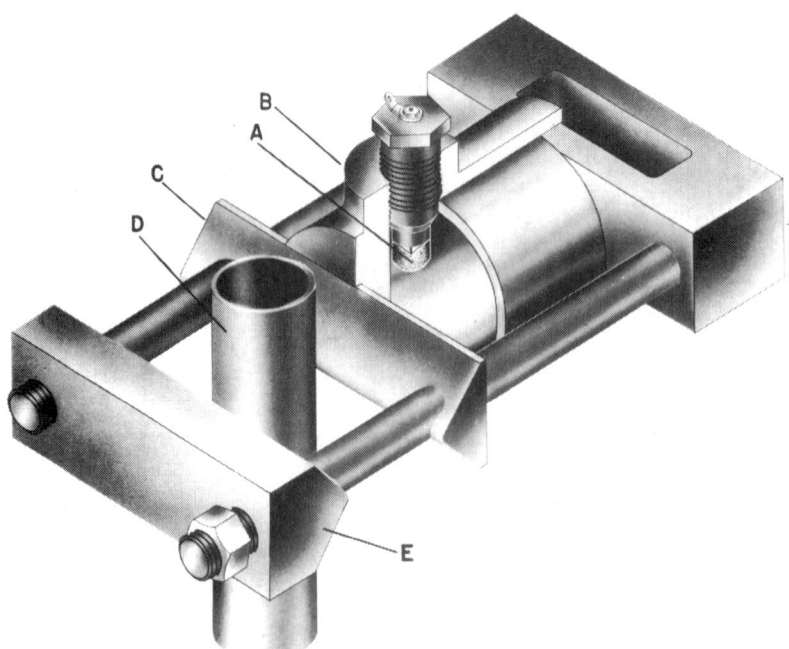

Figure 3 Cold weld bottle sealer: (A) black powder, (B) cylinder, (C & E) steel jaws, (D) copper intake tube.

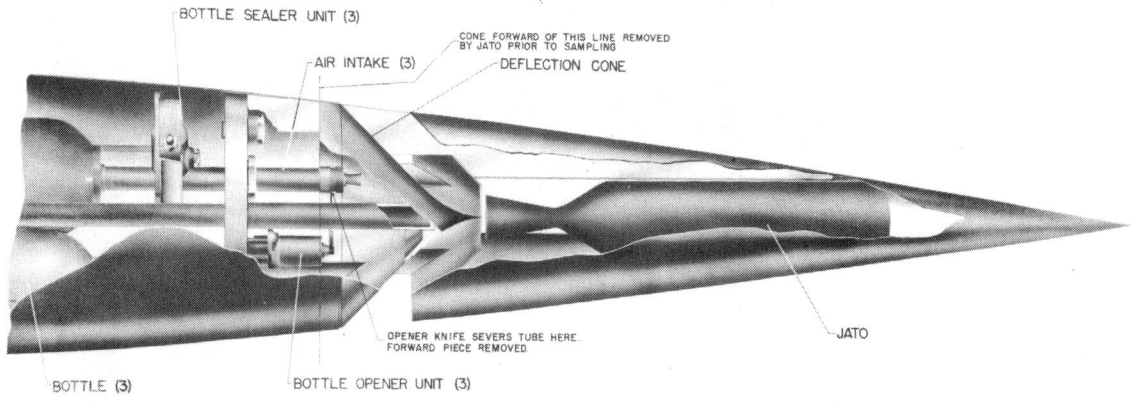

Figure 4 Aerobee nose cone assembly illustrating opener unit, bottle sealer unit and other elements.

Figure 5 Sampling Aerobee payload after use and recovery showing cold weld seals.

209

Table 2
UPPER AIR SAMPLING, DECEMBER 1950 - MAY 1952

Bottle	Rocket	Date of Sampling	Altitude Opening	Altitude Closing	Total Velocity at Closing	Mach Sample	cm^{3}NTP Sample	Total Pressure in Bottle	Analysis			Days Sampling to Analysis
									He Ratio	Ne Ratio	A Ratio	
			km	km	km/sec			μ				
B-6	SC-17	19-12-50	64.0	67.1	0.60	2.0	0.338	43	1.44	1.08	0.93	352
B-8	SC-17	19-12-50	67.1	69.5	0.55	1.8	0.185	22	2.02	1.18	0.89	188
B-9	SC-17	19-12-50	69.5	71.6	0.52	1.8	0.178*	21*	2.41*	1.20*	0.85*	142
B-13	SC-21	26-09-51	56.1	58.7	0.48	1.5	6.10	700	0.998	1.005	1.001	58
B-15	SC-21	26-09-51	58.7	60.7	0.13	1.4	4.13	420	1.035	1.008	0.996	83
C-11-B	V-2-59	20-05-52	58.5	66.1	1.07	3.5	0.40	37	1.133	1.040	0.962	406
C-5	V-2-59	20-05-52	66.1	73.5	1.01	3.5	0.168	21	1.570	1.232	0.90	148
C-7-B	V-2-59	20-05-52	79.9	85.9	0.88	3.0	0.032	3.3	1.396	1.020	0.93	—
C-1	V-2-59	20-05-52	85.9	90.8	0.83	2.8	0.012	1.6	2.943	1.395	0.82	247
C-3	V-2-59	20-05-52	90.8	95.7	0.77	2.5	0.0026	0.34	—	—	0.82	378
C-6-B-L	V-2-59	20-05-52	102.7	105.8	0.62	1.9	3.438	350	2.443	1.045	0.96	—

*Corrected for leakage.

Final Samples

As noted, no reasonable case can be made that the samples collected are other than upper air at the open-bottle altitudes. It may be wondered, however, whether or not that air was modified either chemically or aerodynamically after entering the intake tube. The most difficult possibility to counter is that the intake flow process favors the collection of light gases and that the measured separations are aerodynamically engendered rather than resulting from atmospheric processes. Flow separation is a real phenomenon but attempts to show analytically that it could account for separation in the samples have been defeated by the complexity of the intake flow situation: geometry, velocity, angle of attack and so on.

An early attempt to do so was made by Martin [16], but his conclusion that separation was caused by supersonic flow would seem to be negated by the results from the last two sampling flights. In 1956, two sample bottle Aerobees were flown with payload weights increased so that the peaks of the trajectories came at about 86 km. Thus, the samples were collected at the subsonic horizontal component of the rocket trajectory instead of at Mach 1.4 to 3.5 as in earlier samples. The last samples had also the advantage of analysis by two groups using different analyzers.

The confirming analyses were made possible by the construction at Michigan of a miniature micro-analyzer of the Glückauf type. This analyzer was used not only for analysis of upper air samples but also for an extensive investigation of the magnitude and effects of leaks in some of the bottles. Table 3 gives the results of analyses of samples taken in the last two flights. Following a discussion of results, the method of analysis is described but the point can be made here that analysis of the samples has never been suspected as the cause of the results and may be accepted with complete confidence.

Table 3

UPPER AIR SAMPLING BY AEROBEE FLIGHTS IN 1956

Bottle	Rocket	Date of Sampling	Altitude Opening M.S.L. km	Altitude Closing M.S.L. km	Total Velocity at Closing km/sec	Mach Number	cm^3 NTP Sample	Total Pressure in Bottle 300°K μ	By	Analysis (avg. of 3 ea.) Loss in O_2 Cell[2] %	He Ratio	Ne Ratio	Days Sampling to Analysis
B-25	SC-34	09-08-56	85.3	85.5	0.16	0.55	0.0241	–	Paneth	–	3.14	1.34	–
B-15	SC-35	10-08-56	85.6	85.9	0.12	0.41	0.0234*	2.98	Mich.	23.7	1.65	1.13	73
B-10	SC-35	10-08-56	85.6	85.9	0.12	0.41	0.0318*	5.18	Mich	36.2	1.45	1.10	171
C 23-B	SC-35	10-08-56	85.6	85.9	0.12	0.41	0.0204*	1.96	Mich.	0.2	1.24	1.02	262
									Paneth†	–	1.11	1.04	–
											±10%	±2%	

---
* Total amount of nitrogen plus argon.
† A subdivision of sample in bottle C-23-B.

Discussion of Results

The detailed discussion and intercomparison of samples has been extensively reported in the literature and will not be repeated here. The significant conclusions which may be drawn and those which must remain in doubt are as follows:

1. Separation was measured in all samples collected above 60 km regardless of date, velocity, intake system, angle of attack or other variable. This is especially significant in the case of the samples collected subsonically on the last two rockets.

2. The separations measured were always in the right direction for either geophysical or aerodynamic separation. That is, helium and neon increased and argon decreased, with respect to nitrogen. The separations were, furthermore, reasonably consistent with the temperatures known to exist at the sampling altitudes.

3. Various inconsistencies were encountered:

   a. The amount of sample collected was, in the case of supersonic samples, variably less than the Rayleigh formula predicts. This may have been due to bottle-filling dynamics or other flow phenomena.

   b. The amount collected in the last (subsonic) samples was approximately that of the ambient air, but variable. (Ambient pressure at 86 km is 2.57 X 10^{-3} torr.; these bottles contained 2, 3 and 5 X 10^{-3} torr.)

   c. Variable leaks were encountered in some bottles but they cannot explain the results.

   d. Results from a single bottle were not always identical. This is thought to be due to sample division and transfer, not analysis.

4. Separation as a function of altitude, extended to r = 1 for various combinations of samples, show the onset of separation as occurring variably between 60 and 93 km.A

turbopause at different altitudes for different conditions and even for different gases is acceptable but the 60 km level is difficult to accept in view of the times for separation and the negative temperature gradient. For this observation to represent a geophysical phenomenon one must invoke a model in which air separated at high altitudes is circulated downward. A mechanism for dissipating the energy of compression must be included.

5. The geophysical interpretation is the one favored by the investigators in the sampling program. This may be because we set out to detect separation, but credence must be given to the fact that extensive experiments designed to pinpoint a cause of separation other than geophysical gave negative results.

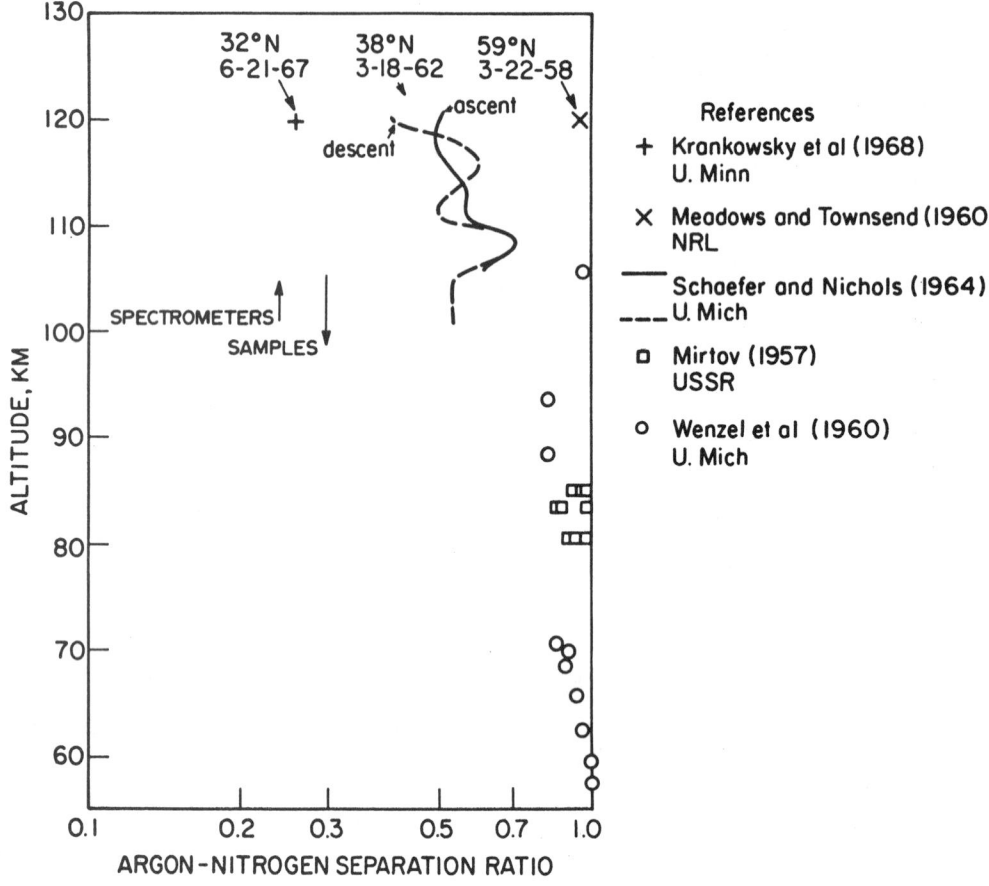

Figure 6   Argon separation ratios vs. altitude showing bottle and spectrometer results.

Although it would be very useful in diagnostic aeronomy to know all of the details of the onset of separation, for most applied purposes the inverse interpretation is quite satisfactory. That is, the greatest separations shown in any samples (representative of air between 86 and 91 km with $r_{He} = 2.94$, $r_{Ne} = 1.40$ and $r_A = 0.82$), result in a mean molecular mass for air of 28.90 compared to 28.96 at sea level, a negligible variation. Thus, data from an experiment yielding one of the structural parameters p, T or ρ in the homosphere can be converted to the other two with manipulations among the equations of state and of hydrostatic pressure only, assuming M constant. In the heterosphere, on the other hand, with the dissociation of oxygen commencing at 100 km and $O/O_2 = 1$ at 117 km, the change in mean molecular mass due to this cause is so great that M cannot be determined from knowledge of separation alone, in any case. Thus, mass spectrometry, to handle both the oxygen phenomenon and the low densities, is resorted to. Figure 6 compares some results of the measurement of argon separation by different investigators.

The Michigan and USSR sampling results are quite compatible. The curves are for the ascending and descending portions of a Michigan quadrupole spectrometer flight at Wallops Island. The two points at 120 km are the maximum and minimum separation ratios for argon at this altitude which have been reported in the literature. The 1958 flight was an r.f. (Bennett) spectrometer flown by NRL at Fort Churchill, Canada, and the 1967 flight of a magnetic spectrometer flown at White Sands, New Mexico, by the University of Minnesota. The reader should consult the references shown for complete accounts. One point illustrated by Figure 6 is that argon separation is a widely variable phenomenon, even more so in the thermosphere than below 100 km.

Sample Analysis

Although some attempts were made to analyze the upper air samples for isotopes of nitrogen and of oxides of nitrogen, the significant results were obtained in analyzing for N_2, A, Ne and He. The apparatus was due to Glückauf [17] with refinements by Chackett, et al. [18], Paneth [19], and Wenzel [15]. The method depends upon the separation of two or more gases by the differential absorption and desorption which occurs when air is brought into contact with an absorber (in this case, charcoal) on a rigidly controlled schedule of time, pressure and temperature.

A brief summary of the Glückauf apparatus and process is of interest. The steel sample bottle, to which had previously been fitted a 1/2 inch diameter copper withdrawal tube with sealing diaphragm, was soldered to the input of the analyzer. The diaphragm was pierced with a sealed, screw-operated point. The air sample was pumped by a Töpler (mercury displacement) pump through a liquid nitrogen trap (to remove CO_2 and H_2O) into a storage bulb of known volume where the pressure was measured with a McLeod gauge. A portion of the sample was then moved along, always with Töpler pumps, to the input pipette of the analyzer and the amount of this fraction measured. Oxygen and hydrogen, if any, were removed here by electrically heating a copper spiral. The amount of gas remaining was again measured. The sample was then transported to a preliminary absorption chamber using easily desorbed oxygen as the transport gas. After contact with hot palladium to get all traces of hydrogen, the sample was moved into the first quantitative absorption cell which was one of 15, later 12, such cells connected in series. The nitrogen and argon were quantitatively absorbed on the first cell and the helium and neon separated as they underwent repeated fractionations in moving along the column. The helium fraction was withdrawn at the end of the column first and measured with a Pirani gage. As the fractionation continued, the neon came off next in exactly calculable sequence according, as noted, to the time, pressure and temperature. The latter parameter was controlled by dewars, containing either liquid N_2 or O_2, which surrounded the charcoal tubes.

Argon was measured by admitting a fresh fraction to the input pipette where oxygen and hydrogen were again removed. The sample then moved to an 800°C barium metal furnace where nitrogen was removed as barium nitride. The argon was then absorbed on charcoal, traces of neon and helium removed by pumping, and the argon desorbed for final measurement with a McLeod gage.

Samples from all successful flights were analyzed at the University of Durham laboratories of Prof. F.A. Paneth and his colleagues. The Durham apparatus evolved considerably over the years and the results from it were confirmed on a similar analyzer built at Michigan starting in 1952. In anticipation of sampling to 100 km, a new analyzer was built at Michigan using the principles of the Glückauf apparatus but scaled down in size by a factor of 10. This analyzer is shown in Figure 7. Other improvements were incorporated, such as the use of Bayard-Alpert ionization gage with a modern microammeter instead of the Pirani gage. The apparatus had no stopcocks and was completely bakable for outgassing. This analyzer was, for example, capable of measuring the helium in 1.5×10^{-4} cm^3 STP of air which is about 7.5×10^{-10} cm^3 STP of helium. Its principal application came about in the analysis of the subsonic samples taken in 1956 and in the associated tests for the effects of leaks, time in the bottles, outgassing and so on.

Figure 7   University of Michigan adsorption micro gas analyzer.

214

In all of the analysis work at both Durham and Michigan extraordinary care was taken to reduce experimental and statistical errors. Ground air samples were always analyzed before and after upper air samples with, invariably, negligible departure from accepted values. In the case of upper air samples, the sensitivity of the analyzers often permitted ten analyses of one sample. The standard deviations in such series typically was less than 1 percent. The foregoing facts give rise to the earlier statement of complete confidence in the analyses.

FALLING SPHERES

In contrast to the relatively limited choice of techniques for investigating composition, especially minimal diffusive separation, many methods for density, temperature or pressure have been conceived and flown. In the 1940's, almost any scheme reasonably supported by theory and technology had a chance of being tried out. Three or four of these survived for many years, even to the present. Survival depended primarily on the quality of data returned and the ease of constructing and flying the apparatus, although in some instances the influence and persistence of the experimenters were a factor.

The Michigan Aero group was involved in several early methods. Starting in 1947, we installed grenades and sample bottles on early V2's. The scientific conduct of the grenade experiment, however, was in the hands of the U.S. Army Signal Corps (see Stroud [20]) who sponsored all of the early Michigan Aero work). During the International Geophysical Year, the Michigan group worked with the Signal Corps on grenades in a co-investigator role. Our own development of methods for structure emphasized aerodynamics. The flow of air around a rocket offers many opportunities for measurement. One can measure the pressure distribution on a right circular nose cone and, by the methods of Taylor and Maccoll [21] and Stone [22] reduce these pressures to ambient density. In a related technique the ram (stagnation) and side pressures existing on a long slender body can be converted to ambient pressure through the supersonic version of Rayleigh's pilot tube formula. We flew both of these methods.

The Taylor-Maccoll treatment also relates the angle of the shock cone surrounding the nose cone to ambient temperature. The Michigan group fitted several rockets with arrays of pressure probes that scanned parallel to the central axis of the cone and detected the sharp pressure transient of the shock wave, thus making possible a calculation of its angle. The method has the unique feature of yielding temperature at the individual point(s) in the trajectory when the shock cone is intercepted. Thus, it does not require a profile, as with density, nor include a long path to the ground, as with grenades. The results from one flight contributed to the Panel Atmosphere of 1952.

All of the foregoing methods require precise knowledge of the rocket velocity and angle of attack and the instrumentation ranges from moderately to very (in the case of the shock angle probes) complex. These factors have not prevented various investigators from persisting in the development and highly successful use of rocket-aerodynamic techniques. The falling sphere technique, however, was conceived by us for avoiding what we perceived as troublesome difficulties. A sphere has no angle of attack and the density can be calculated from the tracking information alone without recourse to pressures. These advantages are real although some new problems, as might have been expected, replaced the old. Nevertheless, it is accurate to say that two versions of the sphere experiment, radar-tracked-inflatable and small-rigid with-accelerometer are among the simplest and most reliable of techniques for upper air structure. From this account, it is correctly inferred that the sphere experiment was adopted as an answer to engineering problems rather than as an artificial version of the meteor experiment. The latter is certainly the historical antecedent of the former but was not the starting point for the sphere idea. The start of the sphere development in 1950 brought to a close our work with other aerodynamic methods.

Density and Temperature From Sphere Drag

The drag equation in convenient form for sphere work is

$$\rho = \frac{-2m}{C_D A} \frac{\ddot{x}_3 + |g|}{(\dot{x}_3-w_3)\sqrt{(\dot{x}_1-w_3)^2 + (\dot{x}_2-w_2)^2 + (\dot{x}_3-w_3)^2}}$$

where

ρ = ambient air density

m = mass of sphere

C_D = coefficient of drag of sphere

A = cross sectional area of sphere

$\ddot{X}_3$ = vertical acceleration of sphere with respect to launcher.

g = acceleration of gravity

$\dot{X}_1, \dot{X}_2, \dot{X}_3$ = east, north and vertical components of sphere velocity with respect to launcher

$\dot{W}_1, \dot{W}_2, \dot{W}_3$ = velocity components of wind with respect to launcher.[*]

Having obtained a profile of density vs altitude from the sphere drop, ambient temperature is calculated with the following equation:

$$T_z = \frac{\rho_o T_o}{\rho_z} + \frac{Mg}{\rho_z R} \int_{z_o}^{z} -\rho(z)\,dz$$

where

z = altitude of interest

---

[*] In the Doppler-tracked flights these were ignored. In later radar-tracked flights, vertical wind was ignored but horizontal winds were solved for. Vertical wind may be solved for in the case of two spheres of different mass to area ratio dropped together. This has not been done.

o = reference altitude

M = molecular weight, taken to be constant to 100 km and currently well-known above 100 km to the limit of the sphere experiment.

R = Universal Gas Constant.

Note that the equation is always integrated downward. This requires a choice of T_0 at the upper reference altitude, say 120 km. After about 15 km of downward integration the integral swamps out any error in a reasonable guess of T_0. This approach is universally used in preference to upward integration from the ground. The latter technique gives a value for T_0 but integrates over the variable and often unmeasured (at time of flight) tropospheric/lower-stratospheric path.

Tracking

The U.S. radar available to us in the early 1950's was the SCR-584 having an accuracy* (sic) (Skolnik [23]) of 20 yds in range and 2 mils in angle. This is not sufficient to measure the parameters of sphere motion well enough to yield acceptable errors in density, temperature and wind. Recourse, therefore, was had to DOVAP (doppler, velocity and position) the r.f. interferometric system developed by the Germans to track V2's and adapted to tracking purposes at White Sands by the Ballistic Research Laboratories. DOVAP was roughly 10 times better than SCR-584 radar and good enough for a try at spheres. However, a price had to be paid in the form of a transponder with antennas in the sphere and a return to an "angle of attack" problem owing to the fact that as the sphere tumbled, doppler cycles were added to or subtracted from the signal by the rotation of the sphere antennas with respect to those on the ground. The unwanted cycles could be excised only with considerable effort.

The First spheres

The first spheres were 1.22 meters in diameter constructed of nylon gores. The polar diameter was occupied by a fiber glass cylinder containing the DOVAP antennas and air under pressure. At one end a valve retained the air until released on deployment. At the other end was mounted the DOVAP transceiver which could be removed through a bulkhead without releasing the air pressure in either the cylinder or the ball, if the latter was inflated. Figure 8 shows the sphere. More than one deployment device was used in four flights of this sphere design. The most successful was a sling shot of large rubber bands mounted inside a cylinder and held taut by the deflated sphere packed around its diametral core. The nose cone then held the sphere in place and was itself drawn tight to the cylinder below by glass fiber cords. The latter were severed pyrotechnically by timer on the upleg of the rocket trajectory (Figure 9).

---

* Freedom from experimental, rather than statistical error.

Figure 8   Early DOVAP-tracked inflated sphere.

Between May 1952 and September 1953, the four flights were carried out at White Sands. The last sphere weighed about 9 kg compared to 28 kg for the first. Figure 10 shows the temperatures calculated from these flights compared with those of the Panel Atmosphere. The mutual confirmation of the method and the model atmosphere was the important result.

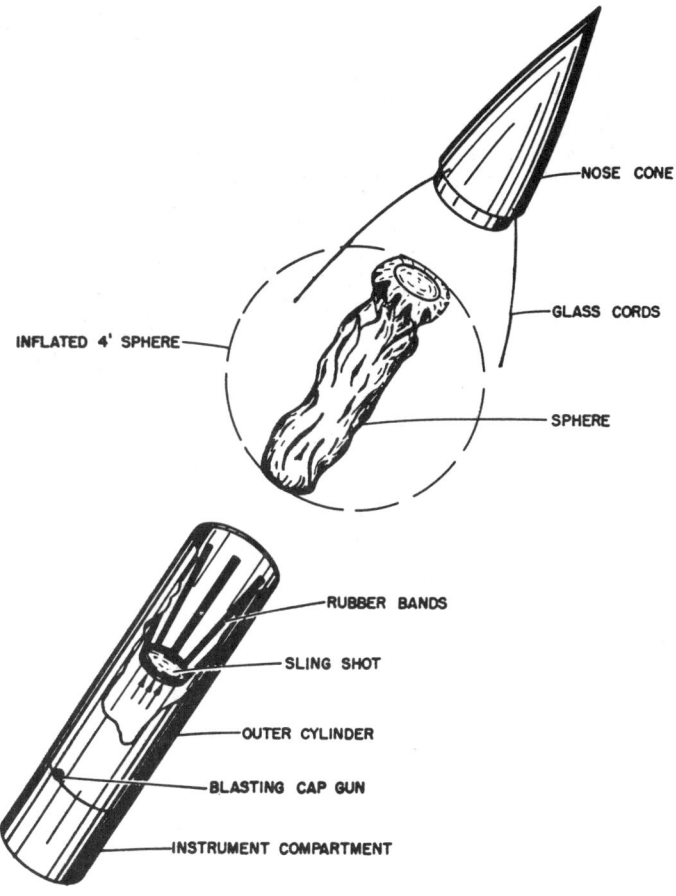

NOSE CONE

GLASS CORDS

SPHERE

INFLATED 4' SPHERE

RUBBER BANDS

SLING SHOT

OUTER CYLINDER

BLASTING CAP GUN

INSTRUMENT COMPARTMENT

Figure 9   Deployment of inflatable sphere from an Aerobee.

Accelerometer spheres

In early 1954, the Michigan group proposed to Air Force Cambridge Research Center that the sphere method could be developed into a small,[*] inexpensive experiment by carrying along an internal proof mass against which to measure drag acceleration instead of using the Earth as a reference for ground tracking. A simple local reference would preclude the measurement of wind but would otherwise have the advantages of size and simplicity in addition to which no ground tracking would be required. The results would come from telemetering alone although temperatures and pressures, it turned out, would be required from the ground to 20 km. But these data are routinely available from weather balloons.

---

[*]   Nearly simultaneously with the development of the small sphere Michigan undertook, under Air Force sponsorship and with the aid of NACA, the development of the two-stage Nike-Deacon and Nike-Cajun rockets. The use of the Deacon was suggested by James A. Van Allen's use of it in the Rockoon. The Nike-Cajun, which still flies, was the precursor of a whole family of multi-stage sounding rockets used in space science.

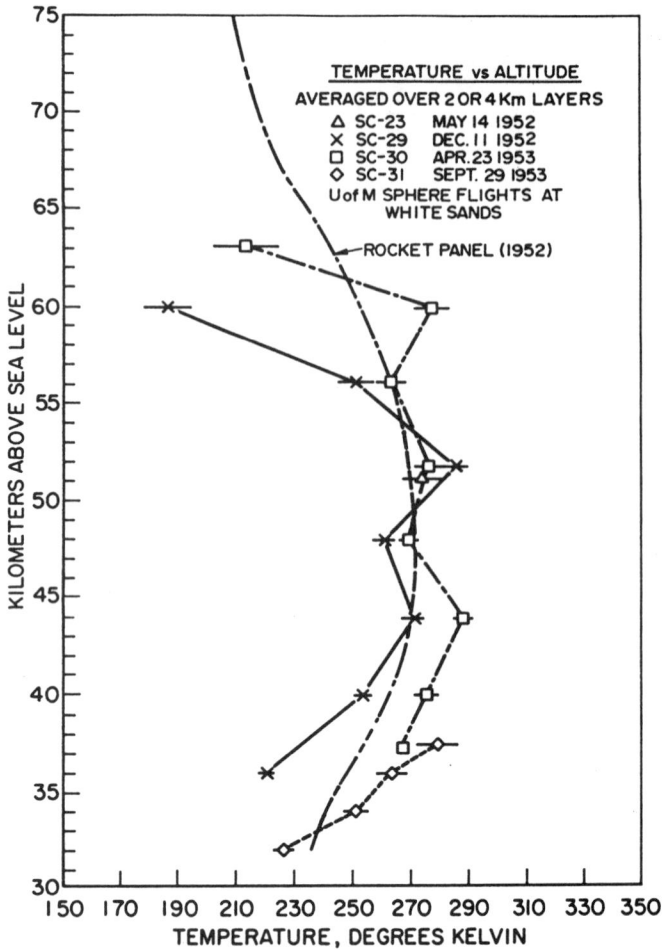

Figure 10 Temperatures measured by four DOVAP-tracked spheres.

Figure 11 illustrates the local reference mass device, which is in essence a transit time accelerometer (Jones, [24]). Figure 12 shows the accelerometer in schematic relation to the sphere. The cylindrical bobbin, about 2.5 X 2.5 cm, is precisely centered by the conical pick-up fingers in a surrounding cavity that is 0.48 cm in all directions distant from the bobbin. On a signal from the intervalometer switch the fingers retract and the bobbin moves under the influence of drag acceleration toward the cavity. When it touches, a signal is transmitted to the ground and compared with one which was sent when the bobbin was released.

From $s = 1/2\, a_D t^2$, one solves for a_D, the drag acceleration. Herein lies the explanation of the sensitivity of the method. With the Earth as a reference, one measures dv/dt and gets a_D as the small difference between g and dv/dt. With the accelerometer a_D is measured directly down to 10^{-3}g. In our work we used the sensitivity to design a small sphere 17.8 cm in diameter which could be deployed from small rockets at low cost. That is, the decreased aerodynamic sensitivity of the small, rigid sphere was compensated by the increased acceleration measuring sensitivity.

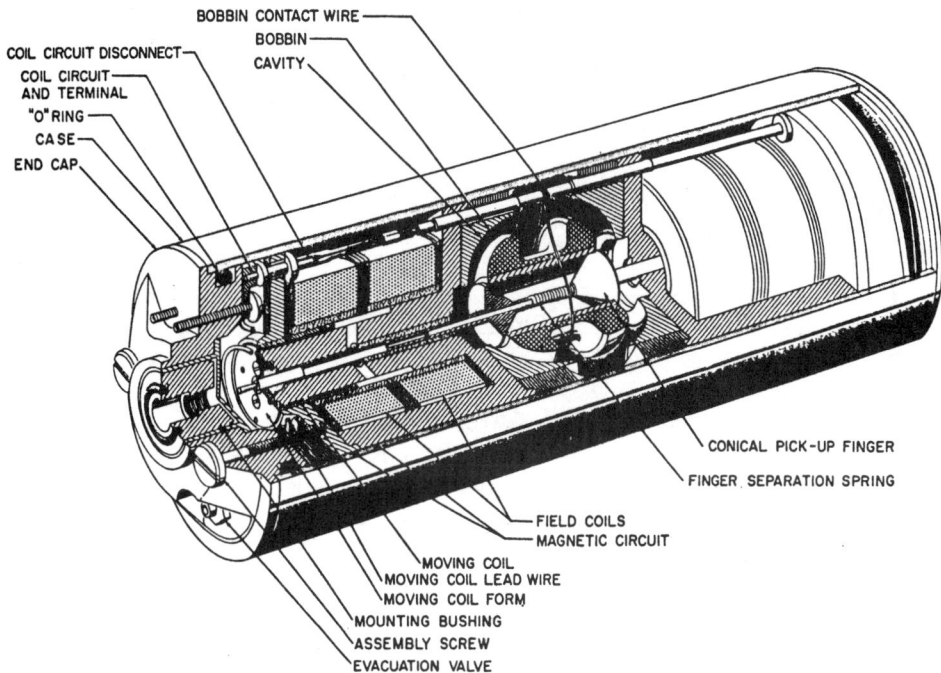

Figure 11   Transit time accelerometer.

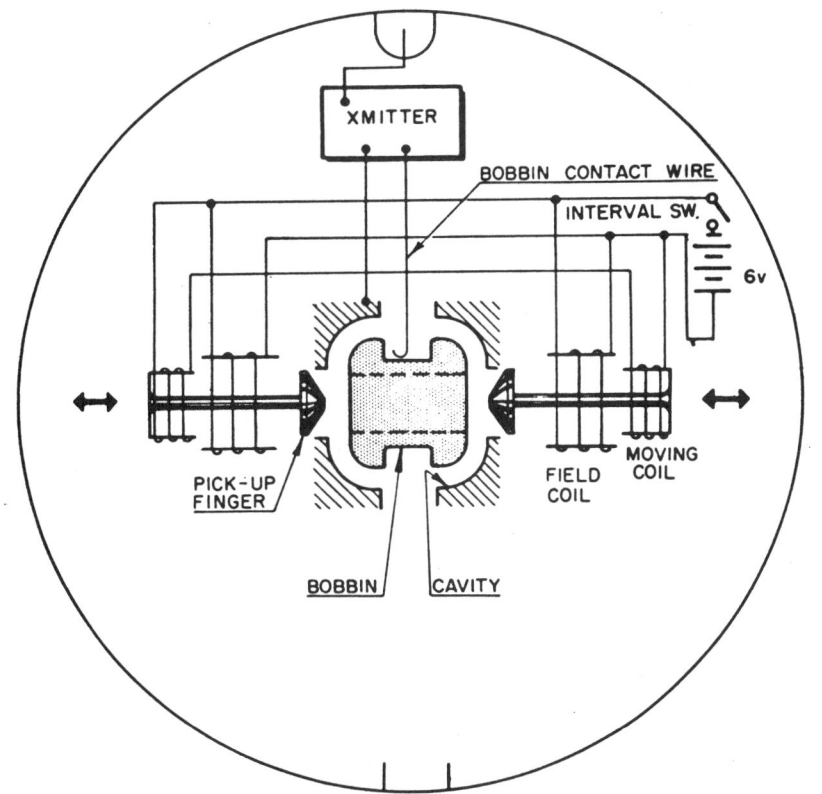

Figure 12   Accelerometer in schematic relation to sphere.

The small spheres measured density from about 90 km down to about 18 km. Near this altitude, the accelerations became large and irregular -- apparently due to vortex shedding. Whatever the cause, the method could not be used successfully to the ground. Hence, the need for pressures to 20 km from balloons as noted earlier.

The first flight took place at Wallops Island on 8 April 1955 in the first Nike-Deacon rocket. Because of last-minute difficulties the accelerometer was left out and the flight tested only the rocket and the sphere deployment and transmitter. All were successful. On 24 June a second flight, complete with accelerometer, was launched on the second Nike-Deacon. Everything worked properly and densities were calculated from 80 to 18 km. The results were in excellent agreement with the Panel Atmosphere, thus setting the stage for many flights of the small sphere. The primary users of accelerometer spheres have been Michigan and Air Force Cambridge Research Laboratories. Michigan's last flight was at Fort Churchill in March 1958. The Air Force flights, including sphere refinements for higher altitude, continued (Faire and Champion, [25]).

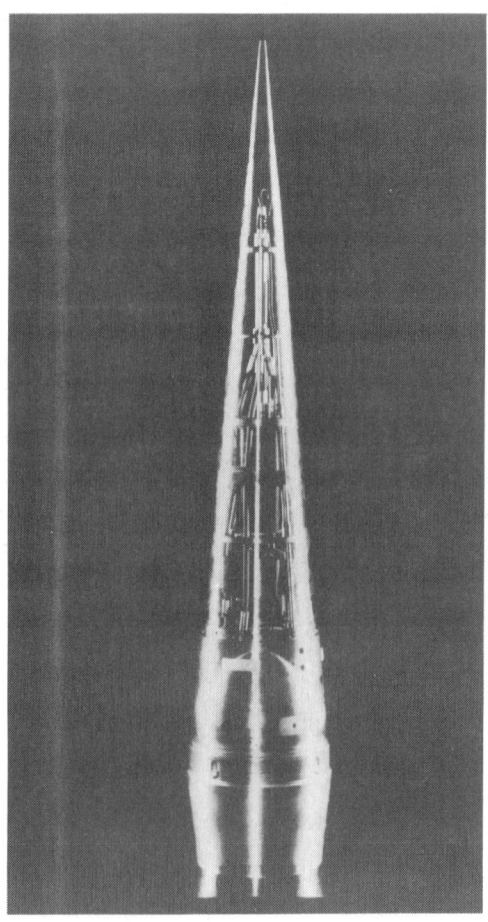

Figure 13   Phantom view of a 17.8-cm accelerometer sphere in a Nike-Cajun nose cone.

Radar Tracked spheres

During the interval of small sphere development radar improvements occurred which brought performance up, approximately, to that of DOVAP. The RCA AN/FPS-16 is a popular radar of this class for which Skolnik [23] cites accuracies of 5 yds and 0.1 mil. This development made possible the use of radar for sphere tracking.

Leviton [26] and his colleagues at Air Force Cambridge Research Laboratories developed Robin, a 1-meter Mylar sphere with internal corner reflector to be carried on the small Arcas rocket. Robin's range was 70 to 30 km and its prime purpose was to provide inexpensive sounding on a daily basis at several bases. In the early 1960's, Michigan adapted Mylar spheres to the Nike-Cajun rocket for investigations up to 120 km. In this application the spheres were 2/3 m in diameter with aluminized surfaces and no corner reflectors. Three spheres were carried in the rocket for deployment redundancy. A particularly satisfying investigation with this combination was a survey of the tropical upper atmosphere with 13 flights at Kwajalein, 9.4°N during 1963 and 1964. Figure 13 is a phantom view of a 17.8-cm accelerometer sphere in a Nike-Cajun nose cone. Figures 14 and 15 show the sphere and payload, Figure 16 the results. The radar for these flights was Tradex having somewhat better accuracy than the FPS-16.

Figure 14   Two-thirds meter aluminized Mylar sphere with inflation capsule.

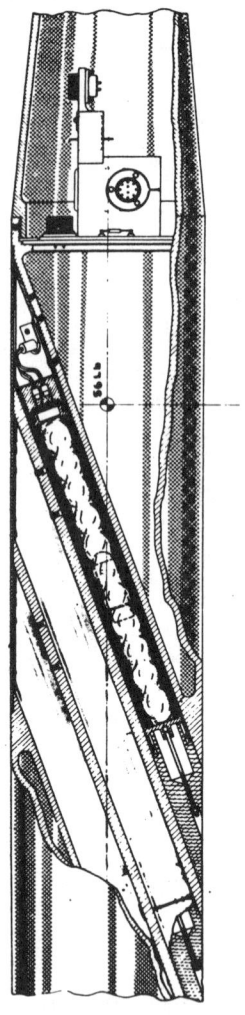

Figure 15   Nike-Cajun payload for deploying three inflatable Mylar spheres.

During the 1960's, Murrow [27] at NASA and Pearson [28] in Australia undertook programs with radar-tracked spheres. The latter program has been the main source of Southern Hemisphere upper air data. Sphere flights reached a peak during the IQSY. In the interval January 1964 to December 1965, 170 flights of various kinds of spheres were carried out by experimenters in 10 laboratories. For surveys of techniques, results and the literature see Jones [29] and Jones and Peterson [30]. The former reference contains a description of an inflatable sphere and accelerometer combination by Faucher and Morrissey of Air Force Cambridge Research Laboratories.

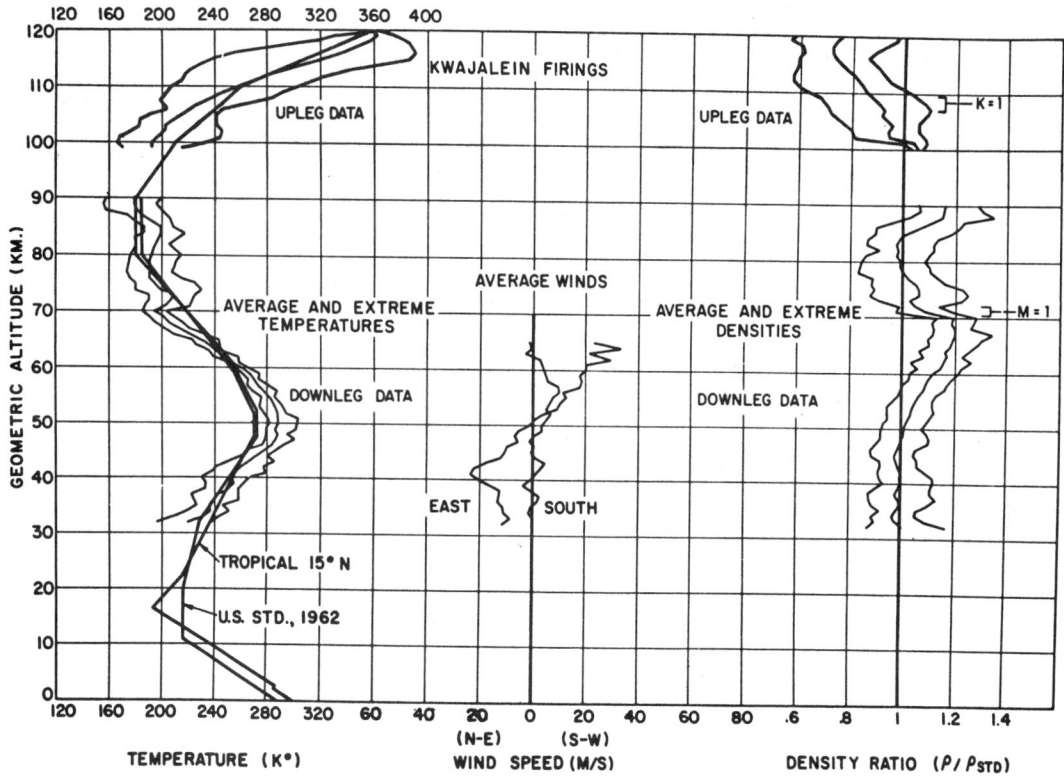

Figure 16 Average and extreme densities and temperatures from 13 soundings during all seasons; Kwajalein atoll, 9°24'N; 1963-1964.

Coefficient of Drag

The coefficient of drag C_D (Newton's Number) in the drag equation is a dimensionless number varying between 0.2 and 2.0 which must be known in order to calculate density from measured accelerations. It is usually given in constant contours on a grid of Mach number and Reynolds number below 130 km and of Mach number and Knudsen number above 130 km. The experimental determination and compilation of useful values is an interesting aerodynamic topic. For a survey of references see Jones and Peterson [31]. For our purpose here it may be stated that C_D values have improved concurrently with the development of the sphere experiment and that values have generally been available as needed.

Results

Falling spheres have contributed extensively to some of the model and standard atmospheres cited earlier. The more interesting contributions, however, have been those in which a flight or group of flights was aimed at a particular verification, phenomenon or the meteorology of a particular place and time. There follows a chronological survey of those which the Michigan Aero group carried out:

a. 14 May 1952 to 29 September 1953. Four flights at White Sands of the DOVAP-tracked first spheres. Confirmed the method and supported the Panel Atmosphere. (Bartman, et al [32].)

b. 8 April 1955 and 24 June 1955. First tests of accelerometer sphere at Wallops Island. Also first tests of Nike-Deacon sounding rocket, precursor to Nike-Cajun and other multi-stage sounding rockets. (Jones and Bartman [33].)

c. 27 October 1956 to 10 November 1956. Five flights of the accelerometer sphere conducted between $40^{\circ}N$ and $65.6^{\circ}N$ on the U.S.S. *Rushmore* to investigate latitude dependence of structure. A latitude gradient in density was measured. (Jones, et al [34].)

d. 27 January 1958 to 4 March 1958. Four flights of accelerometer spheres at Ft. Churchill, 58.7N. These flights straddled an explosive warming which was clearly seen (Figure 17). One sphere was on a Signal Corps/Michigan Aerobee carrying grenades, which also detected the warming. (Jones, et al [35].)

e. 26 March 1963 to 18 June 1964. Sixteen flights of radar-tracked spheres at Kwajalein atoll, 924'N., sponsored by the U.S. Navy. Thirteen flights gave results yielding a complete survey of the structure of the tropical upper atmosphere. (Peterson, et al [36].)

f. 18 June 1964 to 3 February 1966. Results from eight radar-tracked spheres grouped in five diurnal pairs in an attempt to see the diurnal density "bulge" in the vicinity of 100 km to reported by Greenhow and Hall in 1960 from meteor observations. The spheres showed no bulge. (Jones and Peterson [30].)

g. On several occasions there have been opportunities to compare spheres with techniques used by other investigators as in (d) above: Other cases are:

6 June 1962: Sphere, grenades, pitot tube. Jones [29].

28 November 1963: Sphere, mass spectrometer. Jones & Peterson [30].

7-8 August 1965: Spheres, grenades, chaff. Jones & Peterson [30].

ACKNOWLEDGEMENTS

Many of the tens of people in the Department of Aerospace Engineering who contributed to the research are cited in the references. To other colleagues who are not, thanks are expressed here for their participation in what was an exhilarating group effort. Special recognition to Dr. Myron H. Nichols is in order for initiating the program and providing guidance after he left Michigan. Sydney Chapman, during his several sojourns at Michigan, made important contributions to both the sampling and sphere experiments. Professor F.A. Paneth and his colleagues at the Londonderry Laboratory for Radio-chemistry at the University of Durham performed analyses on nearly all of the upper air samples and were most generous in providing the Michigan group with analyzer design information.

Agencies of the U.S. Army, U.S. Air Force and U.S. Navy provided the financial support required. People associated with university and U.S. government laboratories and government operational bases were unstinting in their cooperation. This cooperation was usually arranged through the Upper Atmosphere Rocket Research Panel, which served a national need for several years.

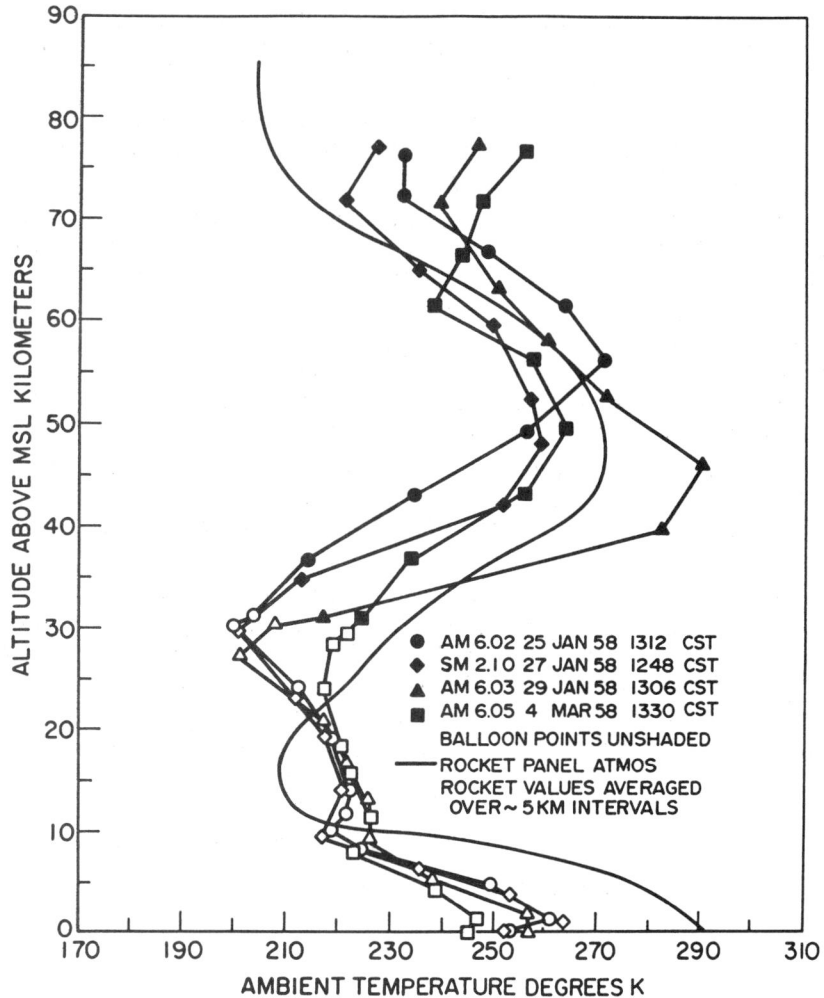

Figure 17 Upper air temperatures showing an explosive warming event; Fort Churchill, 58°45'N; 1958.

REFERENCES

1. H.B. Maris, The upper atmosphere, Part I, *Jour. Terr. Mag.,* 33, No. 4, pp. 233-255, 1928. Part II, Jour. Terr. Mag., 34, No. 1, pp. 45-53, 1929.

2. S.K. Mitra and H. Rakshit, Distribution of the constituent gases and their pressure in the upper atmosphere, *Ind. Jour. Phys.,* 12, pp. 47-61, 1938.

3. F.L. Whipple, Meteors and the Earth's upper atmosphere, *Rev. Mod. Phys.,* 15, No. 4, pp. 246-264, 1943.

4. F.A. Lindemann and G.M.B. Dobson, A theory of meteors, and the density and temperature of the outer atmosphere to which it leads, *Proc. Roy. Soc.*, A102, p. 411, 1923.

5. G.I. Taylor, Waves and tides in the atmosphere, *Proc. Roy. Soc.*, A126, pp. 169-183, 1929.

6. R.A. Minzner and W.S. Ripley, The ARDC Model Atmosphere 1956, *Air Force Surv. in Geoph.*, No. 86, A.F. Cambridge Research Center, Bedford, Mass., 1956.

7. R.A. Minzner, K.S.W. Champion and H.L. Pond, The ARDC model Atmosphere, 1959, *Air Force Surv. in Geoph.*, No. 115, A.F. Cambridge Research Center, Bedford, Mass., 1959.

8. COSPAR Work Group IV. COSPAR International Reference Atmosphere 1965 (CIRA, 1965), North Holland Publ. Co. Amsterdam, 1965.

9. Chapman, S. and T.G. Cowling, *The Mathematical Theory of Non-Uniform Gases*, Cambridge University Press 1939 and p. 244, Dover, 1961.

10. P. Mange, The theory of molecular diffusion in the atmosphere, *Jour. Geophy. Res.*, 62, No. 2, pp. 279-296, 1957.

11. P.S. Epstein, Concerning separation of gases in the atmosphere, *Ger. Beitr. z. Geophys.*, 35, p. 153, 1932.

12. E.J. Schaefer and M.H. Nichols, Upper air neutral composition measurements by a mass spectrometer, *Jour. Geoph. Res.*, 69, No. 21, pp. 4,649-4,660, 1964.

13. B.A. Mirtov, Rocket investigation of the composition of the atmosphere at high altitudes, *Usp. Fiz. Nauk.*, 43, pp. 181-196, 1957.

14. L.M. Jones, The measurement of diffusive separation in the upper atmosphere, in Rocket Exploration of the Upper Atmosphere, R.L.F. Boyd and M.J. Seaton, eds., Spec. Suppl., Vol. 1, *Jour. Atm. Terr. Phys.*, pp. 143-156, 1954.

15. E.A. Wenzel, L.T. Loh, M.H. Nichols and L.M. Jones, The measurement of diffusive separation in the upper atmosphere, *Ann. IGY*, XII Part I, pp. 407-421, Pergamon Press, London, 1960.

16. G.R. Martin, The composition of the atmosphere above 60 km, in Rocket Exploration of the Upper Atmosphere, R.L.F. Boyd and M.J. Seaton, eds., Spec. Suppl., Vol. 1, *Jour. Atm. Terr. Phys.*, pp. 161-168, 1954.

17. E. Glückauf, A micro-analysis of the helium and neon contents of the air, *Proc. Roy. Soc.*, A185, pp. 98-119, 1946.

18. K.F. Chackett, F.A. Paneth and E.J. Wilson, Chemical analysis of stratosphere samples from 50 and 70 km height, *Jour. Atm. Terr. Phys.*, 1, pp. 49-55, 1950.

19. F.A. Paneth, The micro-analysis of the inert gases, *Endeavor, XII*, No. 45, pp. 5-17, 1953.

20. W.G. Stroud, The early history of the rocket-grenade experiment. This symposium, Lisbon, 1975.

21. G.I. Taylor and J.W. Maccoll, *Proc. Roy. Soc.*, A139, pp. 278-311, 1933; J.W. Maccoll, *Proc., Roy. Soc.* A159, pp. 459-472, 1937.

22. A.H. Stone, On supersonic flow past a slightly yawing cone, *J. Math Phys.*, 27, No. 1, 1948.

23. M.I. Skolnik, *Introduction to Radar Systems*, p. 193, McGraw Hill, New York, 1962.

24. L.M. Jones, A transit time accelerometer. *Rev. Sci. Instr.*, 27, No. 6, 1956.

25. A.C. Faire and K.S.W. Champion, High Altitude rocket density Measurements at Eglin, Florida, Space Research VI, COSPAR Symp Mar del Plata, 1965, Spartan Books, Wash., 1966.

26. R. Leviton, The Robin falling sphere. IRIG Document No. 105: Initiation of the Meteorological Rocket Network, Rev. Aug. 1961. Office of Technical Services, Washington.

27. H.N. Murrow and R.M. Henry, Self-induced balloon motions, *J. Appl. Meteor.*, 4, pp. 131-138, 1965.

28. P.H.O. Pearson, Seasonal variations of density, temperature and pressure between 40 and 90 km, Woomera, South Australia, March 1964-March 1975. *J. Atmos. Terr. Phys.*, 28, pp. 1,057-1,064, 1966.

29. L.M. Jones, (ed), Falling Sphere Method for Upper-Air Density, Temperature and Wind, DOSPAR Technique Manual, Paris, 1967.

30. L.M. Jones and J.W. Peterson, Falling Sphere Measurements, 30 to 120 km., *Meteor. Monogr.*, 9, No. 31, pp. 176-189, Amer. Meteor. Soc., 1968.

31. L.M. Jones and J.W. Peterson, Performance, Results, Drag Coefficient., in COSPAR Technique Manual on Falling Spheres, etc., L.M. Jones (ed)., Append. pp. 103-119, Paris, 1967.

32. F.L. Bartman, L.W. Chaney, L.M. Jones and V.C. Liu, Upper-air density and temperature by the falling-sphere method, *Jour. Appl. Phys.*, 27, No. 7, pp. 706-712, 1956.

33. L.M. Jones and F.L. Bartman, A Samplified Falling Sphere Method for Upper Air Density, University of Michigan, E.R.I. Report 2215-10-T, 1956.

34. L.M. Jones, F.F. Fischbach and J.W. Peterson, Seasonal and latitude variations in upper-air density, *Ann IGY*, XII Part 1, pp. 207-216, Pergamon Press, London, 1960.

35. L.M. Jones, J.W. Peterson, E.J. Schaefer and H.F. Schulte, Upper air density and temperature: some variations and an abrupt warming in the mesosphere, *Jour. Geoph. Res.*, 64, pp. 2,331-2,340, 1959.

36. J.W. Peterson, W.H. Hansen, K.D. McWatters and G. Bonfanti, Falling sphere measurements over Kwajalein, *Jour. Geophy. Res.*, 70, No. 18, pp. 4477-4489, 1965.

Additional Sources:

D. Krankowsky, W.T. Kasprzak and Alfred O. Nier, Mass spectrometric studies of the composition of the lower thermosphere during summer 1967, *Jour. Geoph. Res.*, 73, No. 23, pp. 7,291-7,306, 1968.

Meadows, E.B. and J.W. Townsend, Jr., IGY rocket measurements of arctic atmospheric composition above 100 km, In *Space Research*, H.K. Bijl, ed., pp. 175-198, North Holland Publ. Co., Amsterdam, 1960.

_____, and J.W. Townsend, Diffusive separation in the winter nighttime arctic upper atmosphere 112 to 115 km, *Ann de Géoph.*, 14, p. 80, 1958.

Chapter 15

UPPER ATMOSPHERE RESEARCH
AND THE FIRST ROCKET EXPERIMENTS IN THE USSR[*]

B. A. Mirtov and L. A. Vedeshin[†]

On 24 May 1949, scientific instruments were lifted for the first time in the Soviet Union by a rocket to an altitude of 110 km for measuring atmospheric pressure and sampling of air.

Almost the whole mass of the Earth's atmosphere is concentrated in its lower 30 km layer. The higher layers contain only 1-2 percent of the whole air mass. Nevertheless, it is precisely this region of the Earth's gas envelope that has attracted the attention of scientists for a long time. The reasons for this are extremely important both from the scientific and the practical points of view.

To begin with, the upper atmosphere serves as the first barrier along the path of the solar radiation to the bottom of the air basin, the terrestrial biosphere. As it impacts this barrier, the radiation not only undergoes considerable changes in itself but also causes a radical reconstruction of the atmosphere's structure. Aurora and luminescence of the night sky occur, as do disturbances of the magnetic field of Earth. It is known that the state of the upper atmospheric layers, primarily of the ionosphere, affects the nature of radio wave propagation.

Some information about the upper atmosphere is provided by study through ground methods. However, it is extremely difficult and sometimes impossible to obtain a number of most important data by ground methods. This includes data on the short-wave ultraviolet radiation of the Sun as well as on the nature of its corpuscular radiation; of ionization above the reflecting layer of the ionosphere; of composition, density and temperature of the upper atmosphere; etc. This type of information requires penetration of research instruments to an altitude of 100 km and above. At present the attainment of such an altitude is routine and surprises no one, but not so long ago it seemed formidable.

The only technical means to reach 100 km or more was the rocket. In the Soviet Union, the first rocket designed for scientific research was constructed in

---

[*]   Presented at The Ninth IAA History of Astronautics Symposium, Lisbon, Portugal, September 1975.

[†]   Committee of the Soviet National Association of Natural Science and Technology Historians, USSR Academy of Sciences, Moscow, USSR.

1949 under the supervision of S.P. Korolev. From that moment, an entirely new stage began in the study of the upper atmospheric layers.

Rocket research in USSR and in U.S.A. began almost simultaneously and subsequently developed quite independently of each other. The principal feature of our experiments has been that the whole scientific apparatus designed for measuring the parameters of the atmosphere at high altitudes was located in a robot-container, separable from the carrier rocket.

The fact is that the rocket body is not fully hermetic and in the rarefied atmospheric layers there is an intensive emanation of air, filling it prior to takeoff with remains of unconsumed fuel, combustion products of fuel, etc. The "parasite" gas surrounds the rocket by a unique cloud, which may distort the picture being observed and even ruin the experiment. This is highly prominent at altitudes above 80 km, where the pressure drops below 10^{-4} Hg mm.

In the Geophysical Institute of the USSR Academy of Sciences (GEOFIAN), new trends were devised for the research of the upper atmosphere (1946-1949). The scientific apparatus for this research was designed under the supervision of B.L. Dzerdzievskii and E.M. Reikhrudol. It was here, too, that the idea of the separable container was born and, moreover, that a new hermetically sealed container of this type -- FIAR-I (physical research of atmosphere by means of rockets) was constructed. The institute was initially under the direction of O. Yu. Schmidt and later of G.A. Gamburtsev.

Being an absolutely new sphere of research, rocket experiments in the upper atmosphere raised one problem after another. How would the vibrations generated by rocket engines, it was asked, affect the scientific apparatus, which includes brittle thin-walled glass cylinders, electric instruments, clock mechanisms, storage batteries, etc.? What about the performance of instruments and how they would it be affected by their overheating due to aerodynamic braking? How would one conduct the recording of instrument readings (portable autonomous telemetric systems did not as yet exist)? And how would one set up the power supply accessories and what exactly should they be? Should the whole container be hermetically sealed or only a section of it? In what shape should the container itself be? Cylinder, sphere, or parallelpiped?

In the first launchings of FIAR-I, whose length was about 1 m, diameter about 40 cm, and weight 85 kg, the feasability of the direct research of the high atmospheric layers by means of the rocket-container system had to be experimentally established and confirmed. This required separation of the container with its instruments from the rocket at a rigidly prescribed moment of flight and to ensure its descent and landing by parachute. The latter was an independent and complex engineering problem -- to lower the container carefully from an altitude of 100 km onto the ground and preserve the scientific apparatus. The problem was being solved for the first time. It should be mentioned that the parachute system for the FIAR-I container, just as the rocket itself, was devised and tested by the specialists at the Design Bureau headed by S.P. Korolev.

The first Soviet geophysical rocket IRA (academic) was based on the R-I ballistic rocket, with certain changes in construction of its tail and head as well as in the control system. The first launching of IRA took place, as mentioned at the beginning of this paper, May 1949. At 4 hours 40 minutes, the rocket rushed upward along an almost vertical flight path, carrying with it scientific apparatus weighing about 200 kg.

At a prescribed time after engine cutoff, on command from the program device, the containers FIAR-I, two symmetrically arranged tail compartment mortars, were ejected; and, having obtained some additional velocity (with respect to the rocket), accomplished an independent flight.

Due to the fact that the axes of mortars formed a certain angle with the rocket axis, the containers went sideways from it and, outstripping it, left the zone, where the composition of the atmosphere could have been highly distorted by "parasite" gases. The ejection of containers was carried out prior to the rocket's attaining the altitude of sampling. This was done so that the containers would move out as far as possible from the rocket's body, being thus "ventilated" and freed from the remaining contaminating gases. Having attained the ultimate altitude, the containers began their descent suspended by parachutes.

In the first first flights it was established that the apparatus for the direct physical study of the atmosphere was efficient at all the stages of ascent, ejection and descent of containers and also withstood the accelerations and vibrations. During these flights, measurements were conducted of pressure and density of the atmosphere at altitudes 35 to 115 km and air samples were taken at altitudes of about 100 km. The process of recording on the film showed that atmospheric pressure at the apex of the rocket's flight path was 8.10^{-4} Hg mm.

As regards research on the samples' chemical composition, special methods were devised for this using spectral analysis under laboratory conditions.

On the basis of atmospheric pressure gauging, it was possible to plot temperature curves calculated from the barometric formula.

The successful determinations of the physical parameters of the upper atmosphere, implemented during the first rocket flights, have raised the question of organizing this kind of research on a large scale. S.P. Korolev, who played a significant part in setting up this research, always met the needs of experimenters with great willingness, participated directly in conducting all the tests on rockets, and discussed and analyzed the results obtained jointly with the scientists.

The method of air sampling (and its subsequent laboratory analysis) was later replaced by gas analysis method, carried out by means of radio-frequency mass-spectrometer directly during the flight. The first device of this type in the USSR (and one of the first in the world) was made by V.G. Istomin in 1956-57 and was successfully used in container FIAR-2 for research up to altitudes of 200 km. Now the method of mass-spectrography is inseparable from experiments on structural parameters, determination of the terrestrial atmosphere, that of other planets, and of the cosmic space.

From 1951 to 1956, on assignment by the USSR Academy of Sciences, several modifications were devised on the base of the R-1, one of the geophysical rockets used for regular research of the upper atmosphere. The program of geophysical investigations, conducted under the supervision of Academician A.A. Blagonravov, was considerably extended.

However, it was inexpedient to use powerful rockets for mass launchings to negligible altitudes. In this case, small meteorological research rockets could be quite suitable as they could be launched in tens and hundreds annually for a quick meteorological analysis of the state of the stratosphere and ionosphere, as well as for solving geophysical problems.

These operations were conducted by another group of scientists on meteorological rocket MR-1, which was launched in 1951 by specialists of the Central Aerological Observatory (G.I. Golyshev, A.M. Kasatkin, B.T. Shvidkovskii, G.A. Kokin, et al). MR-1, of lower weight and smaller size, probed the atmosphere up to an altitude of 80 km.

The first rocket experiments, which we have described, provided a lot of new information regarding the upper layers of the atmosphere. The obtaining of air samples and their analysis have, for the first time, clearly shown that for the physics of upper atmosphere boundary-turbopause (above it is the region of molecular intermixing of atmospheric gases) the very important region is not at the altitude of 50-70 km, as previously assumed, but at altitude of 90-100 km. This was later repeatedly confirmed by many investigators. The study of the variation of pressure and temperature in relation to altitude made it possible to determine clearly the deep temperature minimum (about $150^{\circ}K$) at altitudes of 80-90 km, which has previously been surmised from indirect observations. Very high velocity winds were discovered high in the atmosphere (100 m per sec and above), forcing revisions to be made to the question on dynamics of the upper atmosphere.

Besides research of the upper atmosphere and ionosphere, the rockets also served as a basis for solving a number of applied problems connected with perfecting the cosmic-rocket technique.

BIBLIOGRAPHY

1. B.A. Mirtov, Gazovyi sostav atmosfery Zemli i metody ego analyza (Gas composition of the Earth's atmosphere and methods of its analysis). Moskva, 1961.

2. A.A. Blagonravov, Issledovanie verkhnikh sloev atmosfery pri pomoshchi vysotnykh raket. (The research of upper atmospheric layers by means of high-altitude rockets.) Vestni AN SSSR, No. 6, 1957.

3. G.A. Sadovoi, 10 Oktyabrya -- 25 let so dnya pervogo startsovetskoi upravlyaemoi ballisticheskoi rakety dal'nego deistviya R-1 (10 October -- 25 years since the day of the first launching of the R-1 Soviet controllable ballistic rocket for remote operation.) Sbornik IIET AN SSSR, No. 19, 1973.

4. I.A. Khvostikov, Vysokie sloi atmosfery. (High atmospheric layers) ... Moskva, 1964.

5. Razvitie raketnoi tekhniki v SSSR (Development of rocket techniques in the USSR) ... Moskva, 1961.

6. L.A. Vedeshin, Razvitie v. SSSR raketnykh issledovanii okolozemnogo prostranstva. (Development in the USSR of rocket research of the upper atmosphere and space.) ... *Sbornik IIET AN SSSR*, No. 15, 1972.

7. B.A. Mirtov and L.A. Vedeshin, Rakety issleduyut atmosferu. (Rockets study atmosphere.) *Aviatsiya i kosmonavtika,* No. 12, 1974.

Chapter 16

EARLY SCIENTIFIC HISTORY OF
THE ROCKET GRENADE EXPERIMENT[*]

William G. Stroud[†]

In the 1950 to 1960 decade, some 30 sounding rockets carrying the grenade experiment were fired in the Arctic, at middle latitudes and in the equatorial western Pacific. The vertical distributions of temperatures and winds at different seasons and at different times of the day were measured. Although there were significant variations in the results from each of the sites, an outstanding feature was the uniformity with latitude of the seasonal variation of the wind field. Over the latitude-altitude ranges sampled, the winds were strong and from the west during the winter months; and weak and from the east during the summer months. The nature of the general circulation pattern in the mesosphere of the northern hemisphere was revealed by the measurements. Of particular interest were those measurements made at the seasonal turnovers because of the insight into the dynamics of this region they provided.

INTRODUCTION

This review of the early history of the rocket grenade experiment covers the period 1948 to 1960 beginning with the early V2 rocket flights at White Sands, New Mexico, when this technique for measuring upper atmosphere temperatures and winds was being tried out, to the completion of the reduction and the publication of the International Geophysical Year (IGY) data from Fort Churchill, Canada, and Guam in the Pacific. In that period, some 30 sounding rockets (V2, Aerobee and Nike-Cajun) were fired; a series of 12 Aerobee rockets was fired successfully at White Sands (32°N) from 1950 to 1953; 10 Aerobee firings were carried out at Fort Churchill (59°N) during 1956, 1957 and 1958; and late in 1958, 9 successful solid-propellant rocket flights were conducted at Guam (10°N).

The basic idea of the rocket-grenade experiment is straightforward: determine the temperature of the atmosphere by measuring the velocity of a sound wave through a layer of the atmosphere defined by successive bursts of high explosives

---

[*]   Presented at The Ninth IAA History of Astronautics Symposium, Lisbon, Portugal, September 1975.

[†]   National Aeronautics and Space Administration, Goddard Space Flight Center, Greenbelt, Maryland 20771, U.S.A.

ejected from the sounding rocket on the upward leg of its trajectory. In fact, the experiment turned out to be much more subtle both in analysis and in execution. Still, it became a powerful tool for exploration of the upper atmosphere, yielding accurate temperature and wind profiles between 30 and 90 km. Over the years, until about 1973, it was extended by the United States to other latitudes from 10°S to 75°N, and to other seasons and other times of the day. In addition, the rocket-grenade experiment has been conducted in Australia, Japan, Sweden, Italy, France and the USSR. It has been possible with these extensive sets of data to draw a definitive picture of the global stratospheric and mesospheric circulation systems [2].

To derive atmospheric temperatures and winds from the measurements made in the grenade experiment, three basic physical assumptions were necessary:

1. That the composition of the atmosphere was constant up to peak altitude. Thus, it is assured that the temperature, T, velocity of sound, c, relationship was valid; i.e., $c = kT^{1/2}$, where k is a constant depending on the ratio of specific heats and the mean molecule weight of the gas.

2. The acoustic wave front remained coherent as it propagated downward through the atmosphere; i.e., that the horizontal variations in temperature and wind were negligible over distances of 15 km.

3. The vertical velocity of the wind was negligible.

Through all these rocket-grenade experiments and much careful analysis, we always found these assumptions valid.

The basic measurements necessary for the analysis were:

1. The accurate position of the explosion in space: in early firings this was determined by ballistic camera triangulation against the star field. Later, DOVAP (Doppler velocity and position), a radio tracking technique, and combinations of DOVAP, radar, and ballistic camera were used.

2. The time of the explosion: this was determined by photocells on the rocket, which picked up the light pulse and telemetered the time to the ground or by ground based flash detectors.

3. The times and angles of arrival of the sound waves at the ground: these were determined by an accurately-surveyed sound ranging array of from five to nine microphones located as nearly as possible directly under the explosions.

4. The surface air temperature from which the acoustic velocity at the surface was obtained: firings were always conducted when the surface wind velocity was nearly zero so that its effects could be neglected in the data reduction.

THE EARLY EXPERIENCES

The capture of some 60 V2 rockets by the United States Army in Europe at the end of World War II and their commitment to upper atmosphere research made possible a major acceleration of the U.S. upper atmosphere research activities, which were scattered throughout university and armed services research and development laboratories. In 1946, a V2 Upper Atmosphere Research Panel[*] composed of representatives of universities, private industry, and military laboratories[†] was formed to plan and coordinate the program. At the regular meetings of this Panel, whose membership was restricted to those who were actually working on the program, there were discussions of the scheduling and allocation of rockets, technical and operational requirements, experiments to be performed, their performance and their results. Looking back at the minutes of these meeting to reconstruct the early history of the grenade experiment one finds that at the May 1946 meeting M. Golay discussed the potential measurement of temperatures and winds using smoke puffs ejected from the V2; and, in November that year, he proposed sound grenades, smoke puffs and sampling experiments for V2 No. 21. These experiments were ultimately carried on V2 No. 25, which was fired at 0630, 2 April 1948 and reached an altitude of 144 km. The report on this firing reads in part:

> "(c) 12 Grenades with TNT charges [were carried]. These were to be ejected at 5 sec. intervals beginning at burnout, but bad temperature characteristics of the driving motor fouled up the ejections. Observers reported seeing 6 smoke puffs, but none of these appeared on the films. Recordings of sound stations on the ground indicated the occurrence of bursts near the peak of trajectory, but these recordings were not conclusive."

Other early V2 firings (Nos. 33 and 56 in September 1948, and November 1949) carrying the grenade experiment produced no temperature or wind data because of failures to obtain accurate times of the explosions (sounding rocket telemetry was not very reliable in those days). Instrumentation of the Aerobee rocket with the grenade experiment started with a firing in March 1950 followed by successful firings in July, October, two in December and then in June and November 1951. For the first time, precise values of the basic parameters were available and their reduction to atmospheric temperatures and winds made possible.

It was not until the summer of 1953 that the first definitive results of the successful Aerobee firings of 1950, 1951 were published [3,4,5]. The difficulty in the analysis was the correction of the acoustic wave travel times between layers for the effects of the horizontal wind. The breakthrough occurred when one of our colleagues suggested the concept of a "virtual source" for the explosion, i.e., the position at which the explosion at a height Z would have to occur if there were no wind below Z in order that its sound wave arrive at the origin of the sound array from

---

[*]   In 1948, the name was changed to the Upper Atmosphere Rocket Research Panel. It continued to function until the early 1960's when NASA institutionalized these activities.

[†]   The first meeting of the Panel was at Princeton University on 27 February 1946; its members were: E. Krause, Naval Research Laboratory, Chairman; W. Dow, University of Michigan; M. Golay, U.S. Army Signal Corps; C. Green, General Electric Company; M. Nichols, Princeton University; J. Van Allan, Applied Physics Laboratory; F. Whipple, Harvard University; G. Megerian, General Electric Company, technical assistant. (I am most grateful to George Megerian who acted as secretary to this activity through its 15-year existence and has both an excellent memory and a complete set of minutes of the meetings.)

the measured direction. Physically, this could be interpreted as the actual location of the source in a coordinate system fixed in a uniformly moving atmosphere.

Some 32 values of temperature and winds for the atmosphere above White Sands were obtained from these first 6 Aerobee firings of 1950 and 1951. At the lower end at 30 km, the fit with the balloon -- radio sonde data was excellent. The temperature peaked at about 270°K at 50 km, falling to 210° at about 80 km. No pronounced seasonal effect in the temperatures was measured. However, the winds showed a strong seasonal effect, being generally westerly in October, November and December, and easterly in June and July. In both seasons velocities up to 90 km/sec in the 50 km altitude region were measured.

The impact of these first results on our understanding of the upper atmosphere is discussed in the concluding section of this paper.

EQUIPMENT

To obtain the basic measurements needed, one employed the complement of equipments illustrated in Figure 1, an artist's conception of the rocket-grenade experiment. Although three different tracking systems for accurate determination of the positions in space of the grenade explosions are shown, one will suffice provided its full capabilities are utilized. At White Sands (1950-53), we used three ballistic cameras (one redundant). This limited the firings to clear nights when the background star fields and explosions were visible. This severe operational limitation was not acceptable for cloudy, stormy Fort Churchill where the radio technique DOVAP was employed. On Guam, the limited logistics possible caused us to go to a combination single ballistic camera (angular measurements) and DOVAP (range measurements). The typical broken cloud structure over Guam caused us some tense moments as we waited for clouds to sweep by so that we could fire through "holes" in the cloud cover.

An important set of basic measurements sometimes not recognized is the geodetic survey required to determine the relative and absolute positions on the sound ranging array and the individual microphones, the tracking-systems equipment and even, in the case of the DOVAP, the launch tower itself. Ballistic cameras had to be located within ±30 sec of latitude and longitude; the relative positions of trackers, launches and sound array within ±0.5 m and the internal positions of the microphones to ±0.2m. Absolute time as accurate as 0.1 sec was required for the star trail exposures. And relative times within the sound ranging array of 0.0005 sec made possible the accurate determination of winds and temperatures. The early 1948-1950 grenade experiments at White Sands were unsuccessful in part because these ground system accuracy requirements were not appreciated.

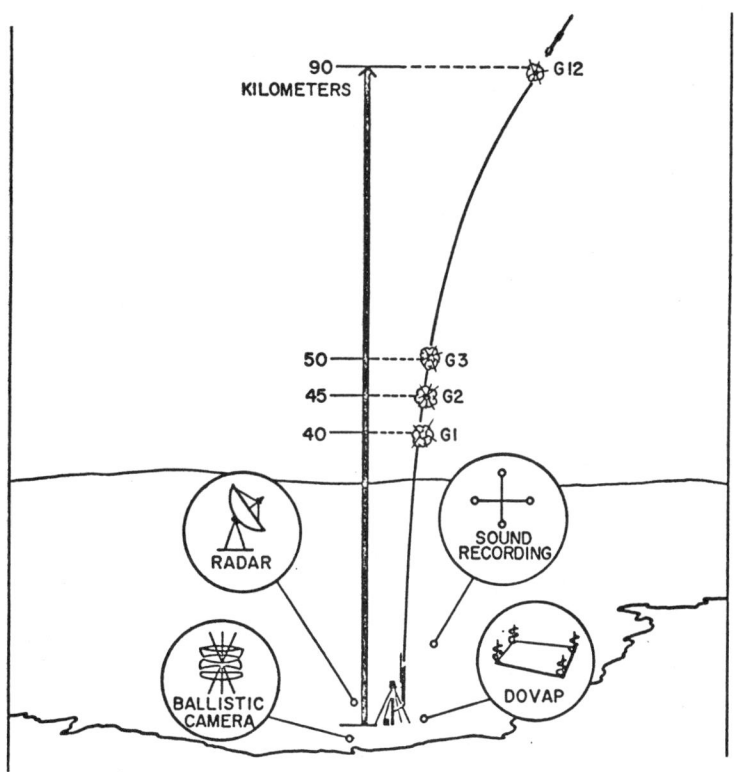

Figure 1 Artist's conception of the rocket-grenade experiment.

METHOD

The basic set of measurements for the rocket-grenade are tabulated in Table I:

Table 1

BASIC MEASUREMENTS FOR ROCKET-GRENADE EXPERIMENT

Times of Explosions, ------------------- $t_{G_1}, \ldots t_{G_n}$

Positions of Explosions, in a coordinate system fixed in origin of sound-ranging array, ------------------------------ $(x,y,z)_{G_1}, \ldots (x,y,z)_{G_n}$

Times of arrival of sound waves at each microphone, -------------------------- $(t_{G_1})_{M_1} \ldots (t_{G_1})_{M_m}$

$$\vdots$$

$$(t_{G_n})_{M_1}, \ldots (t_{G_n})_{M_m}$$

The subscripts G represent the grenade, up to n in number; and M, the microphone up to m in number.

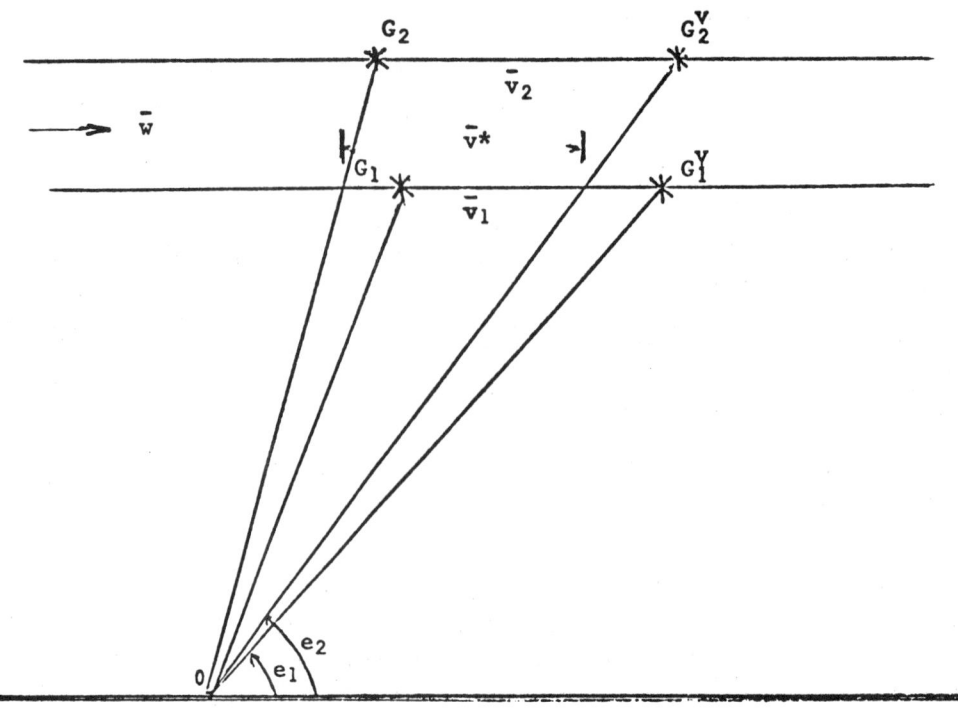

Figure 2 Two-dimensional case for determining wind in the layer between G_1 and G_2.

To calculate the temperatures and winds in the individual layers, we gradually evolved the procedure from the laborious manual calculations of the early papers [3,4] to a much simplified, and more refined technique that made extensive use of a small digital computer [6,7,10,11,12]. The basic principles of the computation are shown in Figure 2 for the two dimensional case. G_1 and G_2 are the actual positions of the grenade explosions and G_1^V and G_2^V are the "virtual sources", the positions from which the sound waves seemed to originate as measured by the angles of arrival of the sound waves at the ground. The calculation proceeds as follows:

$$\bar{v}_2 = \bar{w}_\tau + \bar{v}^* \tag{1}$$

where:

$\bar{v}_2$ is displacement of source of 2nd grenade

$\bar{w}$ is horizontal wind in layer defined by G_1 and G_2

τ is time sound wave spends traveling through the layer

$\bar{v}^*$ is displacement of sound wave from G_2 due to wind field below G_1

The travel time of the sound from G_2 to round is

$$t_2 = \tau + t^* \tag{2}$$

where:

t^* is travel time of sound wave from G_2 spends below G_1.

242

A good approximation is

$$t^* \sin e_2 = t_1 \sin e_1 \tag{3}$$

e_1 and e_2 being the average elevation angles of the sound arrivals from G_1 and G_2.

Since $\bar{v}$ is proportional to t,

$$\bar{v}^* \sin e_2 = \bar{v} \sin e_1 \tag{4}$$

The terms t_1 and t_2 are measured quantities, and v_1 and $\bar{v}_2$ can be calculated from the exact coordinates of the grenade explosions, the temperature and wind field below G_1, and the angles at which the sound waves arrive at the microphone array. These parameters are measured. Thus, the unknowns $\bar{v}^*$, t^*, τ, and $\bar{w}$ can be calculated from equations (1) through (4), and the average wind in the layer between G_1 and G_2 determined.

After determining the wind in the layer, Snell's lay may be used to compute c, the speed of sound in the layer between G_1 and G_2:

$$c \csc e_1 + \bar{w}_\phi = c_0 \csc e_2 \tag{5}$$

where c_0 is the speed of sound at the microphone array, and $\bar{w}_\phi$ is that component of the wind in the layer which acts within the plane of the sound path trajectory from G_2. At the surface of the Earth, the wind is assumed to be zero[*] ; e_1 is the average zenith angle of the sound path from G_2 within the layer between G_1 and G_2, expressed by:

$$\cos e_1 = H/(c\tau) \tag{6}$$

where H is the difference in height between G_1 and G_2. Hence, c can be calculated from [5 and 6]. The temperature T in the layer is related to c by the equation

$$c = [(C_p RT)/(C_v M)]^{1/2} \tag{7}$$

where

R   = universal gas constant

C_p/C_v = ratio of specific heats of air between G_1 and G_2

M   = mean molecular weight of air.

A detailed error analysis [7] demonstrates that the errors in temperature are generally less than 3 deg, and that the wind error is about 5 m/s. The dominant source of error lies in the accuracy with which the arrival of the sound waves at the microphones can be determined.

---

[*]   Firings always occurred when surface winds were negligible.

RESULTS

Variation of Temperature with Latitude and Season

The results reported here comprise the 12 firings at White Sands; 10 firings at Fort Churchill and 9 firings at Guam. Since the Guam firings showed essentially the same result as the White Sands firing, the data from both Guam and White Sands were taken to represent "low latitudes" and the data from Fort Churchill to represent "high latitudes". Even though these were only two points on a latitudinal scale, considerable differences were noted in the structure of the atmosphere between these two points.

The Fort Churchill and White Sands firings were distributed throughout the year, and the firings were conducted at various times of the day; thus, some conclusions were drawn regarding seasonal and diurnal variations.

The results from White Sands and from Guam both showed considerable variation from firing to firing. An analysis of the White Sands firings which were conducted in February, April, June, July, August, September, October, November and December showed no seasonal trend in this variation. This was confirmed by the fact that the 9 Guam firings carried out within the relatively brief period from November 3 to November 25, 1958 also showed appreciable variations in temperature, especially above 50 km. The average temperature profile at Guam, however, agreed very closely with the average temperature profile at White Sands (Figure 1). There was also good agreement between these temperature profiles and those obtained by Groves over Woomera, Australia [8]. The approximate latitudes and longitudes for these sites are: White Sands 32°N, 106°W; Guam 13°N, 144°E; Woomera 31°S, 138°E. The following conclusions were drawn from results:

1. The atmosphere up to 80 km within latitudes of ± 35 degrees of the equator was best described by the standard temperature profile shown in Figure 3. This profile was valid for all seasons of the year.

2. There were deviations from this standard from day to day, but they did not follow a seasonal or latitudinal pattern within this region. These deviations would be small at low altitudes (generally about $\pm 5^{\circ}$K at 30 km) and larger at high altitudes (about $\pm 30^{\circ}$K at 80 km).

At high latitudes the situation was entirely different. The temperatures from five summer firings at Fort Churchill in July and August showed remarkably little scattering, and they were in complete contrast to the temperatures observed in five firings in November, December and January. Although the winter temperatures were consistent from firing to firing, they showed considerably more scattering than the summer firings. The average summer and winter profiles at Fort Churchill were compared to the low-latitude profile in Figure 4. From these it was concluded:

1. In summer the temperature profile at high latitudes was similar to the low-latitude profile up to 45 km. The temperature maximum was about 5° to 10°K higher at Churchill than at low latitudes. At 65 km, high-latitude summer temperatures were about 235°K which was equal to the low-latitude temperature. From 65 to 80 km,

latitudes. At 80 km, high-latitude temperatures were about 25°K below the low-latitude temperatures.

2. In winter the high-latitude temperatures were about 35°K below the summer values at 30 km and about 20°K below at 50 km. This meant that high-latitude winter temperatures were considerably below their low-latitude counterparts up to about 65 km. Between 60 and 65 km there seemed to be a region where temperatures remained roughly the same at all seasons at all latitudes. From 65 km up, winter temperatures at high latitudes increased instead of decreasing. At 80 km they might be as much as 50°K above the temperatures at low latitudes. However, great variability existed in this region in wintertime, and variations of ±35°K from the shown average might occur.

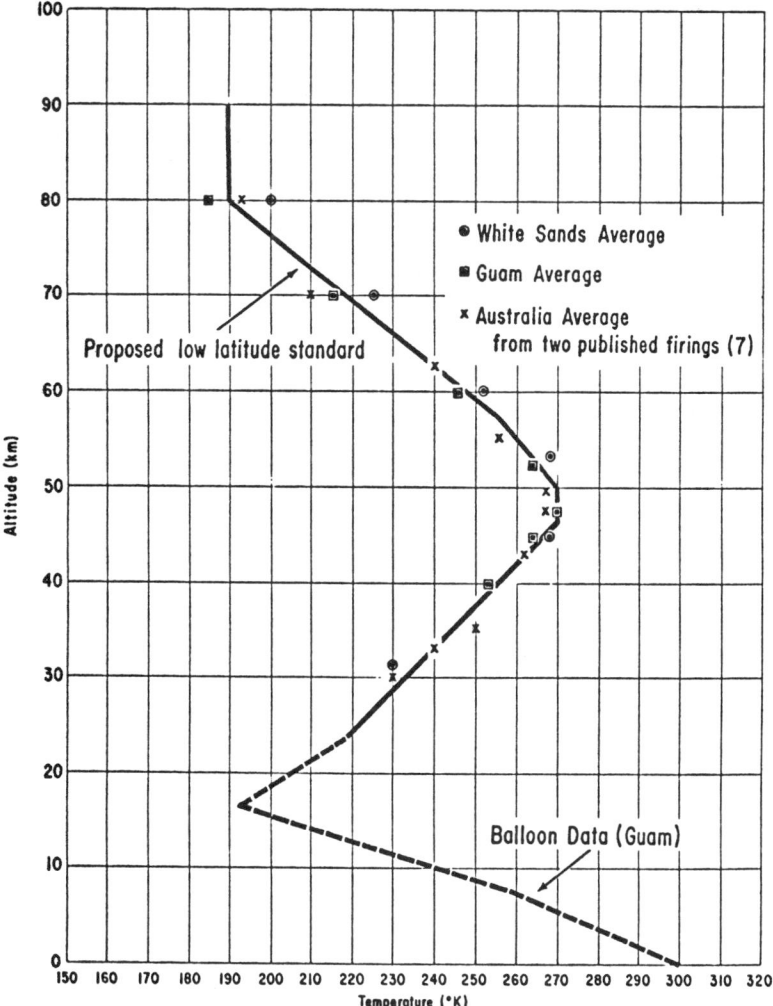

Figure 3 Typical temperature profile for low latitude (30-90 km) atmosphere all year.

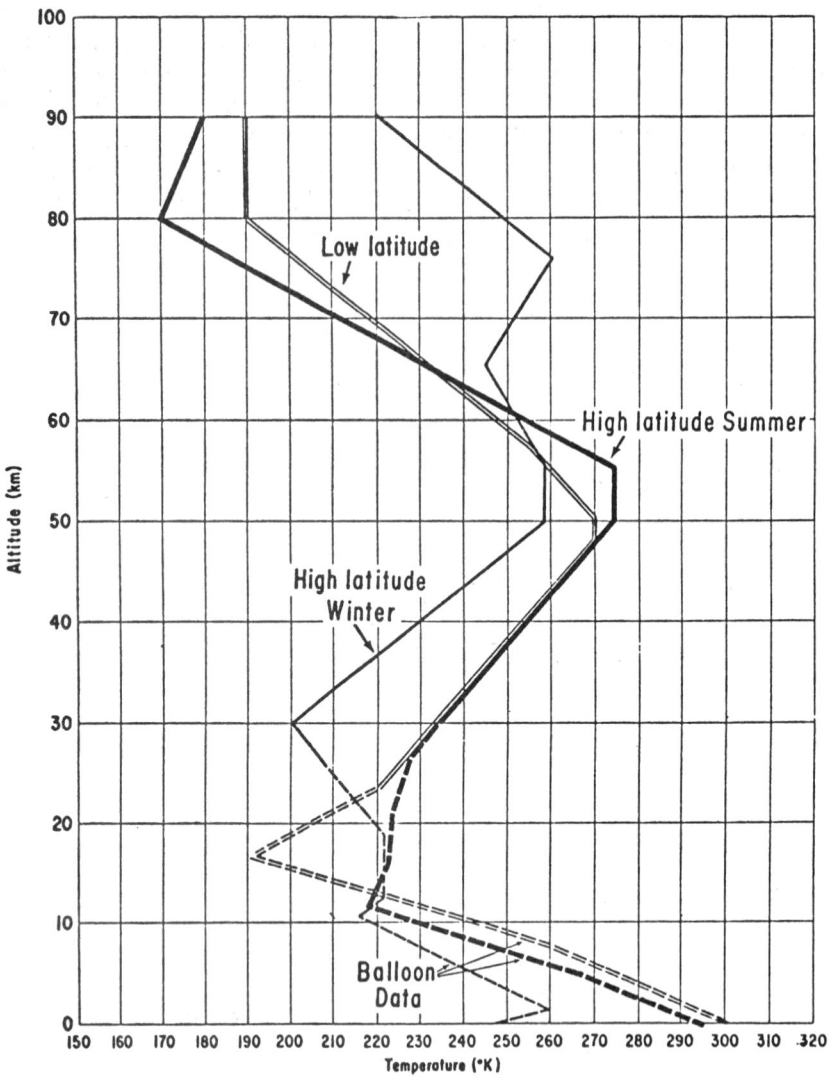

Figure 4 Comparison of temperature profiles for high and low latitude atmospheres (30-90 km).

The variations of temperate with latitude for altitudes of 30, 50, and 80 km in both winter and summer are summarized in Figure 5.

Diurnal Variation of Temperature

The data permitted only a limited evaluation with regard to diurnal variation, since all the low-latitude firings (Guam and White Sands) depended on ballistic camera tracking and were therefore conducted at night. This, incidentally, was also true for the Australian firings reported in [8]. Therefore, the high-latitude data from the Fort Churchill firings were the only ones containing both daytime and nighttime measurements. The only detectable trend was that at 50 km, temperatures were about 5° to 10°K higher at noon than at midnight. This seemed to be true for both summer and winter. No correlation between temperature and time of day could be found at any other altitude; neither was there any indication that temperatures vary with the hour of the night. In particular, the Guam firings, which were spread between sunset and sunrise, were investigated for such trends; the result was negative. However, it was expected that the 5° to 10°K midnight-to-noon variation observed at Fort Churchill also exists at low latitudes.

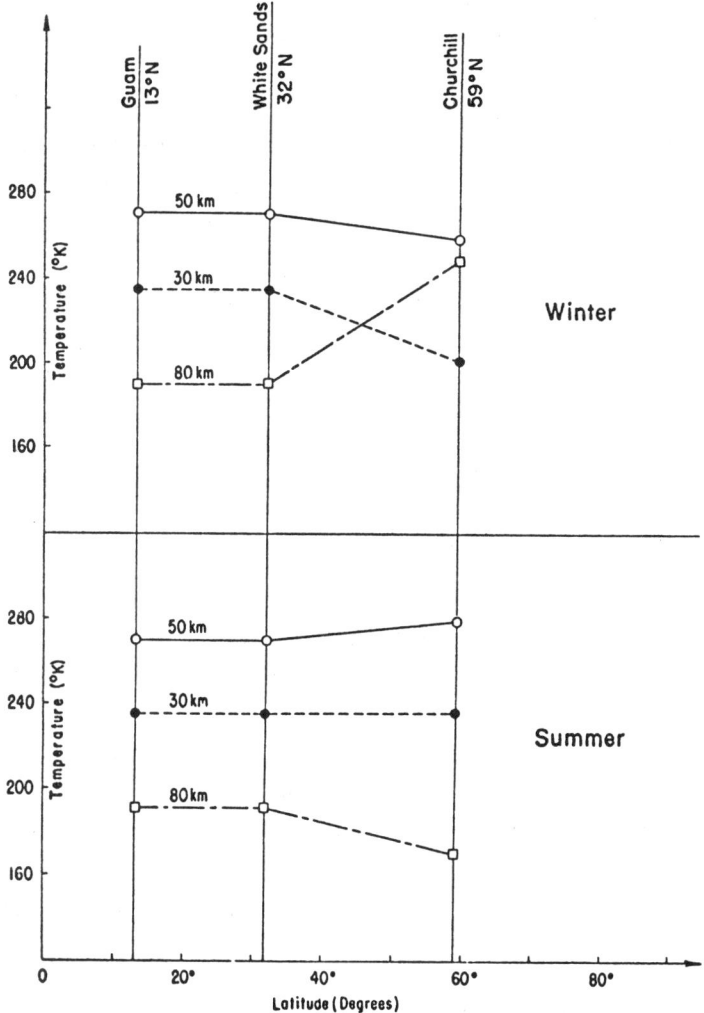

Figure 5 Variation of temperature at 30, 50 and 80 km with season and latitude.

Variation of Wind with Season and Latitude

In contrast to the temperatures, pressures and densities, the winds showed a definite seasonal trend at both high and low latitudes. From 30 to 80 km they were

247

from the west in winter and from the east in summer. The transition between these patterns apparently occurred very rapidly during a few weeks in the spring and fall. The breakdown of westerly circulation at high latitudes in spring was of particular interest, since it was apparently related to the explosive warming observed in the lower stratosphere [10]. A summary of all wind data from the grenade experiments is given in Figure 6.

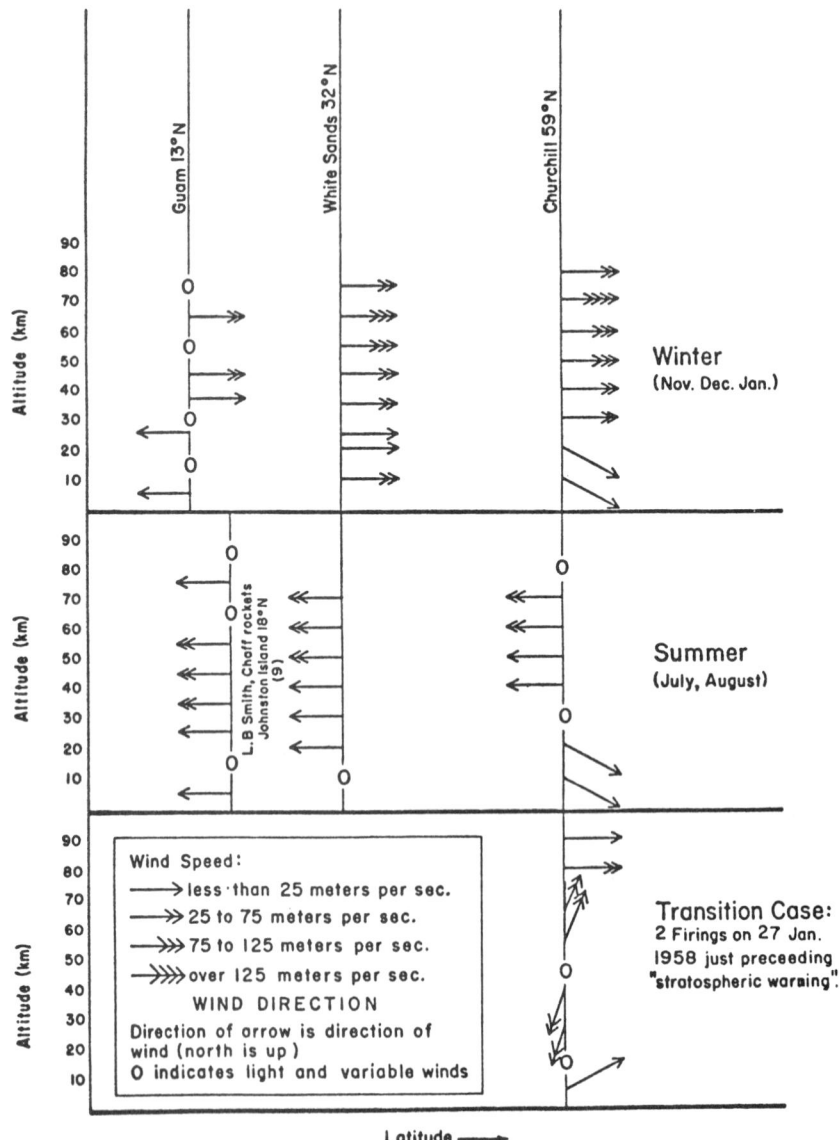

Figure 6   Summary of winds up to 90 km measured at low- and high- latitudes.

A circulation from west to east in winter and east to west in summer followed clearly from the results at Fort Churchill and White Sands. At Guam the data showed that from 30 to 80 km, winds from the west prevailed in November. These data, when compared with rocket-chaff wind measurements taken by Smith [16] over the Central Pacific in the summer of 1958, which showed winds from the east, suggested that the pattern described above holds even at these tropical latitudes. The Australian data by Groves [8] also fit into this pattern.

Generally, at the same latitude the west winds in winter were much stronger than the east winds in summer. They generally increased with altitude up to near 60 km where they reached a maximum. Above 80 km they became variable, indicating a possible reversal in direction. The sharp reversal in wind direction at Guam at 30 km was of particular interest.

Latitudinally, the winds increased toward the pole. Even in November the winds at all altitudes were weak at Guam, but strong at White Sands and extremely strong at Fort Churchill. In the tropics near the altitudes of 20 km and 55 km the weak westerly flow seemed very susceptible to upsets and, sometimes, reversals. In summer the winds at all latitudes, even at Fort Churchill, were much weaker than in winter and from the east.

Undoubtedly, tidal effects on the winds become important above 80 km, but the measurements, especially at these high altitudes, were much too few to allow any further analysis.

It was not possible to derive any diurnal trend in the winds from these measurements. However, it was believed that winds, more than any other parameter in the upper atmosphere, reflected the variations and passages of large-scale meteorological systems, and that these systems sometimes reached high up into the mesosphere.

CONCLUSIONS

The rocket-grenade experiment, once we got it in order, made significant contributions to our understanding of the structure and the dynamics of the atmosphere between 30 and 90 km. Wind field data for this region were practically non-existent prior to the advent of the experiment -- only isolated rocket-borne measurements of smoke trails or puffs were available. There were also a few measurements from the movements of noctilucent clouds and of isolated meteor trails [13]. Those few measurements overlapped the upper end of the rocket-grenade results, i.e., above 70 km, but the data were all consistent -- velocities in the 50 to 100 m/sec range.

The before-and-after-rocket-soundings data on the temperature fields are illustrated in Figure 7 (adapted from [14]).

Data from the anomalous propagation of sound, meteor trails and miscellaneous theoretical calculations had yielded a variety of results, none of which fit in every respect the facts as determined by the rocket soundings of the early 1950's.

In 1952, the Upper Atmosphere Rocket Research Panel, which was the informal coordinating body and information clearing house for the United States sounding rocket program, published the averaged results of the pressure, density and temperature measurements [15]. This Panel atmosphere was a sharp departure from the 1948 NACA Standard Atmosphere, as shown in Figure 7. The temperatures in the 50 km region turned out to be much lower, probably because earlier results, based on the anomalous propagation of sound technique, were not able to factor in the effects of the strong winds in this region. Somehow the earlier models had overlooked or underestimated the implications of the noctilucent clouds; namely, that a deep minimum temperature would be required in the 80-90 km altitude region to maintain a water-ice cloud at those low temperatures.

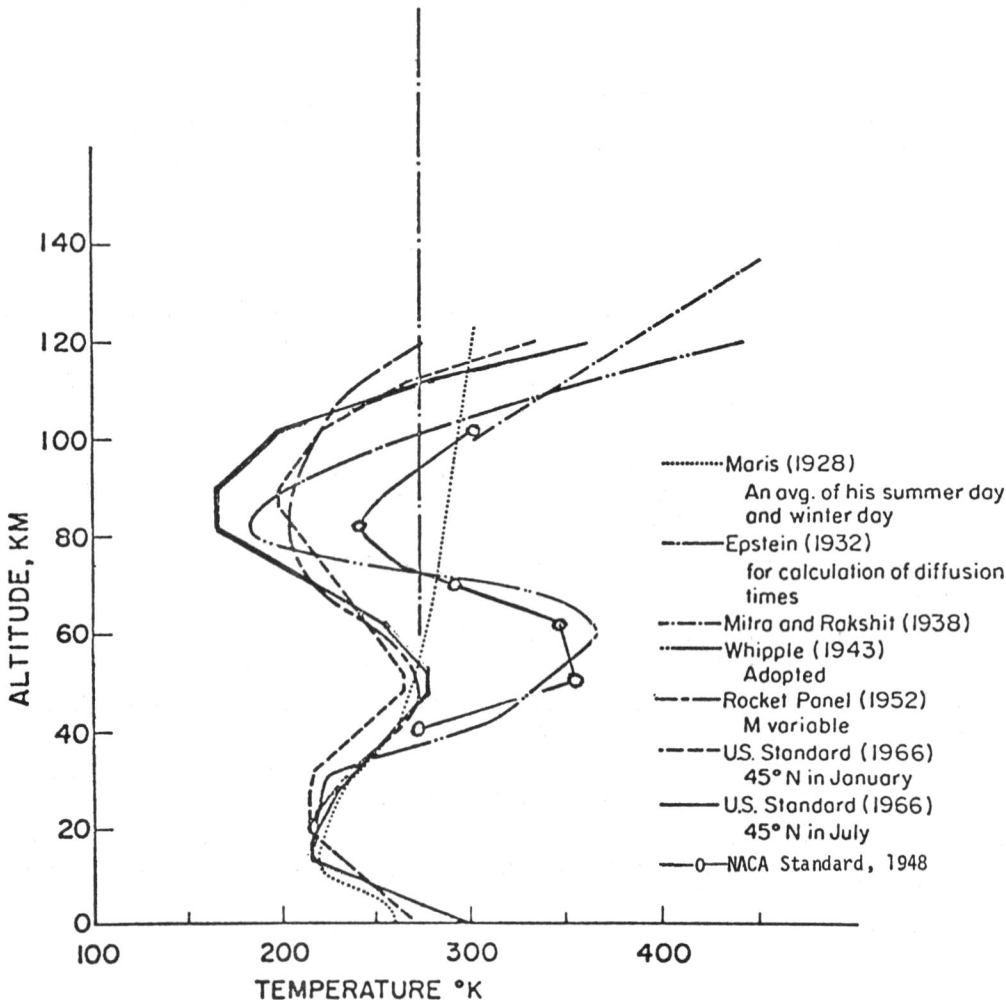

Figure 7 Comparisons of vertical distributions of the atmosphere.

By 1960, we could summarize the results of the rocket-grenade firings as follows:

1. The wind pattern over the entire hemisphere is generally uniform at altitudes between 30 and 80 km, with easterly flow during the summer, westerly during the winter, and sudden reversals between seasons. The wintertime westerly circulation is extremely strong at high latitudes and grows weaker toward the equator. Near the equator sudden disturbances in the established circulation over a limited altitude region (10-15 km) which have been observed by balloons near the 200-mb level also occur at higher altitudes, near 50-60 km.

2. Temperatures, pressures and densities at high latitudes show a strong seasonal variation. Densities in winter are below summer by a factor of two at 60 km and temperatures show a summer-to-winter variation of as much as $+70^\circ$K at 90 km and about minus 20°K at 50 km. No seasonal variation of these parameters can be detected at low latitudes; at all seasons their average is close to the United States Extension to the ICAO standard atmosphere [9].

3. Noticeable diurnal variations in temperatures, pressures, and densities exist at high latitudes. Temperatures near 50 km are 5°-10°K higher at noon than at midnight. Nighttime pressures and densities are therefore somewhat lower than daytime values between 50 and 90 km.

REFERENCES

1. C.M. Cranshaw and M. Keiser, "The Measurement of Temperature at Elevations above 60,000 ft. by Sound Ranging Methods," Evans Signal Laboratory, Belmar, New Jersey, 1945.

2. G. Warnecke and W. Nordberg, "Inferences of Stratospheric and Mesosphere Circulation Systems from Rocket Experiments," from *Space Research V*, Ed, P. Muller, North-Holland Publishing, Co. Amsterdam, 1965.

3. A. Weisner, "The Determination of Temperatures and Winds Above Thirty Kilometer," published in *Rocket Exploration of the Upper Atmosphere*, Edited by R.L.F. Boyd and M.J. Seaton, Pergamon Press, London, 1954.

4. W.G. Stroud, Technical Memo #1570: "Instrumentation of the Rocket-Grenade Experiment," Army Signal Engineering Laboratories, 1954.

5. W.G. Stroud, E. Terhume, et. al., "Instrument of the Rocket-Grenade Experiment for Measuring Atmosphere Temperature and Winds, *Rev. Sci, Instrumentation, 26*, pp 427-432, 1955.

6. W. Nordberg and W. Smith, "A Manual Describing the Rocket-Grenade Experiment," Report X651-63-18, Goddard Space Flight Center, Greenbelt, MD, 1963.

7. W. Nordberg, "A Method of Analysis for the Rocket-Grenade Experiment," U.S. Army Research and Development, Laboratory, Technical Memo, M-1856, Fort Mammouth, New Jersey.

8. G.V. Groves, "Wind and Temperature Results Obtained in Skylark Experiments," Proc. of 1st Internat. Space Sci. Symp., Nice, France, January 1960, published in *Space Research*, ed. by H. Kallman Bijl, Amsterdam: North-Holland Publishing Co., 1960, pp 144-153.

9. R.A. Minzner, W.S. Ripley and T.P. Condon, "U.S. Extension to the ICAO Standard Atmosphere," Washington, U.S. Weather Bureau, 1958.

10. W.G. Stroud, W. Nordberg and W.R. Bandeen, "Rocket-Grenade Measurements of Temperatures and Winds in the Mesosphere over Churchill, Canada," *J. Geophys. Res.* 65(8):2307-2323, August 1960.

11. W.G. Stroud, W. Nordberg and J.R. Walsh, "Atmospheric Temperatures and Winds Between 30 and 80 km," *J. Geophys. Res.* 61(1)45-56, March 1956.

12. W. Nordberg and W.G. Stroud, "Results of the IGY Rocket-Grenade Experiments to Measure Temperatures and Wind above the Island of Guam," *J. Geophys. Res.* 66(2):455-464, February 1961.

13. S.K. Mitra, *The Upper Atmosphere*, The Asiatic Society, Calcutta, 1952.

14. L.M. Jones, "The Structure of the Neutral Upper Atmosphere; Air Samples and Falling Spheres," Paper presented at XXVI Congress, International Astronautical Federation, Lisbon, 21-27 September 1975 (this volume).

15. The Rocket Panel, *Phys. Rev. 88*, pp 1027-1032, December 1952.

16. L.B. Smith, "The Measurement of Winds Between 100,000 and 300,000 ft. by Use of Chaff Rockets," *J. Meteorology* 17(3):296-310, June 1960.

Chapter 17

EARLY FRENCH UPPER ATMOSPHERE RESEARCH USING ROCKETS[*]

A. Vassy[†]

France has been interested in the exploration of the upper atmosphere using rockets since 1946. At that time, the Center of Studies of Self-propelled Projectiles, with a section called "Upper Atmosphere" headed by E. Vassy, was created. A supply of 13 V2s salvaged from Germany was intended for the use by this section. Because of an unhappy chain of circumstances, these V2s did not arrive in France.

Therefore, in March 1949, the Directorate of Studies and Armament Production (Direction des Etudes et Fabrications d'Armament) decided to build a rocket capable of carrying a payload weighing 60 kg to an altitude of 65 km. The implementation of the project was assigned to the Laboratory of Ballistic and Aerodynamic Research (Laboratoire de Recherches Balistiques et Aérodynamiques, LRBA) at Vernon, near Paris. A first shot took place in 1952; then after some improvements, the Veronique missile reached 135 km on 21 February 1954. Experiments could now begin, although it remained necessary to select those that did not require telemetry, which was still unavailable.

It was on 19 October 1954 when the first scientific experiment took place; the missile reached 104 km; it carried a spectrometer with an SFIM recorder to measure the emission spectra as a function of altitude. It was necessary, however, to recover the missile and its still functioning recorder; this was not possible until 1956.

Research with the Véronique missiles then suffered an eclipse, and the French program of rocket research, described by E. Vassy [1] to the 5th International Astronautical Congress (Innsbruck 1954), could not be completed by the International Geophysical Year 1957-58.

In the meantime, some small solid-propellant rockets, of the Monica series, equipped after 1956 with a telemetry device, were launched to carry out pressure measurements; they produced mostly technical results.

---

[*]   Presented at The Ninth IAA History of Astronautics Symposium, Lisbon, Portugal, September 1975.

[†]   Laboratory of Physics and Atmospheric Dynamics, Paris, France.

In 1959, the experiments with Véronique were resumed, although the program still lacked the desired telemetry. As a result, the program was limited to some sodium iodate ejections at altitude -- a program entrusted to Professor J. Blamont. Under this program our team carried out measurements of the Sun's half-light sodium emissions at 3,303 Å and the 5,577 Å line of iodate. These observations took place following the shots of March 1959 and March 1960.

Finally in February 1961, telemetry by then being operational, the 1954 program could start operations with the launching of four Véronique missiles. Under the direction of E. Vassy, three teams worked on scientific experiments:

1. Our laboratory

2. The Ionospheric Institute of Breisach with Professor Rawer

3. The Franco-German Institute of Saint-Louis with Dr. Rossler.

In addition to the measurements of pressure and temperature of the atmosphere, there was also the study of the D Region of the ionosphere with an H.F. spectrometer, the study of the propagation of a long wave, of the sunlight diffused by the atmosphere, and of nocturnal luminescence. For the processing of these data, it was necessary to control the attitude of the rocket; this was achieved by a three-axis gyro-stabilized magnetic sensor and an original method permitting a decrease in the inherent inaccuracies of such sensors.

The program continued with the operations of October 1962 and April 1963. A gamma line spectrometer built by the Atomic Energy Commission was included. As in 1959, the Sun measurements perfected the measurements in rockets.

Eventually, the program described in 1954 was accomplished in 1964 with the launching of a Bélier missile equipped to measure the vertical distribution of ozone above the ceiling of the sounding balloons.

All the scientific equipment used in these programs was conceived and developed in an original way by the several laboratories responsible for the experiments. The coordination of the experiments on each launch fell under the scientific responsibility of E. Vassy or myself depending upon the circumstances. We will now examine quickly the results obtained.

OPERATIONS DURING 1954; RADIOELECTRICAL ABSORPTION BY THE LOWER IONOSPHERE

This experiment was made in collaboration with a team led by K. Rawer [2]. Véronique No. 12, launched on the 19th of October 1954 around noon local time at Hammaguir (31 latitude N, 2 longitude W), carried in its nose cone a spectrometer covering the ranges from 170 to 240 kHz (long waves) and 600-1,000 kHz (medium waves). This spectrometer was connected to a SFIM recorder. The missile reached an altitude of 104 km.

The antenna was a small ferrite rod carrying a resistance coil on the primary circuit. The effective sensitivity of such an antenna was no longer than about 1 cm, but with a sufficiently sensitive receiver, one could receive a great number of broadcasting emissions which were located in the prescribed frequencies. It could be placed in the interior of a missile at the furthest end of the plexiglass nose cone. The ferrite rod was mounted in the direction of the axis of the missile so that a rotation did not influence the antenna pattern.

The primary goal of the experiment was to measure the field of emissions as a function of altitude. The altitude could be identified with the aid of markers that were made each second on the tape of the recorder. The trajectory was observed using optical methods up to an altitude of 31 km and calculated beyond that. The receiver was calibrated in the laboratory.

Of the transcribers recovered after 18 months, only one returned with usable data.

The site of the trial was situated a good distance from the emitting stations. For the medium waves, one had the choice of the two closest stations, eg., Fez (frequency: 701 kHz; distance 380 km) and Rabat I (frequency 610 kHz; distance 520 km), for which the direct line of sight was reached from the altitude of 20 km; the propagation was therefore without any doubt in a direct line between the station and the missile from this altitude. Therefore, these observations could be interpreted without major difficulties. The situation was clearly less favorable for the long wave frequencies. The recorded emissions in this frequency came from Europe, at distances between 2,200 and 3,000 km. Droitwich was chosen (frequency 200 kHz; distance 2,400 km) as a representative of this group of stations outside direct line of sight.

The results (the value of the field at altitude z as a ratio of the measure between the field and the Sun) showed that for each wave there was first of all a slight diminution of the field at a minimum situated between 3 and 6 km; then the field grew and its value overtook that of the Sun.

For the medium waves, the augmentation subsisted up to about 50 km where the values obtained exceeded by approximately 30 dB the value of the Sun. Between 45 and 72 km in altitude the value of the field remained almost constant. Above 72 km the intensity diminished very rapidly until 84 km. After 84 km, the field was too weak to record.

For the long waves, the measuring device was unfortunately useless between 10 and 40 km; at 43 km the value of the field was already slightly inferior to that of the Sun. The field remained more or less constant between 43 and 66 km, it then diminished rapidly between 66 and 77 km where the minimum intensity detectable was reached.

The results, which now have only a historic value, were interpreted correctly, but the experiment served above all as a bench mark for the subsequent shots.

OPERATIONS DURING 1956, 1957, 1959: SMALL ROCKETS

These programs were made with the little rockets of the Monica series, launched from the Levant Isle (43 latitude S, 6 longitude E); apart from technological goals, these rockets carried gauges developed in the laboratory and which measured the temperature and pressure [3]; the results were valuable for the success of Israel's [4].

OPERATIONS DURING 1959 AND 1960: SODIUM EJECTIONS AND SOLAR OBSERVATIONS

In the absence of telemetry, Blamont carried out experiments by ejecting sodium at a high altitude -- an experiment conceived by D.R. Bates. Our program consisted of carrying out observations from the Sun on the twilight and nocturnal luminescence.

In 1959, the ejections consisted of sodium clouds. It was known that the luminosity, visible from the Sun, presented in the first place the doublet D1, D2 (5,893 A). Cooper, Manring, and Bedinger had researched the presence of the doublet 3,303 (4P-3S); they only found a very weak emission, after the first trial had given a negative result. The Véronique rockets were launched at Hammaguir on 10 March 1959 at 18.40 (T.U. = GMT), about 20 min after sunset and on the 12 March at 5.44 (GMT), about 25 min before sunrise [5]. We used an observation post at Colomb-Béchar, at a distance of 120 km from the launch site, and we tried to observe the ultraviolet ray with the aid of an ultraviolet optical spectrograph. We used some sensitive plates above 6,800 Angstrom in the near ultraviolet; that is, we obtained the yellow line and ultraviolet area on the same spectrum, which permitted an evaluation of the relative intensities of the two lines.

A single spectrum was obtained at the time of each launch: on 10 March at twilight with 30 min of exposure and on 12 March at dawn with 15 min of exposure.

Concerning the first, there was no trace of the 3,303 line. For the second, the presence of this line is unquestionable even though the doublet 5,893 was much less intense than it was on 10 March. We add that in the spectrum of 12 March, ray 3,303 was present only in one part of the upper spectrum, which shows that the excitation of this doublet is produced only in a strictly localized zone.

It appears, therefore, that the 3,303 line would be emitted much easier at dawn than at twilight, which explains why the Manring team did not observe the ultraviolet ray in the evening and night launches, and only barely observed it in the morning shot. We maintain that the yellow lines and the ultraviolet lines neither co-exist nor co-vary. It should be well understood that the comparable spectra made on the days following the shots, at the same hour and looking in the same direction, did not reveal the existence of the line.

In 1960, our attention turned to green ray 5,577 normally present in the nocturnal luminescence. We ejected a combination of sodium and potassium and, using a Perot-Fabry interferometer, observed the profile of the green ray in the ejection zone [6]. A launch took place on 2 March. One hr and 30 min after the ejection we observed some very large and asymmetrical rings; 3 hr after the shot, the rings became symmetrical. One could hardly maintain that this occurred because of a widening caused by the Doppler-Fizeau since this happened at very high speeds.

OPERATIONS DURING 1961, 1962, AND 1963

Not until 1961 did the 1954 program begin to develop with the use of an operational telemetry. In the meantime, the measuring devices, entirely developed in the laboratories of the various teams, were ready to be deployed.

We also developed a method of plotting the altitude of the rocket [7], which was known to be indispensable to interpret certain results. Inspired by the American example, we used three magnetometers (made in the U.S.A.) arranged according to an orthogonal trihedral directly connected to the rocket, one axis lying parallel to the axis of rotation of the missile. The fixed trihedral of reference was tied to the Earth. The sensors gave a signal that depended on the influence of the Earth's magnetic field on the axis of their resistance coils; the sensor changed its position within a more or less constant field, the signal varied with the cosine of the angle of the field and of the resistance coil.

If one writes out the system of equations defining the orientation of the rocket by its three Euler angles, one immediately perceives that there is an indetermination [inexactitude]. Several authors have raised this indetermination suggesting an auxiliary sensor, perhaps an optical one. We preferred another method; we made the calculation closer and closer from the instant zero thanks to the derivation, the Euler angles at the zero instant being known by a measurement of the orientation of the missile at the launch site before the firing takes place.

The calculation is, of course, a little laborious. It is simplified as soon as the rocket is in free flight (before the end of propulsion). The determined attitudes, therefore, are revealed as correct; in effect, one has at his disposal several cross-checks thanks to the scientific sensors placed in the missile [8]. During these three operations, we achieved a successful shot of the 11th Véronique at Hammaguir, which permitted us to discover different elements characterizing the atmosphere. Let us summarize the results.

Propagation of Kilometer Waves at Altitude

The measurements using the transmitter of Ste. Assise have shown that during the day the value of the field of the transmitter was slightly superior to the value at night for the same altitude.

Pressure and Temperature of the Upper Atmosphere

The gauge developed by Israel, automatically compensating for temperature variations in the wall of the missile, permitted a profile measurement of temperature with altitude. The 1961 shots showed an important increase in temperature augmentation of the total density of ozone in the atmosphere, the density which was measured from the Sun to the field of launch.

Vertical Distribution of Aerosols

In collaboration with Rossler, we used an instrument to measure the sunlight diffused by the atmosphere to determine the content of aerosols [8]. We observed a minimum at the altitude of the tropopause, followed by a significant maximum toward 25 km.

Nocturnal Luminescence

The measurements designed to measure the altitude of the layer transmitting the green ray of 5,577 provided an unexpected result which one could interpret as indicating the existence of an important layer of dust between 75 and 125 km [10]. The origin of this important quantity of dust at this altitude has not been determined with any certitude; the dust could be either meteoric or volcanic.

OPERATIONS DURING 1964 -- VERTICAL DISTRIBUTION OF THE OZONE

Finally in 1964, the last project announced in the 1954 program made its debut. On 10 November 1964 at the Levant Isle, a Bélier rocket was fired with a device for measuring the vertical distribution of atmospheric ozone [11]; there were also sensors in the rocket to measure attitude and pressure. This rocket rose to 68 km.

The ozonometer, as conceived in the laboratory, was evidently an apparatus measuring ozone by absorption, the Sun being the source used. It functioned during ascent, the period of the flight when the nose is directed upward, and did not require ejection. Data were collected by telemetry during the course of the flight. Aboard was a photometer containing a photomultiplier sensitive between 2,200 and 3,800 Å (maximum at 2,900 Å) and three interferential filters isolating the narrow spectral bands centered on 2,735, 3,095, and 3,450 Å; the filters, mounted on a turning disc, filed past the receiver. A quartz isotope diffuser collected the sunlight.

The results have been studied by Bancarel [12]. They show a distribution which is not conventional; it presents a double maximum at 20 and 25 km; the results obtained toward these altitudes fit together well with those of a radio-sondage ozone made 3 hr before the launch. Above 40 km, the concentrations obtained are close to those obtained in 1949 by the U.S. Naval Research Laboratory, but we should note that the ratio of the mixture is not constant; it diminishes with altitude, between 10 and 20 μ g/g around 35 km falling to 5 μ g/g at 50 km.

CONCLUSION

In conclusion, these are but our team's first steps in the research using rockets. Because of delays in technical methods, ours was not a pioneer effort; but we attempted to work in the area that we had studied previously in the laboratory, using the means available, in order to perfect the data we acquired; and we sought to develop new methods and instruments in order to make an original contribution to space research concerning the upper atmosphere.

BIBLIOGRAPHY

1. E. Vassy, V. Internat. Astronautischen Kongress, Innsbruck 1954, in *Auftrage* der Öesterreischischen Gesellschaft für Weltraumforschung (Wien, F. Hecht, 1954), p. 221.

2. H. Mende, K. Rawer, E. Vassy, Absorption radioélectrique par la basse ionosphère mesurée à bord d'une fusée, *Annales de Géophysique*, vol. 13, p. 231 (1957).

3. E. Vassy, *Sounding rockets* (MacGraw Hill 1959), p. 252.

4. G. Israel, Monomètre thermique utilisable à bord de fusées depuis le sol jusqu'à 90 km, *Comptes Rendus Acad. Sc. Paris*, Vol. 251, p. 1,892 (1960).

5. A. Vassy et E. Vassy, Présence de la raie 3,303 Å dans le spectre d'émission de nuages artificiels de sodium, *Comptes Rendus Acad. Sc. Paris*, Vol. 248, p. 2,235 (1959).

6. M. Perrin et A. Vassy, Etude de la raie verte

7. G. Israel, M. Kiveliovitch et A. Vassy, Restitution de l'attitude d'une fusée au cours de son vol, *Comptes Rendus Acad. Sc. Paris*, Vol. 253, p. 2,317 (1961).

8. G. Israel, et A. Vassy, Résultats concernant l'attitude d'une fusée Véronique obtenus au moyen de capteurs magnétiques, *Astronautica Acta*, vol. 8, p. 264 (1962).

9. F. Rossler et E. Vassy, *Comptes Rendus Acad. Sc. Paris*, Vol. 254, p. 2,041 (1962).

10. A. Vassy, Mesure de la luminescence nocturne en fusée; influence de aérosols, *Comptes Rendus Acad. Sc. Paris*, Vol. 260, p. 1,712 (1965).

11. A. Vassy, J.P. Bancarel et P. Perrot, Résultats d'une expérience en fusée Bélier; répartition verticale de l'ozone, de la pression et de la température, *La Météorologie*, p. 13 (1967).

12. J.P. Bancarel, Contributions à l'étude de la répartition verticale de l'ozone atmosphérique, Thèse de Dr. d'Etat, Paris (1969).

Chapter 18

DEVELOPMENT OF THE FIRST AUTOMATIC STATIONS FOR LUNAR FLIGHT IN THE USSR[*]

G. Yu. Maximov and Yu. A. Matusevich[†]

The first successes of Soviet cosmonautics are inseparably bound with the study of the Moon. And this is not by chance, for the nature and structure of our celestial satellite, despite numerous investigations, is still hidden in riddles. One of these riddles, which has long attracted attention and has been the reason for many, sometimes quite fantastic, hypotheses, was bound with the structure of the invisible far side of the lunar surface. The final elucidation of this question became possible only with the realization of space flight, the dreams of which were transformed into reality at the turn of our century due to the work of the great K.E. Tsiolkovsky and other founders of cosmonautics.

The idea of rocket flight around the Moon and photographing its other side was expressed as far back as the 1920s. The possibility of carrying out this experiment was mentioned by R. Goddard [4, p. 415; 7], F. Tsander [2, p. 57], F. von Hoefft [6], H. Hein [8], and others. They suggested the launching around the Moon of small rockets, equipped with cameras, with subsequent return of the rockets to the Earth.

According to the projections of these pioneering scientists, the angular orientation and flight control of these rockets were to be implemented by means of a gyroscopic control system supplemented, according to Goddard, with correction devices in the form of inertial and optical appliances. However, the above projects were received with skepticism by their contemporaries, including specialists [5, pp. 170-171], who realized that the state of development of rockets and automatic control systems did not, at that time, permit one to consider seriously the reality of circumlunar flight.

For a successful accomplishment of such flight around the Moon and of photographing its surface it was necessary to solve the following problems:

1.   Select an optimum flight path and then launch the rocket at a calculated time.

---

[*]   Presented at The Ninth IAA History of Astronautics Symposium, Lisbon, Portugal, September 1975.

[†]   Committee of the Soviet National Association of Natural Science and Technology Historians, USSR Academy of Sciences, Moscow, USSR.

2. Impart escape velocity to the spacecraft, required for reaching the general vicinity of the Moon.

3. Ensure the required spacecraft orientation and optical axis of the photographic equipment during flight.

4. Develop the necessary reserves of power aboard the spacecraft.

5. Photograph the lunar surface.

6. Transmit to the Earth the results of photography.

Beginning in the middle 1940s, rocket developments in the Soviet Union were developing at a swift rate. In 1948, the first Soviet controllable ballistic rocket R-1 was launched; it was developed in the Design Bureau under S.P. Korolev's supervision [3]. In 1957 the USSR had constructed a multistage intercontinental ballistic missile, capable of reaching any area of the globe. Having constructed this rocket, on 4 October 1957, the Soviet Union was able, for the first time in the history of mankind, to launch an artificial Earth satellite. The subsequent launchings of the second and third Earth satellites in 1957-58 clearly demonstrated the power of Soviet rocket technology and its ability to ensure space launchings.

The next stage in the development of the Soviet space program was accompanied by a series of Moon missions undertaken by the automatic space stations. The first such station, Luna 1, was launched on 2 January 1959. After the flight in the vicinity of the Moon it became an artificial planet of the solar system. Luna-2, launched a few months later (on 14 September 1959) for the first time, reached our celestial satellite and delivered to its surface a pennant with the State Emblem of the Soviet Union.

The construction of Luna 1 and Luna 2 involved spherical hermetically sealed containers 0.8 m in diameter. Arranged inside each container were the radio-telemetry system, power supply accessories, electronic blocks of scientific instruments, a fan for gas mixing and heat removal from transmitter to container machines. Outside the container antennas, scientific instrument sensors and a special pole, were set up. At the end of the pole a magnetometer sensor was located.

In contrast to the first two Soviet Lunas, the third automatic station Luna 3, was somewhat different in construction. It was launched on 4 October 1959, exactly 2 years after the launching of the first artificial Earth satellite by the USSR. On 7 October 1959, photographs were taken of the other side of the Moon by Luna 3, resulting in the enrichment of science by most valuable information for all mankind. The successful carrying out of such an outstanding experiment, a triumph of Soviet space science, became possible due to creative coordination of scientists and engineers of various specialties who managed to construct, within quite a short time, a unique automatic control system of the station's orientation during flight, to develop a single power supply system for the instruments aboard, to solve the problem of selecting an optimum flight path, photographing the other side of the Moon, and transmitting the survey results to the Earth.

The flight path of Luna 3 is shown in Figure 1. The specific feature of this trajectory was the fact that the lunar gravity field was used for its accomplishment.

The return of the station to the Earth after the flight around the Moon took place from the side of the northern hemisphere. As a result of the gravity maneuver, the orbit was close to elliptical with an apogee of about 480,000 km and a perigee of about 47,500 km.

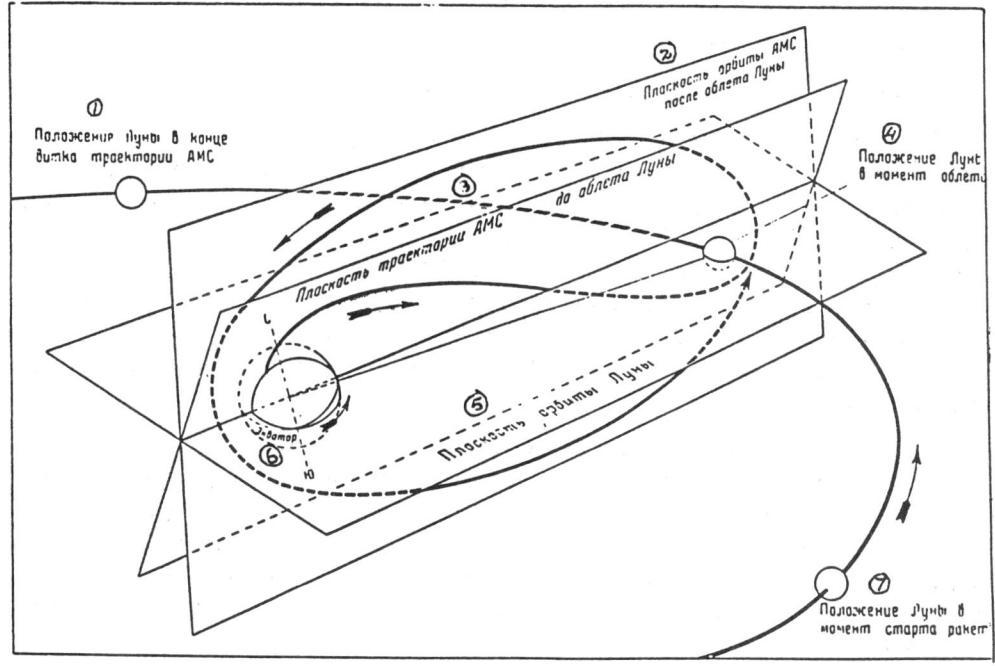

Figure 1 Diagram of flight path of the automatic interplanetary system. (1) Position of Moon at end of trajectory loop of automatic interplanetary station (AMS); (2) Plane of AMS orbit after circumlunar flight; (3) AMS trajectory plane prior to circumlunar flight; (4) Position of Moon during flight around it; (5) Plane of Moon's orbit; (6) Equator; (7) Position of Moon at moment of launch of AMS from Earth.

The solution of such problems as the photographing of the lunar surface and transmission of results to the Earth was predetermined by the vigorous development of the radio-technology and radio transmissions to great distances. The photographing of the Moon from the automatic space station required solving a multiplicity of technical problems connected with selection of exposure conditions, automatic processing of the film, construction of an illuminator of required clarity and strength, etc. All this involved difficulties.

Of these, the most complex and important was the development of the automatic control system to assure the station's orientation during the flight. This system, which was the beginning of the development of spacecraft control systems in the USSR, was devised under the supervision of B.V. Raushenbakh, a member of the USSR Academy of Sciences. Academicians M.V. Keldysh and S.P. Korolev were highly interested, due to the importance and the novelty of the problems, and participated in the construction of the orientation system for Luna 3. In evaluating the results of the work done in this sphere, the fact should be kept in mind that Luna 3's orientation control system was the world's first automatic control system housed in a spacecraft. There was no previous experience whatsoever, in constructing this type of system so everything had to start practically from zero. Nevertheless, Soviet specialists brilliantly resolved this problem.

Luna 3's orientation control system operated on the basis of a two-stage procedure, with the orientation control of the station's movement around the Moon consisting of several stages. Initially, on command from the Earth, the station was oriented toward the Sun. The command was given at the moment, when the Earth, the Moon, the station and the Sun were approximately on the same straight line. In this case, the station was naturally on the other side of the Moon.

For orienting toward the Sun, four optical Sun pickups were arranged at the bottom of the station. With the appearance of a signal at the output of any one of these there was automatic cessation of the station's search rotation, which prior to this was provided by feeding minor displacement to one of the angular movement pickups set up on three reciprocally perpendicular axes and designed for dampening the station's oscillations about its center of mass. The command for search rotation was given also by getting the Sun into the vision field of any of the four pickups (arranged around the illuminator in the nose cone of the station). At the moment of opening the lid of the illuminator the Moon was in the vision field of the lunar pickup. Thereafter, the power supply from the solar pickups was automatically cut off and the station operated in the regimen of lunar orientation.

At a certain precalculated moment the lunar surface was photographed from aboard the station, oriented in this way was by means of a camera. The direction of the optical axis of this camera coincided with the orientation axis of the lunar pickup, which was rigidly fixed to the station's body.

The specific feature of this orientation system was the fact that it operated on a relay principle: the controlling signals, formed by the position and angular movement pickups, were changed in steps, and the orientation jets operated only in conditions of constant thrust. These initial premises were dictated, on one hand, by rigid limitations for the consumption of working fuel in the process of orientation, and on the other by the specifics of space flight. It was economically expedient to expand to some extent the nonsensitivity zone of the pickups (but only up to certain limits, determined by the requirements of the orientation accuracy) and to implement the station's orientation within a certain tolerance zone of the station's angular deviations.

For the same reason, in order to ensure the highest efficiency of the controlling devices with a minimum consumption of fuel, it was decided to assemble discrete logic elements of the computing and transforming block in Luna 3's orientation control system. The orientation jets were estimated to operate in three sets of conditions: (1) in continuous thrust condition, (2) in impulse condition with invariable frequency and duration, and (3) in non-thrust condition. The cut-in of each of these sets of conditions corresponded to certain combinations in the reading of angle and angular movement pickups. Moreover, the direction of correction impulses depended on the sign of deviations arising in the systems.

The fact that the world's first automatic control system of spacecraft orientation, set up in Luna 3 was of a relay type with logic and transforming arrangement, indicates that the development of the cosmic automatic control systems (SAU) was from the start developed in its own way, on the basis of principles, which were not extensively used in aviation and rocketry where use was mainly made of analog automatic control systems, which reduce nonlinearity and auto-oscillations to a minimum.

The fuel for the orientation jets of Luna 3 was compressed gaseous nitrogen, which was contained in a special cylinder.

There were two ways to ensure the required amount of power on board the station:

1. Use storage batteries of high capacity, capable of generating, without recharging, electric energy throughout the flight.

2. Supplement the power reserves on board during flight, which could be obtained by means of solar batteries.

The last variant seemed to be preferable as it enabled the total weight of the station to be reduced. However, for the practical realization of a supply system on the basis of solar batteries the way had to be found for arranging these batteries on the spacecraft. As pointed out above, the time of the oriented flight of the station was less than one hour, which was a lot less than the time planned for its functioning. A certain amount of torsion after the completion of orientation could not guarantee that the station would keep its prescribed position in relation to the Sun throughout the whole flight. Therefore, the designers of the station had to construct the so-called omni-directional solar battery, which at random position of the station in relation to the Sun would ensure sufficient charge of the storage batteries and continuous operation of radio receivers and scientific instruments.

Prior to the launching of Luna 3, it was necessary to make a final checkout of all calculations. To enhance the reliability of the orientation system, the main stages of the station's flight were reconstructed under laboratory conditions. For this purpose, a special test bed was constructed on which the orientation control system with actual Sun and Moon pickups and photo-camera was being perfected. The platform, imitating the controllable object (i.e. the station), was suspended on a multistrand suspension with considerable length of strands. The bed also included a follow-up system, which turned the top point of the strand's suspension in accordance with the course of the platform. The strands were never twisted, thus making visible the absence of moments of external forces.

The last stage of the tests was the playback of all operations logic of the control system during the circumlunar flight, including the photographing of the lunar surface with the orientation of the station at the Moon simulator. The photographs, obtained during this test by multiple working of the camera shutter with the cutoff winding of the film, indicated high precision in performance of the orientation control system.

In conclusion, it is noted that further development of space technology has confirmed the correctness of the main principles employed in the construction of the Luna 3 automatic station. In particular, attention is drawn to solar batteries, which as power generators have found a firm place among the spacecraft's on-board equipment for various purposes; the relay systems of orientation control, now more widely used in the investigation of space; and the two-stage operational procedure of Luna 3's orientation control system, which was subsequently adopted for later space flight endeavors.

BIBLIOGRAPHY

1. Kosmonavtika. Malen'kaya entsiklopediya (Astronautics. A small encyclopedia). Moskva, 1970.

2. F.A. Tsander. Iz nauchnogo naslediya (From the scientific legacy). Moskva, 1967,

3. "Iz istorii aviatsii i kosmonavtiki" (From the history of aviation and astronautics), vyp. 19, Moskva, 1973, pp. 89-93.

4. R.H. Goddard. Report to Smithsonian Institution concerning further developments of the rocket method of investigating space. -- In the book "The papers of Robert H. Goddard", N.-Y., vol. 1, 1970, pp. 413-430.

5. R. Esnault-Pelterie. L'astronautique. Paris, 1930.

6. F. von Hoefft. Die Eroberung des Weltalls. -- "Die Rakete", 1928.

7. "Scientific American", 26 February 1921.

8. H. Hein. Der Schuss in den Weltraum. -- *Kosmos,* Stuttgart, 1925, 22 Jahrgang, H. 5, SS. 145-150.

Part V
PIONEERS OF ROCKETRY AND ASTRONAUTICS

Chapter 19

KEPLER'S "THE DREAM, OR LUNAR ASTRONOMY" AS A PREDECESSOR OF SPACE RESEARCH[*]

Z. Horsky[†]

It is well known that the foundations of a scientific theory about the movement of bodies in space were laid by Isaac Newton. They are as old as the law of gravitation published in 1687 in his famous work *Philosophiae naturalis principia mathematica*. Already in this work we can read a clear and correct description of the conditions under which a body with a given imparted initial speed in a given direction would start orbiting the Earth or would leave the Earth forever [1]. In a rough simplification, it is possible to conceive of all the development of cosmonautics after Newton as a search for conditions of how to reach these speeds and how to ensure that a spaceship survives the physical conditions of passing through the atmosphere and extraterrestrial space, conditions generously ignored by Newton in his considerations.

It follows from the fact that the theory of gravitation created a scientific basis for a future active space research, that predecessors of this research have to be looked for among those scientists who, before Newton, had approached the wording of the gravitational law. And among them the most successful was precisely Johannes Kepler who worked out in Prague his "axioms of a true science about gravitation". They are contained in the introduction to his basic work *Astronomia nova* published in 1609 [2] where, as is well-known, he formulated on the basis of Tycho Brahe's and his own observations the first two laws of the movement of planets, i.e., of those laws whose application is a daily bread of the present-day space researcher. We can only regret that Kepler himself never returned at a later time to the ideas forming the content of the "axioms of the true science about gravitation" and preferred to orient his later research in a different way.

Presumably, it was not a mere chance that at a time when these "axioms" were worded, Kepler intensely examined the idea of reaching another space body, specifically the Moon. We can have an idea about the extent of his obsession with this possibility when reading his work *Dissertatio cum nuncio sidereo* from 1610. In the form of a long letter, Kepler answers Galileo and reacts to his work from the

---

[*] Presented at The Eleventh IAA History of Astronautics Symposium, Prague, Czechoslovakia, September 1977.

[†] Astronomical Institute of the Czechoslovak Academy of Sciences, Prague, Czechoslovakia.

same year *Sidereus nuncius*. Kepler writes Galileo from Prague: "Provide us with ships or veils adapted to the celestial atmosphere -- and people will be found who will not be taken aback by these distances. We might say that the brave ones to undertake this voyage are waiting already. And so, Galileo, you are going to found the astronomy of Jupiter and I myself that of the Moon [3]." Kepler calls Galileo founder of Jupiter's astronomy, because Galileo in his Stellar Messenger reports the discovery of Jupiter's four large satellites. And he considers himself -- not by mere chance -- to be a founder of lunar astronomy, since already at that time he had finished the manuscript known under the title *Somnium sive de astronomia lunari (The Dream, or Lunar Astronomy)*.

And it is exactly this work by Kepler that represents the center of interest of our paper. In this work we can perceive in the most distinct way Kepler as a precursor of space research. In recent research in the field of the history of literature, this work has not been ignored. Studies evaluating the science fiction type of literature and among them especially those dealing with imaginary voyages to the Moon had always to take into consideration this work by Kepler, which is very strong both from the point of view of strictly literary values and from the point of view of its content. Another reason why the authors of these studies have to take Kepler's work into consideration is the fact that one of the best known and most popular works of this type, *The Voyage to the Moon* by Cyrano de Bergerac, is partially and consciously influenced by Kepler's *Dream*. At the same time these studies had always to establish quite a particular position of the *Dream*, the impossibility to classify it within this or that developmental trend of this or that type of literature. But even in Kepler's life work itself the *Dream* and its nature represent a total exception [4].

What is the content and the structure of Kepler's *Dream*? Our knowledge is based on the Latin printed edition published only four years after the death of the author by his son Ludwig Kepler (1634) [5]. The original manuscript was lost, unfortunately. It appears from the published work that it was elaborated in two different stages and that, in fact, it had never been completely finished by the author. Recently, a detailed analysis of the structure of this work was carried out and the history of its origin examined by Professor Edward Rosen, who accompanied his English translation of the *Dream* with a detailed commentary [6]. Many aspects of Rosen's research will serve as a basis for what follows.

Rosen distinguishes three stages in the birth of the work. In the text of the *Dream* itself only two stages are apparent. The first one represents only about one-fourth of the total size forms the essence and the proper text of the *Dream*. It was written in Prague as early as 1608/9. The rest, originating much later, consists of long comments regarding the basic text.

The basic text itself consists again of two quite distinct parts. The first part is pure literary fiction. Kepler begins by references to his time. The dispute from 1608 between the Emperor Rudolf II and his brother the Archduke Matthias, was commented on by the Prague public and compared with examples from the history of Bohemia. Under the impact of these events Kepler also began to study Czech history and was attracted by the fate of the princess Libusha who excelled in the art of witchcraft.

Once, when reading a book, Kepler fell asleep -- and here the fiction part of the narration begins -- and saw himself playing the role of a certain Duracotus. His mother was a witch and also a healing woman named Fiolxhilda. In the figure of Duracotus we can distinguish clearly the person of Kepler himself as well as in the old healing woman his mother. Let us, however, follow only the main elements of the story.

Fiolxhilda, angry with her son, who once interrupted her witchcraft due to his unfortunate curiosity, sells him to the naval service. By accident Duracotus gets to the Danish island of Hven where Tycho Brahe lives. For several years, he studies astronomy under the master's guidance. Even this detail reveals the autobiographical details of Kepler's explanation. After five years, Duracotus returns to his mother who arranges for him a voyage to the Moon. The voyage could take place only thanks to the witchcraft of the mother, to her capacity to call the demons from Levania, a name designating the Moon. The transfer of a human body from the Earth to the Moon closes the fantastic part of the story.

We can find herein a number of rational observations: Kepler foresees the dangerous effects of the solar radiation on a human body outside the atmosphere (he believes that the atmosphere reaches only to the highest peaks of the mountains), and that is why the whole voyage had to take place during the time of the Moon's eclipse, when it is necessary to move inside the shadow of the Earth. Kepler also reckons with breathing difficulties outside the atmospheric envelope of the Earth. To a certain extent he seems to guess even the difficulties connected with overloading. Kepler also predicted, in good agreement with his axioms of the true science about gravitation, the existence of a borderline beyond which, during the movement of a body from the Earth to the Moon, the lunar gravitation will prevail over the terrestrial one. He was also aware of the fact that this borderline must be much nearer to the Moon than to the Earth, given the smaller volume of the Moon and, consequently -- assuming the same density of the Earth and of the Moon -- the smaller mass of the Moon. In the author's humorous allusions as to who is and who is not suitable for such a voyage to the Moon, some researchers are ready to see a kind of future cosmonaut.

As soon as Duracotus had landed on the Moon, he began describing the phenomena he observed there. The description is very systematic and begins, "in the way of geographers", with phenomena to be observed in the sky. After that, an exact description is given of astronomical phenomena as observed from the Moon.

Let us mention just the main facts. The Moon is divided into two hemispheres; one of them is facing us constantly. It is, therefore, possible to watch from it the Earth nearly always in the same position in the sky. The second hemisphere, which is averted from the Earth, will never allow anybody to see our planet. Quite certainly the view of the Earth is the most beautiful phenomenon to be observed from the Moon. Moreover, the observer will see the Earth constantly rotating round its axis! And, according to the gradual swiveling of its spots, he will be capable of measuring time as by a watch. For that reason Kepler -- using the words of fictitious Moon inhabitants -- calls the Earth Volva (from the Latin verb *volvere*), because unlike the Moon seen from the Earth Volva is constantly revolving.

Further on he claims that the movement of the fixed stars has the same appearance on the Moon as on the Earth (with only a different time of the apparent turning of the celestial sphere), while the seeming motion of the planets is when much more complicated than observed from the Earth. These basic findings were very likely a matter of primary concern for Kepler; it is because of them he undertook the daring attempt to observe the sky from the Moon. The defender of the Copernican heliocentric system has thus acquired two decisive arguments:

1. An observer on the Moon will have -- just as an observer on the Earth -- a feeling that he stands on a stationary body in the centre of the Universe that is turning in its totality round him. If this feeling can be proved to be fallacious on the Moon, it must be fallacious on the Earth as well.

2. An observer on the Moon will see with his own eyes that the Earth is revolving round its axis. In the spirit of the Copernican astronomy and in agreement with the tendencies of Giordano Bruno's philosophical cosmology, Kepler tried in the first place to deepen the antianthropocentric world outlook.

In the subsequent text of the *Dream* a detailed analysis of the phenomena belonging to the field of spherical astronomy follows, conceived specially for the Moon. When he has covered this topic and when Kepler begins to assess the physical conditions on the Moon (e.g. predictions of big droughts or, on the contrary, of long rain periods due to a long-term exposure of the lunar surface to the solar rays and after that due to a long night during the long lunar day), the *Dream* comes all of a sudden to an end. Kepler has fully exhausted and covered the field that, as an astronomer, he could master with absolute certainty and accuracy; as soon as he was obliged to guessing only, the author suddenly woke up from a deep dream with his head buried under the pillows.

This is the form in which the manuscript of the *Dream* remained for more than 12 years; only later on did Kepler return to the text again and added the 223 remarks and notices, some of them never to be completed. They were created at a time when Kepler worked subsequently in Linz, Ulm and Zagan. The remarks are about three times longer than the text itself. When Kepler's son Ludwig made up his mind to publish the *Dream* in the year 1634, he commented on the remarks that his father had written noting them to have gradually been prepared between the years 1620 and 1630. But, as Rosen [7] proved convincingly, work on the remarks could have begun by the end of the year 1621; or, more likely, during 1622 at the earliest.

It is worthwhile to take into account the environment in which the basic text of the *Dream* originated, as well as the stimuli influencing its conception. Rosen believes that the oldest stage of Kepler's *Dream* is his student dissertation at Tübingen University in 1593 [8], which dealt with the topic "How would the phenomena occurring in the heavens appear to an observer stationed on the Moon." The content of this thesis, however, remains unknown. It was never exposed to public discussion as it was too Copernican to be admitted to a public judgment.

On the other hand, we can hardly accept the view that this thesis was included in the known Kepler's text the *Dream*. It seems that Kepler in Prague returned once again to his original student idea, but treated it in a new way. The influence of the Prague scientific environment is apparent in the text of the *Dream*. And not only because Kepler himself talks about this matter publicly in his introduction to the work.

The autobiographically conceived Duracotus was initiated to astronomy by Tycho Brahe and Kepler himself collaborated with Tycho in Bohemia in the years 1600 and 1601. We also know from Kepler that in his idea to work up a lunar astronomy there was participation by his Prague friend Johannes Matthaus Wackher of Wackenfels, imperial councilor to Rudolf's court. (He was born in 1550 in Constance and died in 1619 in Vienna.) This very individual thinker has up to now escaped attention in the history of the astronomy. Studies about the Prague scientific milieu around 1600 usually do not quote his name as among the foremost representatives of mathematics and astronomy such as Tadeáš Hájek z Hájku (Hagecius), Tycho Brahe, and Johannes Kepler or the outstanding designers of instruments Erasmus Habermel and Justus Bürgi (known also in mathematics as an inventor of logarithms). Next to these Prague scientific personalities Wackher seems to fade, the main reason very probably being that he never published his astronomical views and considerations and that he was regarded by his contemporaries rather as a philosopher and politician. Nevertheless, his cosmological views were very bright and independent. They are known especially, thanks to Kepler's mediation.

Wackher was a zealous and enthusiastic defender of the philosophy of Giordano Bruno. In cosmology he fully understood the meaning of Bruno's speculative completion of heliocentrism. He advocated Bruno's idea that there are also planets revolving around the fixed stars -- suns [9]. He even predicted Jupiter's rotation around its axis in the same sense as the four satellites discovered by Galileo orbit the Jupiter [10]. Wackher enabled Kepler to carry out his first observations using a telescope [11].

In speculative cosmology, Wackher was even more courageous than Kepler himself. He advocated without any objection the view that the Sun is only one of the stars, whereas Kepler for a long time refused Bruno's idea that the stars should be formations analogical to the Sun. In his *Dissertatio cum nuncio sidereo* (1610) Kepler, in agreement with Giordano Bruno, admitted at the most that the stars, unlike the planets, produce their own brightness, he denied, however, that any of the fixed stars could approach or even equal in size and brightness the Sun [12]. Only later, in his *Epitome astronomiae copernicanae Kepler*, -- did he make some concessions in his outspoken resistance against Bruno's views [13]. This likely was in part because of Wackher's influence.

Wackher also influenced Kepler in another sense: He made him give up the rest of his anthropocentric world outlook concerning the Universe. Kepler tells us that he had animated discussions with Wackher concerning the Moon and that he wrote *Lunar Astronomy* to please Wackher [14]. The conception of the dream originated, therefore, in Prague in the course of discussions with the then most outspoken advocate of Bruno's philosophy and whose influence is obvious in the *Dream.*

Wackher's attitude to Bruno's philosophy is even more valuable and praiseworthy if we take into consideration the fact that he defended Bruno's views even after their author had been condemned and burnt. On the other hand, this fact also proves a high degree of tolerance in the Prague scientific community, before the Battle of the White Mountain, in the very community that enabled Kepler to develop his astronomical theories.

These tolerant and free conditions in the scientific life of Prague are in a sharp contrast with another important event from Kepler's life closely connected with his *Dream.* In 1617, during Kepler's stay in Linz, his mother was accused of witchcraft and risked a sentence of burning. She was lucky that Kepler had not yet decided to have his *Dream* printed. The autobiographical elements in the introduction were too obvious and very likely would have turned into dangerous aggravating circumstances in a trial against his mother. Kepler himself was worried that some hand-written copies of the *Dream* might fall into undesirable hands. In the trial against his mother, which took place in Leonberg and dragged on until 1621, Johannes Kepler actively and successfully defended her. Although she was acquitted, the poor old woman had been jailed during all the time of the trial and was perhaps even tortured before her release from prison in the autumn of 1621. But her health was broken and she died shortly later -- on April 13, 1622.

We can therefore regard as correct the view of Professor Rosen that Kepler was not writing his comments to the *Dream* as early as 1620 as claimed by his son, but very likely only after the successful end of the trial and his return to Linz in 1621; or maybe even later, after the death of his mother in 1622.

Kepler worked on the additional remarks until his death. It turns out that they develop mostly the pedagogical part of the *Dream*, whose text allows one to develop more broadly an explanation of this or that piece of astronomical knowledge. The remarks reveal for us the systematic personality of Kepler working in the same way as when he wrote his voluminous textbook *Epitome astronomiae copernicanae*, which chronologically precedes their origin.

NOTE

People who recently stood on the real Moon saw in the sky exactly the same phenomena as predicted by Kepler in his *Dream.* In the spirit of his prediction they also lived a fallacious feeling that they stood on the surface of a body stationary in the middle of the Universe. Kepler was also the first one to define the relationship of lunar gravitation as compared with that of the Earth, what is the cause of their differences, and what consequences they bring about during the motion of a body sent from the Earth to the Moon. We may admit that Kepler at least partially guessed what obstacles the human organism would have to overcome during its voyage through space. It may seem today that all this is too little when compared with the broad range of considerations required by the theory of space research. If, however, we add to all this Kepler's laws of the movement of the planets and the mighty inspirational force of his work that was followed by Isaac Newton and his successors; and if, moreover, we remind ourselves that more than three-and-a-half centuries divide us from Kepler's discoveries, we will not hesitate in calling him one of the true precursors of scientific space research.

REFERENCES

1. Isaac Newton, *Philosophiae naturalis principia mathematica*, 1687, lib. I., def. 5.

2. Johannes Kepler, *Gesammelte Werke*, Bd. III -- *Astronomia nova*, ed. Max Caspar, München 1937, pp. 25-26.

3. Johannis Kepleri, *Dissertatio cum nuncio sidereo*, Pragae 1610, p. 26; Joannis Kepleri, *astromoni Opera omnia*, ed. Ch. Frisch, vol. II., Francofurti a.M. at Erlangae 1859, p. 502; Walter Gerlach -- Martha List, *Johannes Kepler*, München 1971, pp. 137-138.

4. Marjorie Hope Nicolson, *Voyages to the Moon*. New York, The Macmillan Company, 1948, p. 41 sqq.

5. Joh. Keppleri, *Mathematici olim Imperatorii Somnium, seu Opus posthumum de astronomia lunari. Divulgatum a M. Ludovico Kepplero filio, Medicinae Candidato*. Impressum partim Sagani Silesiorum, absolutum Francofurti, sumptibus haeredum authoris. Anno M DC XXXIV.

6. Edward Rosen, *Kepler's Somnium. The Dream, or posthumous Work on Lunar Astronomy*. Translated with a Commentary by ... The University of Wisconsin Press, Madison, Milwaukee, and London, 1967.

7. Edw. Rosen, *op. cit.*, pp. XIX, XX.

8. Edw. Rosen, *op. cit.*, pp. XVII & 207-208

9. *Diss. cum nuncio sid.*, Pragae 1610, p. 22; O. o., ed. Ch. Frisch, vol. II., Francofurti a.M. et Erlangae 1859, p. 500.

10. *ibid.*, p. 29; i.e. p. 503.

11. Edw. Rosen, *op. cit.*, p. 167.

12. *Diss. cum nuncio sid.*, Pragae 1610, p. 22; O. o., ed. Ch. Frisch, vol. II., Francofurti a.M. et Erlangae 1859, p. 500.

13. *Principiorum doctrinae sphaericae pars secunda, O. o.*, ed. Ch. Frisch, vol. VI., Francofurti a.M. et Erlangae 1866, p. 136 sqq.

14. *Diss. cum nuncio sid.*, Pragae 1610, p. 15; O. o., ed. Ch. Frisch, vol. II., Francofurti a.M. et Erlangae 1859, p. 496.

Chapter 20

ALBERT FONÓ: A PIONEER OF JET PROPULSION[*]

István György Nagy[†]

The outstanding Hungarian engineer Dr. Albert Fonó (1881-1972) displayed creative work for a span of nearly seven decades. He received his diploma in engineering at the Budapest Technical University in 1903, and afterwards worked in several factories in Hungary and abroad. Returning home he obtained a doctor's degree in engineering in 1909. From that time on he was a consulting and design engineer. In this capacity he was one of the founders of the International Federation of Consulting Engineers.

His activity was connected chiefly with energetics; in this field he acquired an international reputation. He was an extremely productive and many-sided inventor: he worked out 46 patents in 20 themes.

Besides his inventions covering the field of propulsion he dealt with different other subjects, too. In this, his activities in the field of jet propulsion are treated. Some of his patents pertaining to automation and metrology are noted. It is remarkable that Fonó was one of the first who designed a hydrofoil in 1926; in these experiments he cooperated with Theodore von Kármán.

He got a honorary professorship at the Budapest Technical University in 1947 and in 1954 became a member of the Hungarian Academy of Sciences. In his eighties in 1959 he was elected president of the newly-formed Hungarian Astronautical Society. He never regarded this position as a mere formal charge and very actively participated in the activities of the society. From 1968 on he was member of the International Academy of Astronautics.

The author of the present paper was privileged to be acquainted with Albert Fonó and work with him in the Hungarian Astronautical Society.

---

[*]   Presented at The Eleventh IAA History of Astronautics Symposium, Prague, Czechoslovakia, September 1977.

[†]   Hungarian Astronautical Society, Budapest, Hungary.

THE AERIAL TORPEDO

The first invention in which Fonó applied the principle of jet propulsion dates back to the World War I, to the year 1915. With his device, which he designated as "aerial torpedo", he wanted to improve the efficiency of field-artillery guns [1].

From the second half of the 19th century on, artillery weapons entered into a rapid development. Rifled guns and breech-loading became general. Also, guns with recoiling barrel were introduced. The firing range and accuracy of guns and their rate of fire increased considerably. In the course of development new types of guns appeared with greatly improved mobility. The technical development is characterized by the fact that between 1870 and 1914 the firing range of field artillery guns was doubled and on the average attained 8 kilometers (about 5 miles).

Nineteenth century rockets could not compare with rapidly developing guns, and consequently they were set aside by the military. The Austro-Hungarian Army used them for the last time in 1869. In Great Britain, Hale rockets were withdrawn from use in 1905. There were some attempts to modernize artillery rockets about the turn of the century. The best results were obtained by the Swedish artillery officer W. Th. Unge. His invention, which first bore the name "aerial torpedo", was taken over by the German firm Krupp. Experiments with this rocket were stopped in 1910 because its accuracy was not sufficient [2].

Fonó had in view to increase the range of field artillery. As is well known, this is attained by boosting the muzzle velocity of the projectile. This method is limited since at higher speed substantially higher air resistance has to be overcome. In order to demonstrate the inventor's train of thought we quote some sentences from his description [3].

> "... The difficulty of achieving greater range evidently lies in the fact that the energy must be stored in the form of kinetic energy. If it were possible to store the necessary energy in another manner and make it available in overcoming air resistance, then an obvious improvement in the shooting distance would be possible.

> We propose that chemical energy instead of kinetic energy be introduced in the form of a combustible fuel in the projectile. This fuel is to be burned along the way with the approaching air, and the derived heat converted into work to overcome the air resistance. If in this way a forward acting force can be applied to the projectile, then it is evidently possible to accelerate the shell during flight ... It would be possible with a relatively small initial velocity of the shell and with a relatively small reaction force on the shell to achieve very great range and an appreciable impact energy at the terminal point. It would also be possible with relatively light guns to shoot heavy shells to great distances."

As shown in Figure 1, in order to sustain the velocity of the artillery shell Fonó proposed a propulsion unit that contained every characteristic of ramjet engines. According to the technical description of the aerial torpedo "the device works so that the heat developed by fuel combustion increases the temperature of the air streaming opposite and thus augments its volume. With proper choice of cross-sectional areas the air of increased volume is discharged at higher velocity than the velocity of intake" [4].

Fonó submitted his proposal to Austro-Hungarian Army Headquarters (Armee-Oberkommando), which quickly rejected the proposal with the plea that "no practical results were to be expected; consequently, the proposal could not be considered further" [5]. The prompt rejection points to the fact that military experts did not examine Fonó's proposal with required thoroughness. There is no doubt that the unfavorable decision was influenced by another fact, too: Headquarters reckoned with a relatively short war and did not want to venture into a probable long-lasting development of a new type of weapon.

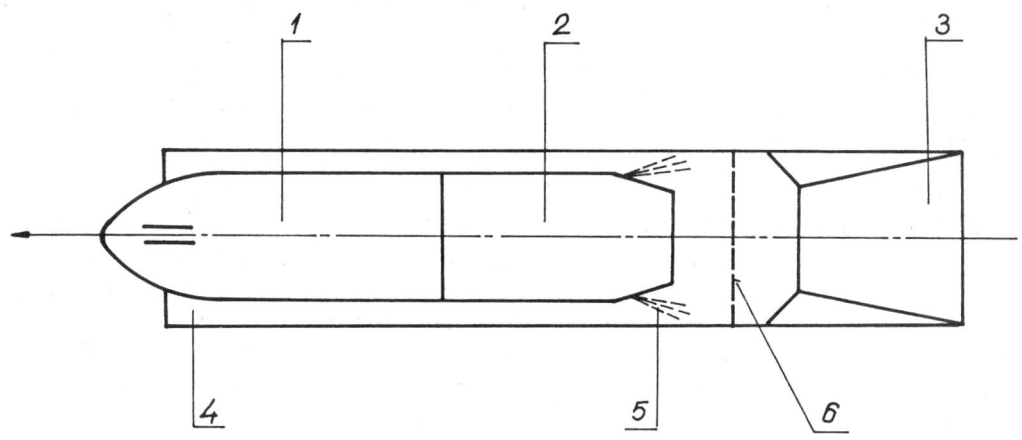

Figure 1 Sketch/plan of Fonó's "aerial torpedo" (1915). (1) The shell proper; (2) Fuel; (3) Expansion nozzle; (4) Compression nozzle; (5) Carburation; (6) Ignition

As to air-breathing jet propulsion engines, their early conception dates back to the time when the first airplanes appeared. Between 1907 and 1913, the French engineer René Lorin (1877-1933) worked out a number of such designs. From him also originates the principle of ramjet engines [6].

The air frames of early airplanes were fit merely for subsonic speeds. This is why conventional engines with propellers were quite suitable to their operation. In this field, the use of jet propulsion became timely only two decades later with the development of new aircraft construction.

Fonó was not acquainted with Lorin's ramjet concept when he worked out his aerial torpedo. We have to emphasize that Lorin did not envisage the use of ramjets at the supersonic speeds needed by this type of engine to achieve useful thrust [7]. This characteristic was realized by Fonó, who at the same time indicated the only possibility of their application would be the propulsion of projectiles at supersonic speeds (in 1915). Figure 1 is a sketch/plan of his 1915 aerial torpedo.

Certainly Fonó was the first to propose the combination of projectile with air-breathing jet engine, so his design we might regard as the first concept of present jet-propelled missiles.

There is no doubt that Fonó's concept is sound, and it is true that the invention provided an opportunity to develop a new type of missile. This is definitely demonstrated by later designs and experiments of a similar sort. The British inventor B.C. Carter obtained a patent in 1926 for a ramjet-propelled artillery projectile [8]. The GIRD experiments in the Soviet Union, performed by Yu. A. Pobedonostsev and his team between 1933 and 1935 with gun-launched ramjet-driven field artillery shells, were of greater importance [9]. Simultaneously with these experiments, R. Leduc in France worked out a design of a projectile of the same sort [10]. In Germany, with the participation of the Austrian engineer K. Oswatitch, large-scale experiments were carried out during World War II to develop such projectiles [11]. Evidently, all these attempts were broken off with the appearance of modern artillery rockets.

THE AIR-JET ENGINE

Long after the war, Fonó took up the problem of jet propulsion again. He elaborated, in 1928, the "air-jet engine" suitable for high-altitude supersonic aircraft and applied for a German patent. In the patent specification [12] he pointed out that in order to increase considerably the speed of aircraft their flying altitude had to be increased. In high-speed flying, conventional air-screws are overstrained; moreover, from the point of view of aerodynamics, propulsion of that sort is disadvantageous. Said problem could be solved only by introducing jet propulsion.

Fonó emphasized that jet engines proposed previously by other inventors were not suitable for supersonic flight. Consequently, in his patent application he defined a propulsion unit characterized by a compression nozzle having an initially diminishing cross-section in the direction of the air stream. Having specified his patent Fonó described three types of jet engines. Two types were real ramjets, while the third was a ramjet combined with an air-vane-driven compressor. The last-named propulsion unit could not start by itself; therefore, Fonó applied for an additional patent [13] in which he specified a system with a compressor driven by a separate source of power. In such a way, the propulsion unit also became suitable for subsonic speeds.

The very exhaustive German patent investigation was unusually prolonged but at last established the novelty of Fonó's inventions. The patents were granted in 1932 (with the priority date of May 1928), and so there is no denying the fact that these patents are the earliest [14] covering all the essentials of present aircraft and missile air-breathing jet engines.

Fonó for a time tried to dispose of his patents. He entered into negotiations with the Fokker and Junkers aircraft factories but these firms were unable to solve many technical problems and to meet the expenses of development. Under such circumstances, some years later the inventor let his patents expire. The task of developing aircraft jet propulsion fell to other engine builders.

REFERENCES[*]

1. A. Fonó, *Életem és müködésem* [Recollections] (1965) MS in the Hungarian Transport Museum, Budapest.

2. F.C. Durant III, G.S. James (ed.), *First Steps Toward Space* (Washington, Smithsonian Inst. Press, 1974), pp. 261-266. Now available as Vol. 6, *AAS History Series,* Univelt, Inc., San Diego, California. (Hereafter cited as *First Steps*.)

3. A. Fonó, *Lufttorpedo, ein Vorschlag* (10 February 1915) MS in the Hungarian Transport Museum, Budapest.

4. A. Fonó, On Ram Jet Propulsion, *Acta Technica Acadeniae Scientiarum Hungaricae*, vol. 12, pp. 384-385 (1955).

5. K.u.k. Technisches Militärkomitee, Sekt.I, Nr. 3675 (7 April 1915), see W.H. Avery, Air Torpedo -- A Proposal of Albert Fonó, *ARS Journal*, vol. 30, p. 1102, (1960).

6. R. Lorin, De la turbine à gaz au propulseur à réaction, *L'Aérophile*, vol. 21, p.229 (1913) and Une expérience simple relative au propulseur à réaction directe, L'Aérophile, vol. 21, p.514 (1913).

7. W.H. Avery, op. cit., p. 1102 and M.J. Zucrow, *Aircraft and Missile Propulsion* (New York, Wiley, 1958), vol. 2, p. 349.

8. M.J. Zucrow, op. cit., vol. 2, p. 349.

9. *First Steps*, pp. 171-175.

10. J. Stemmer, *Die Entwicklung des Raketenantriebes* (Zürich, Hoffmann, 1944-1945), vol. 3, p. 34.

11. M.J. Zucrow, op. cit., vol. 2, p. 350.

12. Luftstrahlmotor für Mochflug, German patent 554906.

13. Luftstrahlmotor für Mochflug, German patent 560075.

14. M.J. Zucrow, op. cit., vol. 2, p. 349.

* The author wishes to express his appreciation to Dr. Pál Vajda for his kindness in putting some source-materials at the author's disposal.

Chapter 21

S.P. KOROLEV AND SOVIET ROCKET TECHNOLOGY[*]

B. V. Rauschenbach[†]

In the history of science and technology, an enormous role has always been played by those who have blazed new trails and whose names are associated with great discoveries and achievements, especially in fields that have attained vitally important significance for all of humanity.

In our age of numerous fundamental discoveries and rapid scientific and technological progress, a special place among the new applications of human energy is occupied by cosmonautics which has absorbed into itself the achievements of a large number of sciences. It is possible that, in the future, humanity will call the 20th century the Age of the Opening Up of Space.

At the beginning of our century, there appeared in science at first little noted works of K.E. Tsiolkovsky, who theoretically substantiated the feasibility of cosmonautics. The middle of the same century has been marked by the activities of many scientists and engineers who set for themselves the task not only of the further development of the ideas of cosmonautics, but also of the practical implementation of this ages-old dream of humanity. Among these scientists, a quite exceptional place belongs to S.P. Korolev.

If you were to follow all the activities of Korolev from the beginning of the 1930's, when he was closely involved in the problems of rocket technology, up to the last days of his life, you would be astonished not only by the energy with which he worked, but also by his strict sense of purpose. The impression is created that, from the very first days of his own work in this engendered field of technology, he had already seen Gagarin's future flight.

Understanding the conditionality of clearly defined periodizations, we will try all the same to divide Korolev's activities into three stages:

1. The period of emergence of rocket technology (1930-1946).
2. The period of development of powerful rockets (1946-1957).
3. The period of development of spacecraft (1957-1966).

---

[*] Presented at The Eleventh IAA History of Astronautics Symposium, Prague, Czechoslovakia, September 1977.

[†] Committee of the Soviet National Association of Natural Science and Technology Historians, USSR Academy of Sciences, Moscow, USSR.

EMERGENCE OF ROCKET TECHNOLOGY (1930-1946)

The first period is characterized by the fact that rocket technology was just springing up. In order for it to get firmly established, to develop and to gather strength, it was faced with feasible "terrestrial" tasks: the installation of rocket ships and the use of rocket engines for short-term improvement of aircraft flight characteristics and as a secondary aim -- the development of classical design rockets as craft for scientific purposes with a planned vertical lift altitude on the order of several kilometers.

This stage was necessary, inasmuch as, in opening up the possibility of involving industry in the work on rocket technology, it made possible the development of liquid rocket engines [LPRE] and their systems not on an amateur basis, but rather using all the capacities and traditions of power machine building. The task of developing automatic flight control systems became a reality and it became possible to involve in the work powerful scientific organizations. All this was associated with the fact that the results of the majority of the named operations were supposed to be put to practical use immediately upon their completion. It is precisely this possibility of the immediate use of developed designs that made "profitable" not only the final result -- the entry of man into space -- but also the intermediate stages.

By 1931, Korolev had decided to dedicate all his activities to rocket technology and later on to space technology. This decision was influenced by Tsiolkovsky's ideas, with which Korolev had become acquainted in previous years; and as a result of a meeting with F.A. Tsander, a zealous space flight enthusiast. Tsander, at that time, had attained fame as the author of works associated with the exploitation of space and as an engineer who had already begun tests with the OR-1 rocket engine [Experimental Rocket engine No. 1]. Korolev immediately understood that here was an opportunity to begin practical work on the achievement of space flight. With his own energy, he undertook to organize this matter and Tsander's works, which for many years had drawn no response, immediately attained a practical direction. At the end of 1931, an agreement was signed according to which financing became available for the work on installing a rocket engine in a rocket aircraft.

Overall supervision of work was entrusted to Korolev and the development of the rocket engine, which received the designation OR-2, was entrusted to Tsander. Korolev not only took upon himself the overall supervision of the work and not only supervised the completion of the light-engine, tailless aircraft, the BICh-9, into which it was proposed that the OR-2 be installed, but also, as a test pilot himself, conducted flight tests of this unusual craft. Although this work was not yet completed, it made it possible to gather a group of rocket technology enthusiasts around Korolev and Tsander. Soon the originally social organization GIRD (Jet Propulsion Study Group [JPSG]) had actually become a scientific research and experimental design organization, had obtained solid financing for its work, and sharply expanded its own areas of study.

Korolev was appointed the head of this organization and no one had any doubts about this appointment, inasmuch as Korolev's exceptional creative and organizational capabilities had been clearly manifested from the very start of JPSG's work.

Typical of Korolev's activities as head of JPSG and, after the formation of the Jet Propulsion Scientific Research Institute as a result of the merger of the JPSG and the Gas Dynamics Laboratory (1933), as the leader of one of the foremost schools of study of this institute, were initiative, boldness in the formulation of tasks and, simultaneously, a maximum sobermindedness -- all this work had a clearly defined purpose and could undoubtedly be realized.

In 1933, they launched the modestly sized GIRD-09 and GIRD-10 rockets developed under his supervision; the latter, developed according to Tsander's design studies, had all the typical features of ballistic missiles with LPRE's. Korolev's basic efforts were directed at that time at developing winged flying craft. This trend in his activities is completely understandable -- the relatively modest capabilities of the rocket engines of that time made it possible to lift the necessary loads only by using the lifting force of wings. Under Korolev's supervision, winged rockets were developed with the "201" and "212" LRE's, the first of which would be comparable today to air-to-air missiles, and the second to surface-to-surface missiles. These rockets were already equipped with automatic flight control systems and the "201" also had a remote guidance-to-target radio system. Both rockets were developed in the period from 1934 to 1938; and, in 1939, flight tests of the "212" rockets were conducted and the completion of the "201" rocket had begun.

In 1937 and 1938, ground tests were conducted on the Korolev-designed RP-318-1 rocket plane, in which pilot V.P. Fedorov completed the USSR's first flight [of a craft] with a working rocket engine in 1940. In those same years, Korolev developed a plan for a record climb into the stratosphere in a rocket plane with a sealed cabin.

This broadly developed work was suspended prior to the war in order to concentrate all the Jet Propulsion Institutes' forces on the development of rocket artillery, in particular, the Katyushas that later became famous. At this time, and until the end of World War II, Korolev continued to work on the application of LRE's in aviation, participating in the installation of rocket engines in combat airplanes.

DEVELOPMENT OF POWERFUL ROCKETS (1946-1957)

The second period of Korolev's activities began in 1946 when, after the end of the war, there was an opportunity to return to long-range developments and he was appointed chief designer for the development of sets of automatically controlled long-range ballistic missiles. By this time the development of rocket engine construction in the USSR had reached such a level that lifting large masses without using aerodynamic forces, in accordance with the principle of ballistic missiles, had become a complete reality. At the same time, along with Korolev, chief designers were appointed for engines, for control systems, for radio systems, for ground equipment and so on. The group of chief designers, headed by Korolev, was faced with a most important defense task, associated with the development of a new and terrible weapon.

During this period, having turned out to be in charge of grandiose projects, Korolev developed a highly flexible and clearly defined organization for a complex set of operations and established the Chief Designers' Council. In this small council, he managed to create an amicable working atmosphere, in which the most important principle of leadership became common sense and the interests of the matter at hand. All this made it possible to develop one missile system after another with unimaginable speed. The development of large-scale ballistic missiles required not only the development of new and varied engines, control systems, ground equipment sets and so on, but also of a qualitatively new approach to the designing of the rockets themselves.

All rockets built up to this time (not only in the USSR but also in other countries) had been designed and produced based on aviation technology developed contemporaneously with them. They thus still lacked many specific rocket features, which alone would make it possible to bring the relative fuel reserve up to the necessary level. Therefore, Korolev and his associates, conducting an extensive cycle of tests and experiments, developed in the end rocket designs that completely met the requirements that had confronted them. The various types of long-range rockets developed in the period from 1946 to 1957 were, for their time, prominent examples of rocket technology. The triumphal completion of this work was the successful flight test in August of 1957 of the world's first intercontinental ballistic missile.

The potential feasibility of developing a launch vehicle based on intercontinental missiles capable of placing spacecraft onto space trajectories was clear from the very beginning. Therefore, it would be a mistake to think that the work on the exploitation of space began after the launching of a missile over intercontinental distances. The sense of purpose of Korolev's work, who never lost sight of the prospects for exploiting space, was evidenced in particular by the fact that the theoretical and experimental work in preparation for the development of space flight was begun long before 1957.

By 1949, under Korolev's supervision, the first geophysical rocket had been developed, which had been intended for vertical probing of the atmosphere up to altitudes on the order of 100 km. Launches of similar rockets, of ever more improved design, were conducted and continued even after the launch of the first satellite. In the end, the altitude attainments of such sounding rockets exceeded 500 km. The task of such rockets was the study of the upper atmosphere and space. In addition to what has been mentioned, animals were carried on rockets of this type and a study of the effect of space flight conditions on a living organism was conducted. Thus, it is possible to state that the various experiments on penetrating space and accumulating space flight experience were begun several years before the signals of the Earth's first artificial satellite were heard on the ground.

In addition to the regular launches of research rockets, from the beginning of 1950's, intensive theoretical work was conducted on questions concerning the exploration of space. A study of the problem of attaining space velocities with rockets was begun in 1950 in our country under Korolev's leadership. This was work in which the paths to the achievement of space flight were studied not as a possibility in principle (which Tsiolkovsky had already indicated) but rather as something realizable on the basis of the existing level of technology, taking into account its short-term prospects. Beginning in 1954, the possibility of developing artificial Earth satellites was studied attentively. Korolev was also the leader of this work cycle.

Thus, by 1957, when, along with the intercontinental ballistic missile, its space version was also prepared, the answers to a whole series of principal questions associated with the development of spacecraft had already been obtained in the process of launching research rockets and as a result of the theoretical work of an applied nature. Therefore, the 4 October 1957 launching of the Earth's first artificial satellite, which opened humanity's space era and turned out to be completely unexpected for many people, was the result of years-long and purposeful work.

If you return to the first satellite, then you are struck by its utmost simplicity of design, the practically complete absence of scientific equipment, the elementary nature of the radio transmitter installed in it and Korolev's evident desire to get by with an absolute minimum of necessary and adequately evident measures, capable of giving the radio transmitter the opportunity of operating over the course of a specific and comparatively insignificant amount of time. Paradoxically, this simplest of articles quite naturally became the symbol of the new era, associated with the enormous scientific and technological achievements of humanity in one of the most complex fields of human endeavor. The first satellite is of value not in and of itself (all the same, it made it possible to refine our ideas about the density of the upper atmosphere and radiowave propagation), but as a junction point in the development of technology. On the one hand, it symbolized the completion of a difficult path in the development of rockets, which have become space rockets; and, on the other hand, it was an embryo from which space technology grew. Even after the launching of the first satellite, the process of improving space rockets continued as well and Korolev's main efforts after 1957 were directed towards the development of spacecraft.

DEVELOPMENT OF SPACECRAFT (1957-1966)

The third period of Korolev's activities, which began after the launching of the first satellite, was characterized by the rapid, explosive development of space technology and the appearance of spacecraft intended for the most diverse purposes. A listing of all these craft, developed under Korolev's leadership, which are distinguished from one another by diagrams of design decisions, designations, sizes and so on, would be inappropriate here. We will limit ourselves, therefore, to only a general description of the basic trends in space technology that arose under his direct leadership.

The trend, which was a natural continuation of the work associated with the development of the first satellite, was the further development of various types of automatically operating spacecraft for the study of near-Earth space. The second satellite, launched a month after the first one, contained equipment for the study of the Sun and cosmic rays and the experimental animal -- the small female dog Layka. On the third satellite there were already 12 different scientific instruments. In the future, the degree of complexity of the scientific programs and the quantity of launched satellites increased more and more and in the process of their development, a new field of technology was born and developed -- space technology.

The originality of space technology was the result of the solution of a series of tasks, which had not been encountered in engineering until this time. While making no claim to completeness, we will name here just some of the problems confronting Korolev and his associates. It was necessary to develop methods for the selection of trajectories for the movement of spacecraft and for the prediction of their evolution. This required the development of new chapters in celestial mechanics, which began to change from a pure science to an applied one. Space confronted engineers with the problem of the operation of movable joints in a vacuum, which turned out to be sharply different from terrestrial conditions, and weightlessness, for all practical purposes, caused the complete disappearance of the thermal convection of gases, which filled sealed areas. The contribution of thermal radiation to the task of a spacecraft's heat exchange increased sharply, and this required new methods for calculation and the development of new technological equipment for controlling the temperature within a spacecraft. The task of power supply involved the development of solar batteries. This list could go on and on.

The solution of such tasks required the closest of cooperation in the work of the design, production and research organizations. This process of mutual enrichment of science and technology proceeded in close cooperation with the USSR Academy of Sciences, of which Korolev was a member, with the very active participation of Academician M.V. Keldysh.

The development of space technology initiated by the development of the first artificial Earth satellites proceeded further not only along the path of development of automatic satellites for scientific purposes, but also of interplanetary-type spacecraft, the development of satellites for economic purposes, and the advent of manned spaceships.

Even before the launching of the first artificial Earth satellite, Korolev's associates, under his supervision, were developing the corresponding projects. It is not surprising, therefore, that by January 1959, the first rocket had been launched towards the Moon and in that same year a pennant with the emblem of the Soviet Union had been placed on the lunar surface and photographs had been obtained of its far side. In 1966, less than a month after Korolev's death, a spacecraft made a soft landing on the lunar surface -- Korolev's last work in the lunar studies program. At the same time, work was also conducted on the study of Venus and Mars. Korolev's highest achievement in this field was the first flight of a man-made object to another planet and the placing of a pennant with the emblem of the Soviet Union on the surface of Venus (March 1966).

During the development of similar-type spacecraft, it was necessary to solve a large group of new tasks. First and foremost among them was that of controlling motion. Already, on board the Luna 3 automatic interplanetary station, the world's first attitude control system had been installed without which it would have been impossible to direct the immobile camera installed on it towards the Moon. The task of getting to Venus required not only attitude control, but also the capability of carrying out accurate flight trajectory correction maneuvers. Luna 9, which made a soft landing on the Moon, in addition required the development of a system for landing on a world without an atmosphere. In addition to the tasks of controlling the motion of a spacecraft, there arose in parallel the enormous task of ultra-long-range radio communications, trajectory measurements and flight trajectory prediction with extremely high accuracy. It is natural that all these tasks were again solved in cooperation with scientific and production organizations. Korolev coordinated all this work and had the deciding word during the selection of the basic technical trends of this set of operations.

If the interplanetary flight of the spacecraft developed under Korolev's leadership opened up new paths to science, then the Molniya-1 communications satellite developed under his leadership was a shining example of the solution of a complex but very necessary economic task. Many years after his death satellites of this type in combination with the Orbita system ground stations continued to implement radiotelegraph, radiotelephone and television communications over long distances. In particular, it is precisely these satellites which have been ensuring up to the present time the transmission of Moscow television programs to the Far East.

Manned flights into space are justly considered to be the high point of Korolev's creativity. He always considered manned flights to be especially important and he was influenced not only by considerations of scientific and technical necessity, but of no less importance those of a moral nature. Here in addition, in all probability, was evidence of long-held and steadfast feelings -- it must not be forgotten that in his youth he was a glider and an aircraft pilot and in conversations with friends he frequently lamented the fact that age and health had deprived him of the opportunity to fly in space.

It is perfectly natural that the new direction required the solution of new problems -- life-support systems, the development of manual ship control systems, the ensurance of a safe descent to the Earth's surface, and, consequently, the solution of the task of thermal protection of the descent craft, and so on. All this work was begun early and carried out efficiently, at an impressive pace. At the same time, the requirements for the gradual completion of the systems and of guaranteeing complete reliability were taken completely into consideration. The completion of the Vostok manned spacecraft was begun in the spring of 1960 when a series of ship-satellites were placed into orbit and the latter of these were exact copies of the future Vostok and carried animals as passengers. In less than a year, five ship-satellites were launched, which made it possible to conduct a reliable completion and testing of all the on-board systems.

It goes without saying that parallel with the completion of the technology, the training of the cosmonauts was begun under the general supervision of S.P. Korolev.

On 12 April 1961, with the launch of the Vostok with Yuriy Alekseyevich Gagarin on board, humanity completed the second epoch-making step in the exploitation of space -- it was not an automatic craft, developed by the genius of man, that penetrated space, but man himself.

Following Gagarin's flight came other manned flights and after the Vostoks the Voskhods were launched, and later the Soyuzs also, the planning for which had been started under Korolev's supervision. It must be noted that Korolev personally supervised the flight control of all the spaceships launched during his lifetime.

KOROLEV IN PERSPECTIVE

This brief outline of S.P. Korolev's activities indicates his exceptional role in the development of the USSR's space rocket technology. He was constantly at the center of all the new space rocket programs, beginning with the design study, the postulation of the scientific problems, the preparation of industry and right up to the supervision of flight control.

In summing up his activities, it is possible to note the following three features of his working style:

1. A systematic approach. A clear understanding of the fact that modern space rocket technology is a "big system," where all of its component elements are identically important -- from the ground launch complex to the spacecraft. Personal participation in the solution of key tasks, which arose during the development of this large system, is vital.

2. A clearly defined work sequence. Each step should not only lead to the remote goal, but also have independent significance.

3. An incessant craving for what is new. After having developed any kind of example to space rocket technology and having brought it up to the necessary level of perfection, Korolev frequently "made a present" of the developed theme with all its long-range studies to some related enterprise for the further development of the space rocket technology trend opened up by his work. He himself again proceeded to the unknown.

Chapter 22

HARRY BULL, AMERICAN ROCKET PIONEER[*]

Frank H. Winter[†]

BACKGROUND

In the infancy of liquid propellant rocket technology, during the early 1930's, one technical problem perhaps stood out above all the rest. This was cooling. Rocket engines which could not be sufficiently cooled would simply burn through the chamber wall, sometimes explosively, shortly after ignition of the propellants. In brief, this heat barrier made them useless for long-duration applications. Hence, liquid rocket engines of the period were unsuitable for any practical uses despite the highly optimistic aims of the experimenters of the newly created American Interplanetary Society (1930), later more sedately called American Rocket Society (ARS). Their European counterparts, the members of the Verein für Raumschiffahrt (the VfR, founded 1927) in Germany and various Russian groups faced the same barrier and the same initial frustration. (The British Interplanetary Society (1933) was prohibited by law from experimenting.)

As early as 1923, the Rumanian-born astronautical pioneer Hermann Oberth in his *Die Rakete zu den Planetenräumen* proposed the earliest logical -- and probably inevitable -- technological solution to the cooling and combustion stability problem, a regenerative system in which one of the propellants circulates around the combustion chamber in a cooling jacket, thus cooling the motor and simultaneously preheating the fuel prior to its injection into the combustion chamber. Yet this concept does not appear to have been generally known in America even up to the 1930's. The very first modes of cooling adopted and in turn abandoned by the ARS and VfR were in fact water jackets and the like. Such methods were very inefficient.

Before reviewing these techniques, it suffices to say that it was not until the pioneering work of Harry Bull, a young engineering student of Syracuse University, that the United States' first partially regeneratively-cooled rocket motor was actually built and successfully fired. The results were subsequently published and disseminated through the ARS journal *Astronautics*.

---

[*]   Presented at The Tenth IAA History of Astronautics Symposium, Anaheim, California, U.S.A., October 1976.

[†]   National Air and Space Museum, Smithsonian Institution, Washington, D.C., U.S.A.

Figure 1 Harry W. Bull (1909-1971), according to a portrait made a year or so before his death.

Bull went on to initiate other design ideas, though it was his partially regenera-tively-cooled motor which is of special interest as it helped lead James Wyld, a later ARS member, to develop his own regenerative system. It in turn led to the stable, long-duration liquid propellant motors that would later power the Air Force Bell X-1 rocket aircraft, the Navy's Lark missile, and other significant early American rocket projects. Bull's story is all the more remarkable considering that he worked entirely independently, using his meager personal funds and the machine shops and laboratories of Syracuse University, and miles away from the heart of the American East Coast rocketry community which was then located in and around New York City. He was, nonetheless, a charter member of the ARS and also known to Robert H. Goddard, the American rocket pioneer of Worcester, Massachusetts, who at least distantly encouraged him.

Fortunately, through the generous donation of Bull's papers to the National Air and Space Museum of the Smithsonian Institution by his widow, Mrs. Bertha K.

Bull of Midland, Michigan, further details of his pioneering work and his life are now available.

Harry W. Bull was born 4 April 1909 in Syracuse, New York, the son of Horace P. Bull (who became the managing editor of the Syracuse *Post-Standard*) and Clara B. Bull. In 1928, Harry entered the L.C. Smith College of Applied Science at Syracuse University and graduated with a B.S. in mechanical engineering in 1932. In addition to mechanical engineering, he particularly excelled in chemistry and the other sciences. These abilities, coupled with his natural studiousness, resourcefulness, and energy, were to mold young Bull into an imaginative and productive rocket pioneer [1] (Figure 1).

In 1927, while still in high school, he penciled his earliest known thoughts on interplanetary travel. Although elementary by today's standards they demonstrate an early awareness of the possibilities of rocket-powered space travel and the direct influence of Dr. Robert H. Goddard. The youngster had also vaguely heard of the 1927 Exhibition of Interplanetary Machines in Moscow. Bull was compelled to write to Goddard to seek direction. Bull later recalled:

> My early interest in rockets was brought about by the vivid accounts of Dr. Goddard's experiments which newsmen claimed were aimed at sending a rocket to the Moon. My rocket goals were aimed entirely at developing a rocket that would climb to relatively high altitudes. Goddard was interested in reaching 100 miles (160 km) and I would have settled for 10 (16 km) [2].

In addition to this testimony, Bull received the first of several letters from Dr. Goddard himself on 19 March 1928. The professor, while cordial, was also characteristically noncommittal in revealing any details of his propellants to the enquiring youngster. Not to be discouraged, even by his new idol, Bull wrote:

> Prof. Goddard's great advancement in the art of rocket making need not stop me from experimenting [3].

The first experiment had been conducted in the fall of 1927 in what was then the outskirts of Syracuse. It was a very crude solid propellant rocket, 10 in. (25.4 cm), 2 in (5.08 cm) in diameter, and with a 0.38-in (9.5-mm) brass nozzle. Performance was equally modest: the rocket simply exploded after flying to a very low altitude. The novice experimenter recalled that this setback did not deter him "in the least" and that on the contrary, he embarked upon an exhaustive program, primarily static tests to determine the effectiveness of propellant combinations, both solid and liquid, as well as working towards the most efficacious rocket engine he could build. As a student of mechanical engineering at Syracuse University, his notes continue:

> I found that considerable equipment was available that would lend itself to research in the field of rocketry. During my college days and for two years after graduation I performed 829 tests. The great bulk of testing data has long since been thrown out but the little foldout insert included here and a small bundle of reports labeled 'Early Rocket Research' still remain which may be of casual interest to someone in the future [4].

Throughout these tests, which lasted from 1928 to 1933, Bull worked entirely alone. He financed his work as well as his collegiate career through a small stipend from home and through a part-time job as a photographer with the *Post-Standard* where his father also worked. Though he readily admitted that, "Not being mechanically inclined and also conservative by nature, my father was less than enthusiastic about my rocket experiments [5], nevertheless Bull persisted in his efforts.

Nonetheless, it was by means of the *Post-Standard* and its affiliated wire news services that Bull and his rockets were afforded national attention and that his dwindling financial resources required to continue his experiments were given a needed boost. Bull tersely summed up this giddy episode in his notes:

> My interest in rockets increased after I entered college. During my junior year, in the midst of the depression, money was scarce and everything I made went for tuition. To increase my earnings I decided to build a rocket sled. Money I planned [to earn] was to come from three sources: copyrighted news photos, talks to the many organizations in the city and a booklet telling how to build a sled [6].

THE ROCKET SLED

This clever, though hardly scientific scheme, had been inspired by the rocket sled, car, and plane experiments undertaken in Germany from 1928 to 1930 by the experimenter Max Valier in union with Fritz von Opel, the publicity-seeking automobile magnate. While spurned for his "stunts" by the VfR, Valier's object was dramatically to arouse public interest in the potential of the rocket. By so doing, he hoped to advance the cause of rocketry and astronautics in the long run by not only demonstrating the power of rockets, but also by attracting potential patrons who could financially help to speed the advance of the state of the art. In America, like the VfR, Dr. Goddard was also diametrically opposed to what he considered were entirely frivolous devices and always took a more sober, strictly scientific approach. He advised Bull in a letter of 16 May 1932 -- after Bull had already conducted his famous sled ride -- that:

> To begin with my most definite advice first, I frankly believe the department store 'stunt' would not advance your knowledge of rockets particularly, and would not add to your standing in the eyes of reputable scientists [7].

Goddard's rational, fatherly advice, Bull heeded, though at that point the sled stunt was already behind him. It had begun late in 1930.

About that time, following a series of unsuccessful trials with solid propellant rockets of his own manufacture, Bull visited the Rochester Fireworks Company. There, he was given a tour of the factory and some technical literature as well as powder and rocket samples by the Superintendent, Edward Klein. An attempt was then made to duplicate the Rochester rockets. Spindles and different sized rammers were lathed and welded in Syracuse University's Machinery Hall during Bull's spare time. Great difficulty was met, however, in reconstructing a rocket press such as used by the Rochester Company and which was capable of ramming in the propellant under a maximum pressure of 9 tons/in^2 (18,000 psi, or 1,265 kg/cu cm). Violent explosions often occurred, one of which ruined the young experimenter's test stand set up in the university's Hydraulics Laboratory.

Because of the stability of the firework company's ready-made rockets and the obvious inherent dangers and costs involved in constructing his own rockets for his anticipated man-carrying sled, Bull seems to have eventually opted for the commercially made units but constructed the sled himself. His mother and sister, Jane Bull, sewed the fabric. The rockets themselves appear to have been 6 lb (2.7 kg) caliber black powder skyrockets manufactured by the Rochester Fireworks Company. Without stars and sticks, the rockets were 3 in (7.62 cm) in diameter, approximately 18 in (45.72 cm) long, and produced approximately 15 lb (6.8 kg) thrust for 3 sec. Thirty-six rockets in all, eighteen on each side, powered the finished sled. Theoretically, they would produce at least 540 lb (245 kg) thrust for 3 sec if ignited simultaneously [8]. (It is noted that Max Valier similarly relied upon large commercial pyrotechnic rockets for his own sled.)

Designated the BR-1 (Bull Rocket 1), Bull's sled was an elongated streamlined teardrop-shaped fuselage, 14 ft (4.3 m) long, tapering to a point at the rear. The maximum diameter at the front, which resembled a dirigible, was about 3 ft (0.9 m) and the whole was mounted upon three steel runners, two up front and a single one in the rear. The two front runners were about 10 ft (3 m) apart and fixed, while the one at the rear was movable and connected to the single vertical rudder. Both rear rudder and runner were steered by a rudder bar in the pilot's cockpit.

The cockpit had a regulation airplane windshield and headrest that were dismountable in order to enable the pilot to get in and out. The sled thus resembled a small wingless aircraft, minus its horizontal tail surfaces. The interior framework was of white pine and spruce wood slats, band iron trussed with wire also serving as reinforcements. Over the frame was stretched glider cloth which was clear nitrate-doped and painted with aluminum (aluminum dust and dope), further adding a sleek, airplane appearance to the little craft.

The rockets were strapped by steel braces mounted on top of both of the front runners. In contrast to such Valier's rocket sleds as the Bob Rak 1, the Bull Rocket 1 was pulled rather than pushed. Bull made his own hit-wire fuses operated by three 1.5 v dry cells and activated by a six-point rheostat panel in the cockpit. The first contact on the rheostat or "control board" fired ten rockets; the second, six; the third, eight; the fourth, eight; while the remaining two were for reserve. Simultaneous ignition was therefore not contemplated and Bull estimated then an initial discharge of 18 rockets would be sufficient to get the craft under way with another ten rockets fired shortly after maximum speed had been attained. Following that, a few seconds later, the remaining eight rockets were to be ignited to enable the "boat" to complete its ride to a distance of 1,500 ft (457 m) at 20 ft/sec (6.1 m/sec). Total cost of this project was $22, of which $15 went for the rockets (some of the steel was donated by Syracuse University and Bull's helmet and goggles were loaned by a friend) [9].

An ordinary heavy ice sled served as the first test bed for the system, two of the large Rochester rockets being lashed to it and ignited in a trial on a deserted skating rink. Bull simply reported that "The sled shot across the ice for some 150 ft (45.7 m) in a straight line" and that "Photographs were taken of the trial." The BR-1 itself was then taken one night to a small lake in a cemetery for ignition tests and a week later, on 9 March 1931, the final run was made in front of the Syracuse Yacht and Country Club at South Bay on Lake Oneida [10].

The sled was to have gone on 7 March but a short circuit prevented ignition. Bull had then to re-wire the boat far into the night in readiness for another attempt on the 8th, only to face another day's postponement due to a gale. Finally, at 3:30 p.m. on 9 March, before a crowd of from 500 to 1,000 spectators, including Fox Movietone, Paramount "talking" newsreel men and other press representatives, Bull rode his BR-1 in a short but thrilling ride over mushy ice to 50 ft (15.2 m) in 2/5 sec, or 75 mph (120 km/hr) from standstill.

Slush had clogged the runners and the little sled had swerved almost as soon as the flames of the ten boosting rockets had shot out. This was despite the fact that fellow students, including Charles F. Chatfield and Andrew Pauceck, had done their best to clear the still mushy ground. As it was, they had been compelled to help push the sled prior to ignition and had not cleared back in time so that their overcoats and trousers became scorched and their eyebrows and hair singed. (Bull's sister says her brother later bought a new coat to replace one of the burnt ones.) A third helper, Henry Levine, who had clocked the run with a stopwatch and a measuring tape afterwards, confirmed the distance. Bull was elated, but not as much as he had hoped. Fifteen minutes later, he attempted another ride and then a third. Both were similar to the first run. Though all of the runs were still considered successes and seemed to prove that with clear-ice conditions the BR-1 was entirely capable of far greater distances and speeds of up to 90 or more mph (145 km /hr) [11] (Figure 2).

Figure 2   Bull's BR-1 rocket sled prior to test run on Lake Oneida, Syracuse, New York, on 9 March 1931.

Through the press witnesses gathered on frozen Lake Oneida that afternoon, an enormous amount of publicity on the experiment was generated around the country. Bull's notes show that he collected some 1,500 news stories, the majority of which he was later forced to discard. Generally, the BR-1 was hailed as "this country's first rocket sled" and Bull did not lose the opportunity to announce that it could lead to far profounder developments. "The ultimate aim of these experiments," he afterwards wrote in some by-lined articles, "is the development of a motor suitable to propel airplanes capable of flying in the stratosphere" and that "If, in future tests with liquid propellants, I meet with success, I will apply this new type of rocket to a small plane or glider." The promises were reminiscent of Valier's, following his own successful and similarly highly publicized rocket sled and automobile runs. Almost exactly two years previously Valier had written that, "My final aim is not the automobile, but an airship with a rocket impulse powerful enough to pierce the atmospheric armor of our globe." In both instances, the German and the American envisioned the eventual emergence of the spaceship [12].

In both cases also, these pledges were hardly braggadocio but said in full earnestness by two very dedicated pioneers. Two people who knew Bull, John W. Herrick, a fellow student at Syracuse and afterwards an engineer with Aerojet-General, and William J. Sauber, a chemical engineer who worked closely with Bull at the Dow Chemical Corporation in the 1960's, both attest to his innate modesty and absolute dedication. Herrick recalled that Bull persisted with his experiments, even after being chided by some of his classmates for setting his sights on the Moon. Sauber remembered Bull as above reproach and an exceptionally modest and highly capable man who rarely spoke much. Similarities in character might be suggested of Bull and Goddard, although insofar as the rocket work was concerned the latter was both an advanced and brilliant physicist who had considerably more resources at his disposal as well as a chosen lifetime of work [13].

AFTERMATH AND FIRST LIQUID EXPERIMENTS

Bull's originally stated goals of the sled ride were met. In addition to receiving plaudits from the public, a letter of congratulations from the Chancellor of Syracuse University, Dr. Charles W. Flint, and an average of 18 to 20 other letters daily (most of them containing bids for his services in one form or another). Bull was also able to raise needed money for his schooling and experimentation by selling copyrighted photos (though not as much if the professional news photographers had not been there, the newsmen having been called by Bull's father). One particular offer of note came from William G. Swan, a stunt pilot representing the Million-Dollar Pier in Atlantic City, New Jersey. Swan offered Bull $30 a day for 100 days if he would exhibit a rocket glider that he had proposed building. Bull was through with stunts and considered his serious experiments and university work of primary importance.

Interestingly, Swan did complete his rocket plane and on 4 June 1931, three months after Bull's rocket sled debut, apparently became the first American to fly a rocket-powered aircraft. Earlier, in May, Bull took time out to construct a miniature space rocketship model and deliver an accompanying lecture at an air show at

Luna Park, New York City. Also important to his goals -- or rather, dreams -- he began delivering lectures on rocketry and space flight to the Syracuse Technology Club and similar groups. While in New York City, he also conferred with fellow members of the American Interplanetary Society and, probably in January of 1931 met with the great French astronautical pioneer Robert Esnault-Pelterie.

Curiously, Bull also became known to the Russians. Fulfilling his plan to sell an instructional booklet on how to build the sled, Bull wrote and copyrighted a detailed and well drawn 10-page leaflet in 1933 entitled *How to Build & Run a Rocket Ship* (copyrighted by the Thermo-Reaction Company, which was in fact situated at Bull's home address). He sold 528 copies, including one to Professor Nikolai Rynin of Leningrad, the eminent Soviet space and rocket encyclopedist. Unfortunately, Bull's brochure was received after publication of Rynin's famous nine-volume *Mezhplanetnye soobshcheniya (Interplanetary Flight and Communication)*; otherwise, it doubtless would have been included therein. The booklet was also sold in Mexico, Canada, and Germany (one purchaser being Willy Ley the renowned popularizer of rockets and space) [14].

The few monies derived from the sales of the booklet and the pictures were sagaciously spent not on developing a rocket airplane immediately -- as the public had been led to believe -- but upon a more cautious path: a systematic program of seeking the most efficient fuel combination and a reliable form of rocket engine. As phrased by one contemporary newspaper some months after the sled run:

> The 22-year-old inventor, who gained national prominence through his sensational series of tests with a rocket-propelled ice boat last March on Oneida Lake, has been confining all his spare time for several months to experiments of a 'static' nature in his open air laboratory near Syracuse. Aware of the fact that several men have lost their lives in attempting to make discoveries with the rocket motor, Harry is putting emphasis on the stationary method of approach. In other words, he is forgetting the possibilities of the motor's application to fields of transportation until he has satisfied himself that the motor itself can be perfected to the best of modern scientific knowledge [15].

The paper then went on to describe his new test stand for determining the thrust of liquid fuel motors, operating temperatures, pressure differences, and the velocity of the escaping gases. While the liquid stand was his first, and indeed one of the earliest in this country[*], Bull had actually conducted some crude static experiments with compressed air and gasoline when he first entered college in 1930. These comprised tests 17-34 in his series of 829. He apparently recorded the pressures of the incoming vaporized gasoline and air besides the recoil or thrust. A simple spring scale measured the latter parameter and was found to be quite small because of the low air pressure (30 psi or 2.1 kg/sq cm). Even earlier, in his high school days, perhaps in 1927, he had noted that an:

> ... apparatus for testing the recoil of different combinations of gases was constructed. Rolls of paper which were moved by clockwork recorded the duration and strength of the recoil. An electrical clutch permitted the apparatus to be operated from the next floor [16].

---

[*]   Cleve Shaffer in San Francisco seems to have built an earlier though much more rudimentary test stand. For its part, the American Rocket Society did not construct any until at least 1932. Goddard, of course, predated the others.

In 1929, possibly using the same or a similar apparatus, he sought a double reaction formula:

It seemed possible to explode two gases in two separate chambers and then permit the two exhausts to mingle and explode again. Possibilities were:

$$3H_2 + N_2 = 2NH_3$$

then combine again

$$O_2 + 2N_2 = 2N_2O$$

Simpler combinations were give[n] which included such elements as hydrogen and chlorine, hydrogen and nitrogen, oxygen and chlorine and nitrogen. Difficulty was found in igniting some of the mixtures, others exploded readily, but so little of the gases were to be had that nothing new was found out [17].

Static tests were made also on a pendulum arc stand with solid propellants including Dupont Superfine FF powder. Recoils were produced of up to 26 lb (11.8 kg). These experiments, which were to determine the most efficient relation between chamber volume and nozzle length, were reportedly "carried out very smoothly." But, it was not until 1931, after the sled run, that Bull carried out a long-term static test program of liquid research. He likewise investigated gaseous combinations, steam propulsion and other means. According to his abstracted notes:

[A] most complete and accurate apparatus for testing rockets was next built. Valves were carefully made, steel containers turned on the lathe, pressure and recoil indicators installed, and a composite combustion chamber made which moved on roller bearings [18].

A local newspaper paraphrasing Bull's fuller report on the stand paints a more graphic description:

All these experiments are taking place on the rocket testing stand he has built and from which he records his findings. It has the appearance of a large tube, mounted on three legs. The tube acts as a safety enclosure for the rocket combustion chamber which it surrounds. In case the chamber being tested should become overheated and explode, the tube will protect those near the stand. Bolted to the inside of the protecting tube are two rods on which the rocket chamber is free to slide. The distance the chamber moves is recorded by a pointer to which a spring is attached so that the power the motor is developing can be read from a scale above the apparatus. (3.2 mm) of the rocket chamber will cause the pointer to move three inches (7.6 cm) on the scale. In this manner the power of the different combustion chambers (and fuel combinations) can easily be measured. Mounted on the left side of the protecting tube are the fuel tanks which supply the rocket being tested. These are made of tool steel and are capable of withstanding a pressure of more than 40,000 pounds per square in (2,812 kg/sq cm) or a total pressure of 500 tons. The tank containing the liquefied oxygen is fitted with a special relief valve which maintains the fuel at any desired pressure. This is accomplished by varying the force which holds the valve down and for this purpose a tank of water is used. The oxygen is lined with glass to prevent the intensely cold fuel (actually, the oxidizer) from coming into contact with the sides of the tank. Directly below the fuel tanks are valves controlling the flow of the fuel into the combustion chamber. The   valves are equipped with dials which may be read from a distance when remote control is used [19] (Figure 3).

The individual combustion chambers themselves were machined from solid blocks of 2-in. (5.1 cm) steel stock and were composed of four heavily gasketed and bolted sections. That is, they were segmented so that any of the sections could rapidly be removed without the necessity of construction an entirely new chamber. Damaged or flawed parts could easily be inspected, a microscope being used for this purpose, and modifications, replacements, or improvements could be facilitated. Bull's "composite combustion chamber" also kept experimentation expenses down. The fuel inlets were drilled in the rear, semi-spherical section, or in the forward center section, while the forward section was reamed to serve as the nozzle. It was by this modest but effective system that the inventor was able to conduct a wide and evolutionary series of combustion chamber tests that were eventually summarized by Bull at the request of the American Interplanetary Society and published in the July 1932 issue of the Society's journal *Astronautics*. Even earlier, progress of Bull's work was cited in the predecessor of *Astronautics*, the *Bulletin of the American Interplanetary Society*, for March 1932.

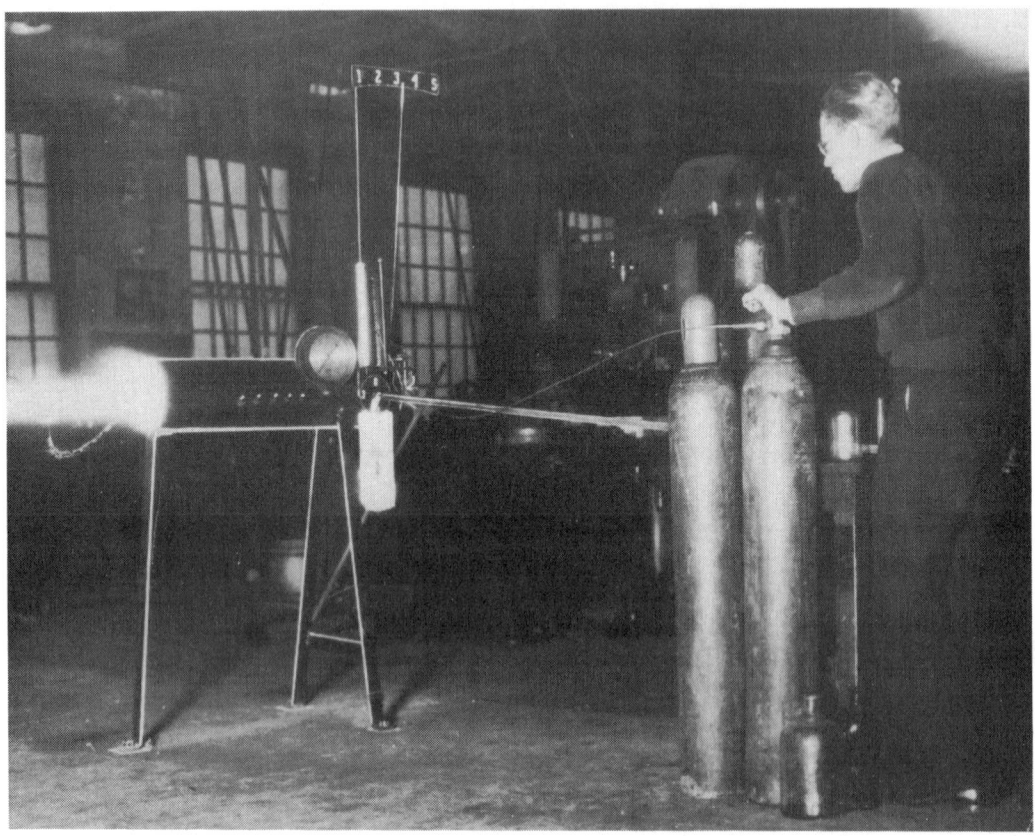

Figure 3   Bull testing liquid-propellant rocket engines on test stand bolted to the floor of the Chemistry Laboratory at Syracuse University in 1932.

Reporting on the activities of the VfR, G. Edward Pendray next turned his attention to the United States. (It is to be borne in mind that these were the days before the first ARS experiments which, at the time of writing, were only in their embryonic planning stages.) "In the meantime," wrote Pendray, "Americans have not been idle. Besides Dr. Goddard there is Harry W. Bull, of Syracuse, New York, and Cleve Shaffer, of San Francisco. Both of these men are members of the American Interplanetary Society. The results of their experiments are being made available to other members, so that there need to be no duplication." Pendray then briefly discussed the experiments of Shaffer (he conspicuously lacked data on Goddard's researches, which were unpublished) before returning to Harry Bull:

> More important still are the experiments of Mr. Bull, at Syracuse ... While the German experimenters have also made proving stand tests, those now being made by Mr. Bull will probably be the most complete ever undertaken, and when they are finished the Society will have available an extremely fine set of results upon which specifications for future rocket motors can be confidently based [20].

Bull's engine tests were based upon the American Interplanetary Society's "primary unit" (a water-cooled motor designed by the society and included chambers: (1) with different lengths and diameters, (2) with sloping and parallel walls, (3) with opposed rear fuel injection, (4) with forward spray fuel injection, (5) "chambers water and air cooled," (6) designed for vaporizing fuel, (7) with different nozzle diameters, (8) with different fuel inlet diameters, (9) using different fuels, and (10) provided with "auxiliary air cones" (i.e. thrust augmenter tubes).

In order to gauge his advancements, Bull similarly utilized the Society's "primary unit" as a standard. The usual fuel was gasoline and liquid oxygen, generally operating on a capacity of 100 cc of gasoline. The average thrust was 2 lb (0.9 kg), a very small value, but the duration of combustion was variable. "That is," wrote Bull, "the chamber which will operate for the greatest length of time on 100 cc of gasoline, while giving a recoil of two pounds, is the more efficient chamber." To illustrate this principle, he pointed out that the final chamber design produced approximately the same thrust and consumed the same quantity of fuel as the first or primary unit, but that it ran over seven times as long. Under normal conditions the first configured chamber, with water cooling, forward fuel injection and parallel chamber walls, burned for 15 sec. The final design, with four gasoline and eight oxygen injectors, and cooling fins welded to the inside and around the nozzle, lasted for some 110 sec, or almost 2 min. Thus, while Harry Bull's engine was tiny, his partially-regenerative cooling system was a significant breakthrough and showed that prolonged and safe rocket operation was now practicable [21] (Figure 4).

Though Bull concluded that this was "undoubtedly far from the ultimate goal," he recognized that "to my knowledge, it surpasses any of the rocket power units of today." It certainly was the longest duration rocket then ever fired in the U.S. and, perhaps, a link towards America's first fully regeneratively-cooled motor that was to appear just half-a-dozen years later, in 1938. James H. Wyld, the originator of this engine and one of the four founders of Reaction Motors, Inc., which later utilized the principle in the Bell X-1's 6000C4 rocket, did not fail to acknowledge Bull's contribution. Wyld rightly credited Hermann Oberth with proposing the regenerative principle in 1923 and suggested that Max Valier was close to actually testing such a system in a rocket automobile before his death in 1930.

However, two other sources conclusively proved that the regeneratively-cooled motor could work in practice, as based on experimental results. One was the article "Der Verbrennungs Raketenmotor" ("A Rocket Combustion Motor") by the Austrian rocket pioneer Eugen Sänger that appeared in the Swiss periodical *Schweizer Bauzeitung* in January 1936. In it, Sänger presented an account of a series of experiments undertaken in 1933 with small regeneratively-cooled motors burning light oil and gaseous oxygen. (Sänger's work is detailed in the paper "The Development of Regeneratively Cooled Liquid Rocket Engines in Austria and Germany, 1926-42" by Dr. Irene Sänger-Bredt and Rolf Engel.)

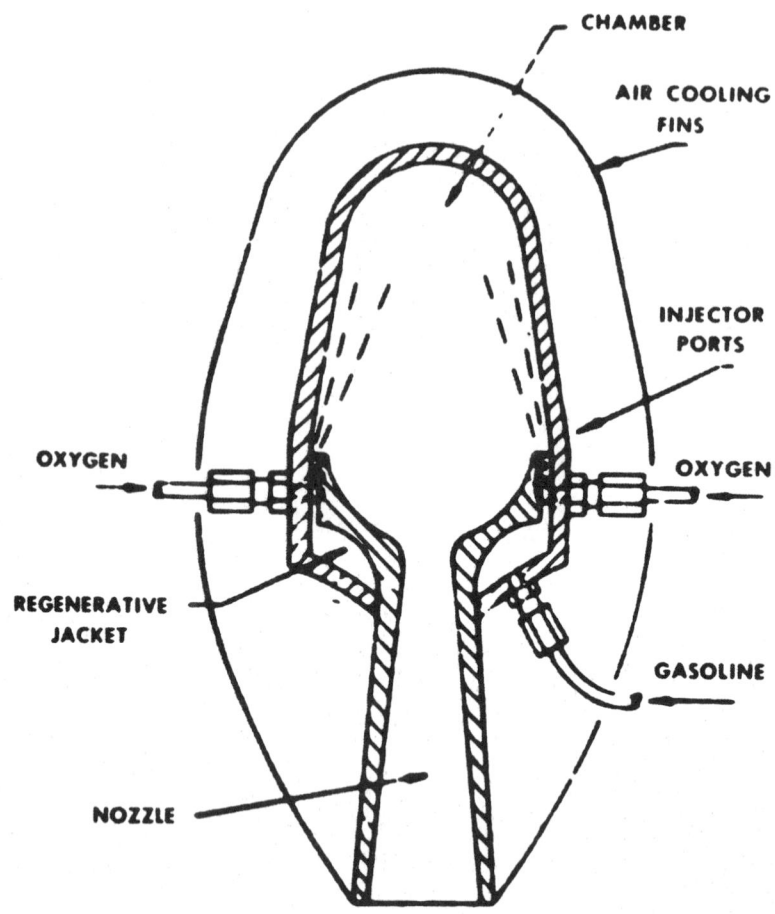

Figure 4 Diagram of partially regeneratively cooled rocket motor prepared by Harry W. Bull in 1932.

Sänger sent the article to ARS member Peter van Dresser who may have given it to Wyld, who is known to have been able to read German. In any event, the Sänger article was translated into English and appeared in *Astronautics* in October 1936 and almost certainly would have been seen by Wyld. Furthermore, Sänger's experiments also appeared in his *Raketenflugtechnik*, or *Rocket Technology*, published in 1933, which apparently was available in the U.S. by 1936 since van Dresser alludes to it in his survey article "The Rocket Motor" in the March 1936 issue of *Astronautics*. The other sources available to Wyld were various accounts of Bull's experiments made the same year Sänger undertook his work. (Van Dresser described both the Sänger and Bull experiments in his survey article.)

302

A year later, Wyld wrote:

The regenerative cooling jacket made its first appearance in practice (in the U.S.) in a small motor constructed in 1933 [1932] by Harry W. Bull of Syracuse, N.Y., a member of the American Rocket Society. Bull's motor was fired on gasoline and oxygen gas, and gave very promising results [22] (See Figure 5).

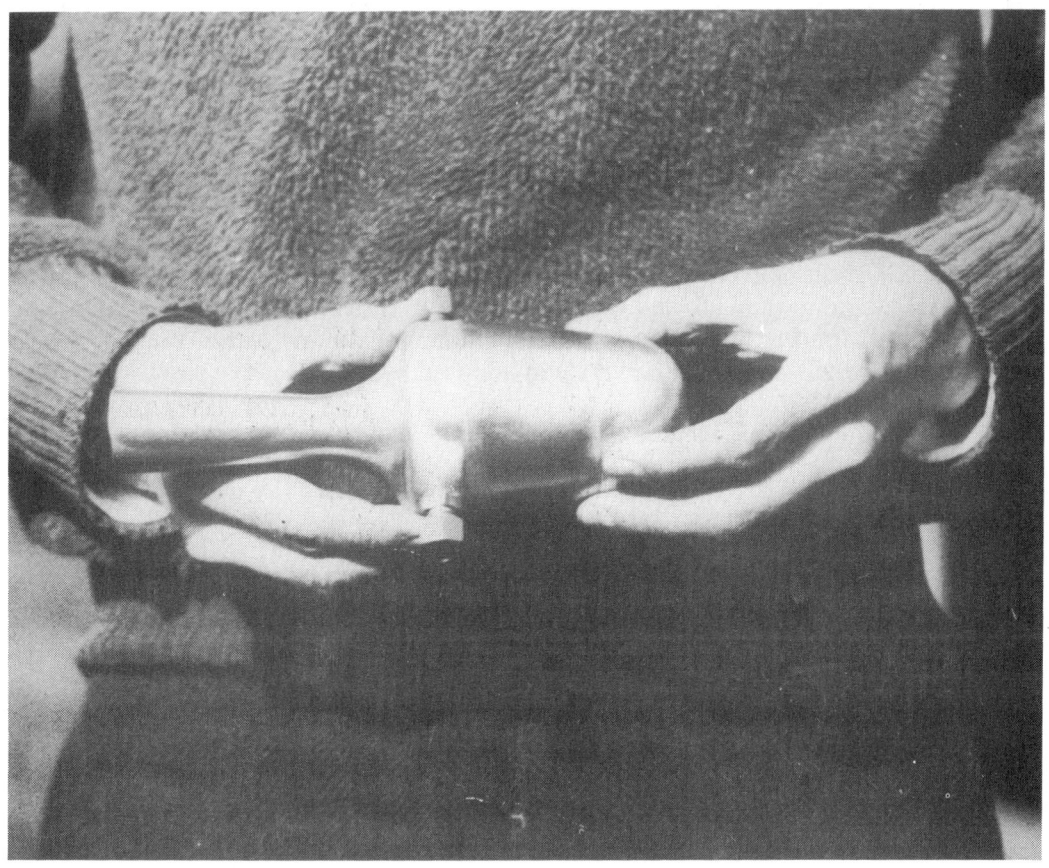

Figure 5 Bull holding partially regeneratively cooled rocket motor, 1933-34. This motor developed approximately 2 lb of thrust for up to 2 min, burning liquid oxygen and gasoline.

A search through Wyld's extant papers at the National Air and Space Museum further shows that soon after he joined the American Rocket Society in 1935, he made a thorough study of all the literature, including back issues of the society's journals, and that he was particularly struck by Bull's approach to the problem of cooling rocket motors. His own design, however, grew out of his overall survey and original thinking. He knew that some form of regenerative cooling was necessary to replace the inadequate water-jacket, refractive-lining, aluminum block and ceramic nozzle methods that were tried[*]. Wyld also realized, as noted in a letter of 27 April 1935 (and continued on 5 June) to G. Edward Pendray, that the main drawback of Bull's system was that it was a ground test and that "probably large tanks were used to provide gas pressure to force in the gasoline; hence the fall in pressure during the run was insignificant and was insufficient to cause an oversupply of oxygen [23]."

The only German (or Austrian) rocket designs with which Bull himself within this period was familiar were the essentially water-cooled early (1931-1932) Mirak and Repulsor types of the VfR reported in the pages of the *Bulletin of the American Interplanetary Society* and in *Astronautics*. But Bull's regeneratively-cooled configuration was distinctly different from the German and Austrian designs. In short, the American developmental story of the regeneratively-cooled rocket motor was wholly independent from that of Europe. Moreover, Harry Bull must still be accorded credit for arriving at the first workable partially-regenerative system in the U.S. as well as establishing the longest-duration running American rocket known up to that time. It may also be said that except for Goddard, he built the first complete rocket test stand in the U.S. and devised several other technological innovations. As late as 1944, for instance, Cedric Giles commented in *Astronautics* about Bull's thrust augmentor which had already been adopted by the ARS:

> After a series of combustion chamber tests, H. Bull reported in 1932 the increase in power and longer firing times of chambers having Venturi-shaped cones 15 in. [38.1 cm] in length and 3 in [7.62 cm] in diameter placed slightly in front of the nozzle. In tests of two identical chambers each using the same amount of fuel and giving the same average reaction, the Venturi employed chamber ran 110 sec to the 56 sec of the other [24].

LATER WORK -- SEARCH FOR PROPELLANTS

Other innovations followed. After his composite chamber tests in a search for a more efficient motor, Bull next concentrated on propellants. His object was to find an inexpensive liquid fuel that was likewise of maximum efficiency. This phase of his research, lasting until 1933 and comprising more than 700 individual tests, appears to have been the most exhaustive program of rocket propellant study to date (some of his tests, however, were repetitive in order to verify results). Unfortunately, Bull lacked both adequate testing apparatus and technical literature to produce any appreciable results. Nevertheless he was possibly the first to experiment with nitric acid as a rocket propellant and one of the first to try hydrogen peroxide, as well as hybrid combinations and monopropellants. This research was very broadly outlined in *Astronautics* (September 1934) and also communicated to leading chemists of the day.

In his quest for fuels, Bull posted a sort of "wanted" notice on the bulletin board of the Syracuse University Chemistry Laboratory and he corresponded with as many interested and knowledgeable individuals upon the subject as he could. For example, to Charles G. Philip, member of the British Interplanetary Society and author of one of the first popular English-language books on space flight, *Stratosphere and Rocket Flight* (1935), he wrote to enquire of the characteristics of liquid

---

[*] FY -- (Goddard's film "curtain" cooling, tested in 1929, and patented in 1935 -- his first cooling patent -- was generally now known.)

acetylene. Bull also consulted his chemistry professors and scrutinized all the chemistry books he could find for usable data on explosives and propellants. There is also a curious note appearing in *Astronautics* for October 1932 seemingly indicating that Bull similarly exchanged his engine and propellant ideas with other universities. The essentials of this report, however, have since been found to have been misleading. According to *Astronautics*:

> A new group of rocket experimenters has been formed at Tri-State College, Agnola (Angola), Indiana. Mr. [later, Professor Walter E.] Burnham, aeronautical instructor; Professor [Raymond T.] Rousch, dean of the Mechanical Department; and John W. Herrick, aeronautical engineer are members of the group. They have already begun work on a spherical combustion chamber with a nozzle of circular section; and will try out the reaction of various hydrocarbons and nitroglycerin. The group has been in close communication with member Harry W. Bull, formerly of Syracuse University [and] have followed closely Bull's experimental experience [25].

In actuality, according to his recollections, Herrick, had simply written a letter of general inquiry to Bull soon after he had transferred from Syracuse University to Tri-State. He had been a fellow student with Bull in engineering classes. Although at the time more concerned with gliders than with rockets, Herrick had nonetheless witnessed the sled experiment and had been an early member (No. 13) of the American Rocket Society. In 1932, he wished to know how Bull was progressing and to inform him that he was then interested in forming a rocket group at Tri-State. Lack of money prevented the group from coming about, however, and no experiments were conducted [26].

When the progress of Bull's overall propellant studies eventually were made public, through his *Astronautics* survey article of September 1934, a real "mystery" did present itself. This was created by Bull's reticence in identifying his newly found ideal fuel which he called "Atalene." In his *The Coming Age of Rocket Power*, written in 1945, G. Edward Pendray sums up Bull's survey and how, after a long series of tests, he was led to discover the mysterious Atalene:

> ... Harry W. Bull, a rocket experimenter at Syracuse, New York, made one of the most elaborate series of tests on possible fuel substances ever reported. He tried high-pressure steam; then a series of liquids with low boiling points [for "vapor," or gaseous propellant rockets], including carbon disulfide, alcohol, ether, carbon tetrachloride, methyl sulfide and chlorine [as well as nitrogen tri-oxide, nitrite, ethylene oxide, methyl tetramethylene, pentane, ethyl bromide and methyl sulfide, and other substances]. 'After many explosions -- I ceased experimenting along these lines,' Bull reported in *Astronautics*. He next tried a rocket motor using solidified carbon dioxide. He found it difficult to liberate the gas rapidly enough. Next he experimented with a powder and paraffin mixture, intended to give a low exhaust temperature, but after several tests decided it was impractical. He followed this with a motor burning magnesium metal, and next developed a powder rocket having the powder arranged in sections or tubes of small diameter to prevent too rapid burning. Experiments then followed with these fuel combinations: nitroglycerin; alcohol and 30 percent hydrogen peroxide; turpentine and nitric acid; gasoline and various nitrates. Concluding his tests by developing a special monopropellant of his own (composition not revealed) which he called 'Atalene,' ... It was, as he described it, 'cheap, colorless, leaves no residue on burning, can be stored for months, [is] safe to handle and will not backfire.' For ignition, however, it required to be heated to 400 degrees Fahrenheit (204C), and this he reported to the American Rocket Society. 'Five months were spent building new designs ... Many types of fuel heaters were tried before the final plan of spraying the fuel into a magnesium flame was perfected.' 'Perfected' however was the wrong word. Shortly thereafter one of the experimental motors exploded violently, driving

a jagged section of one-inch [2.54 cm] pipe into the experimenter's leg. Fortunately it left no permanent injury [27] (See Figure 6).

Figure 6 Bull loading propellant at his rocket test stand on the outskirts of Syracuse, New York in 1933.

Admittedly, many of Bull's fuels were somewhat strange and generally low-yielding, particularly the low-boiling point liquids and the 30 percent hydrogen peroxide (the highest strength then available according to Clark). However, James Wyld could still appreciate the value of the monopropellant Atalene from the engineering point of view:

Bull also appears to have been the first to experiment with a monopropellant liquid-fuel motor, on which full details have unfortunately never appeared. In this type of motor, which was later extensively developed in Germany for glide-bomb propulsion and jet-assisted take-offs, the fuel and oxidizer are combined in a single propellant, which is so arranged as to burn only in the motor combustion chamber. The obvious nature in this plan is the likelihood of a flashback from the motor to the main fuel tank. The dangerous nature of monopropellants was brought home to Bull when he was seriously injured in an explosion of his motor, and he soon afterwards dropped his experiments. The scheme has been widely worked on by others in later years but has not yet (1947) attained as high a degree of safety, efficiency, or reliability as the bipropellant type, in spite of the attractive simplicity of the idea [28].

John D. Clark, in his history of liquid rocket propellants, also acknowledges Bull as an early monopropellant investigator but credits the Italian rocketry pioneer Luigi Crocco as perhaps being the first to experiment with this form (in 1932). (Crocco's experiences along these lines are told in his own words in *Smithsonian Annals of Flight*, No. 10, pp. 44-48.) Bull would thus appear to have been the second but certainly the first in the U.S. When high strength (80 percent) hydrogen peroxide became available in Germany, Helmuth Walter at the Chemical State Institute in Berlin secretly pioneered in 1934-1935 a monopropellant system using it with potassium permanganate as a catalyst. Afterwards, his firm in Kiel successfully adapted the fuel to JATO (jet assisted take-off), the Me-163 powerplant, and other projects alluded to by Wyld.

In America, since Wyld made his statement, monopropellant technology has advanced considerably and small motors utilizing such fuels as hydrazine (usually with an iridium catalyst) have proved highly reliable, inexpensive, and lightweight thrusters for satellites and space probes. Bull's own monopropellant, the hitherto cryptic "Atalene," can now be at least partly identified from his retrieved notes. It was a solution of 60 percent perchloric acid and 40 percent hydrocarbon (carbon disulfide and ether are given as two considerations though another substance may also have been chosen for the final formula). Rather than a catalyst, Bull resorted to the magnesium flame ignition system described above. It was while in the latter stages of testing the overall system, on Sunday, 18 June 1933 (as has also been briefly related), Bull encountered a serious explosion. It was a disaster that virtually ended his rocketry career. Paradoxically, he felt so confident about the fuel that he had special stationery printed reading, "Harry W. Bull -- Atalene Explosives [sic] -- Reactions Motors -- Gravity Releases." Bertha Bull says nothing came out of this "venture" [29].

Like Goddard, Bull preferred to undertake his work undisturbed and away from the general public, on a rather wooded lot adjacent to a farm on the outskirts of Syracuse. However, the explosion had again thrust Bull into public attention. According to the Syracuse *Post-Standard* the following Monday:

Harry W. Bull of 326 Hickock Avenue who built and demonstrated the first rocket ice boat, escaped serious injury early yesterday afternoon when a small rocket motor he was testing in a field at the end of Lancaster Avenue exploded prematurely and hurled a piece of steel into the calf of his left leg. He was taken to Crouse-Irving Hospital in a private automobile. Several stitches were taken in the wound. The young inventor went to the large field a short distance east of East Colvin Street to test the motor of a new rocket he designed and constructed in his laboratory at home. He attached a long electrical wire to the motor and then began to warm up the small power plant with a mixture of chemicals. As he started toward the switch, 100 ft [30.5 m] away, to set off the rocket, there was a loud report. A piece of steel from the tubes, the part of the cylindrical motor that exploded, imbedded itself in the calf of his leg and he fell to the ground. He was only a few feet away from the motor when the explosion occurred [30].

Bull's future wife, Bertha, who was present at the time, concludes with her own account:

> I was with Harry when this accident happened. I could not drive a car at this time and so I started to run for help down the road. By the time I found someone Harry had dragged himself to the car, gotten in and was driving towards me. The man I located got in and drove us to the Crouse-Irving Hospital where Harry spent several days. He was on crutches later and had a very painful recovery but he was determined to exercise his leg, as much as it hurt, and soon was able to walk without crutches. This episode made him think that it would take a great deal of equipment and a huge sum of money to get anywhere in the rocket field. After much persuasion by me and his parents he decided to give up the dangerous pastime [31].

Harry Bull's researches and interest in rocketry, and especially his dream of flight in space, did not end as abruptly as all that. He wisely ceased experimenting, but continued to design and theorize. He was also fervent enough that he still entertained the hope of actually working with or getting assistance from Goddard, always his idol. As late as 15 October 1935, Goddard had written to Bull from Roswell, New Mexico:

> I arrived in Roswell about the middle of September for another year's work [under a Florence Guggenheim Foundation grant] on the research. Although it is not on quite the scale of the previous work, it is a good opportunity, considering the present state of affairs. Sometime, when I am in the East, it may be possible to arrange matters so that I can see you, and explain the conditions under which I am working more fully [32].

Earlier, soon after he graduated from the University of Syracuse with his B.S. degree in Mechanical Engineering on 6 June 1932, Bull had inquired several times about the possibility of a teaching or laboratory assistant position with Goddard at Clark University. Goddard's responses were always cordial and expressed an interest in Bull's experiments, but could only be noncommittal on the question of employment. Following graduation, Bull did obtain a job in the field of chemistry, though far removed from rocketry. He joined Church and Dwight Co., a chemical processing concern at Solvay, New York, close to Syracuse. He remained with them for two years until the spring of 1935, when he became associated with the Tennessee Valley Authority in Chattanooga, Tennessee. There, he was engaged in aerial and topographical drafting and compilation. In 1935 also, he was married (18 May).

Bertha K. Bull recalled that prior to the move to Chattanooga, "all the rocket motors and other hardware were disposed of." Presumably this included the bulk of Harry's notes as well. While many of the details are thus unfortunately lost, a few of his latter ideas are known in a general way. During his final experimental days, for example, he contemplated hybrid rocket propulsion and appears to have conducted some preliminary tests. There was also a rather dubious "kinetic repulsor," or "entirely new reaction method" which was briefly covered in his rocket fuel survey article in the September 1934 issue of *Astronautics* as well as in *Popular Science* for January 1935. Cedric Giles, in his article "Elevators and Levitators" in the *Journal of the American Rocket Society* (December 1946), briefly sums it up as electromagnetic-powered and consisting of:

... two reciprocating weighted disks mounted on a shaft in a cylinder .. When the discs were suddenly thrown apart, by explosive or other means (electromagnetic force), the one striking a flat steel plate would give a weak force, derived from the impact, while the other disc thrown against a spring actuated a strong impulsive force. The difference in the efficacy of the two forces was about three times more force by impulse than by impact, which caused the cylinder to move forcibly in the direction of the spring [33].

A.V. Cleaver, writing in the *Journal of the British Interplanetary Society* in June 1947, properly characterizes Bull's electromagnetic-mechanical levitator as "fallacious," though the search that led him to it was undoubtedly borne out of a long-term frustration in seeking cheap and alternative fuels and propulsion means for his envisioned rocket aircraft. More valid was his well executed design of a 10 mi (16 km) sounding rocket which was to be powered with a full-scale version of his partially regeneratively-cooled rocket engine [34].

As was the fashion with many rockets of the early 1930's, such as the first ARS models and first VfR Miraks, Bull's plan placed the motor in the nose and forced in the liquid oxygen/unspecified hydrocarbon fuel into the combustion chamber by compressed nitrogen. Bull's configuration, however, had a more streamlined, aluminum body, but its unique features consisted of the partially regeneratively-cooled engine, the centrally-located payload section, the rear-mounted parachute release, and the pendulum-activated guiding rudders. Though the design was not publicized, it appears to have been communicated to the Society as James Wyld commented upon the rudder system in his letter to G. Edward Pendray of 5 June 1935: "Harry Bull has proposed stabilizing a rocket by fins operated by servo solenoids, controlled by a pendulum. This seems unnecessarily complex; servo air cylinders would be better, but I think the pendulum itself would do the trick directly." Pendray also alluded to this plan in his article "Men of Space," appearing under the pseudonym Ugo Andres in *New Outlook* for October 1934: "The injury [to Bull] was not serious ... and he is now out of the hospital, determined to continue. He has drawn plans for several types of control apparatus to guide a rocket in flight which will soon be tested out ..." The tests, of course, were never made.

Interestingly, and perhaps unknown to Bull, Goddard was thinking of a similar pendulum stabilizer about the same time and successfully proved the technique in a flight of 8 March of the same year. Though he afterwards preferred the gyroscope. Goddard was likewise testing a rear-mounted parachute arrangement, his release mechanism being more sophisticated than that of Bull's which worked by an explosive activator. Bull's remaining fragmentary notes on the sounding rocket also show that he had considered dual combustion chambers (that he felt were actually easier to cool) as well as spin-stabilization. High-pressure rotary valves and a high-pressure feed pump are also roughly sketched, as are some of the approximate dimensions of the proposed rocket: diameter, 5 in. (12.7 cm); height, 5 ft (1.52 m); fin span 16 in. (40.6 cm); and fin height, 2 ft (0.61 m). Bull's summary notes further reveal that he was on the verge of constructing this rocket as he actually built a 10-ft-high (3.04-m) launch tower of steel wire, brass tubing and aluminum turnbuckles. The stand, however, was never to be used. The accident had cut short all future testing plans [35].

With the cessation of the experiments and more especially his move to Chatanooga and the beginning of an entirely new phase in his life, Bull's active rocketry career also ceased. He stayed with the Tennessee Valley Authority until January 1937, when he joined the Dow Chemical Company at its headquarters in Midland, Michigan, the same firm he had written to four years previously for potential ingredients for his rocket propellants. Beginning as a design engineer and eventually, in 1962, becoming Director of Packaging for Dow, Bull pioneered in another field, chemical packaging. He developed equipment for the spinning of synthetic fibers, paper coating, product packaging and film coating. As such, he has been credited with a number of processes and machine patents and was the author of many technical papers on the subject.

In October 1968, Bull retired due to cancer. During his last years he again returned to his remaining rocketry notes, putting them in order, as he had said, for the interest of "someone in the future". However, according to Bertha K. Bull, even after his experiments "his interest in rockets never lessened and he followed the progress of such experiments through books, magazine articles, etc. until his death." Harry Bull died in Midland on 1 July 1971 [36].

In retrospect, Bull's studies and test work suffered from lack of funds, adequate technical direction and professional assistance as well as being remotely situated from the heart of the American rocketry community. Nevertheless, there is no question that he was naturally gifted and that the impact of his research was recognized by his peers. Provided with adequate resources and able assistants close at hand, his accomplishments would have been all the more durable.

ACKNOWLEDGEMENT

The assistance of Mrs. Bertha K. Bull of Midland, Michigan is gratefully acknowledged. All illustrations were provided by her and are published with her courtesy.

REFERENCES

1. *The Syracuse City Directory*, 1930, pp. 400, 1639; Letter to the author, Lois Ann Peel, Alumni Files, Syracuse University, 6 February 1973.

2. Harry W. Bull Papers, The Library, National Air and Space Museum, Smithsonian Institution, Washington, D.C., hereafter cited as BP.

3. BP.

4. *Ibid*; Letter to the author, Jane Bull Churchill, Syracuse, N.Y., 27 July 1976.

5. *Ibid.*

6. *Ibid.*

7. Letter to Harry W. Bull, Dr. Robert H. Goddard, Worcester, Mass., 16 May 1932, in BP.

8. BP, especially "Rocket Notes III."

9. BP.

10. BP, especially "Rocket Notes III."

11. BP; "Rocket Sled Leaps at a Dazzling Pace," *The New York Times*, 10 March 1931, p. 16, col. 3; "Delays Rocket Sled Test -- Gale Sweeps Lake," *New York Times*, 9 March 1931, p. 44, col. 2, and other newspaper accounts; Churchill Letter, loc. cit.

12. BP; Harry W. Bull, "Will Continue Rocket Tests, Bull Reveals," *The Post-Standard* (Syracuse), 10 March 1931, p. 11, col. 1; "Valier Plans Calais-to-Dover rocket Flight; Pictures Berlin-New York in One Hour," *The New York Times*, 1 March 1929, p. 9, cols. 3-4.

13. Telephone Interviews by the author with John W. Herrick, Palos Verdes, California, 27 July 1976, and William J. Sauber, near Midland, Michigan, 27 July 1976; Letters to the author, Bertha K. Bull, Midland, Michigan, 2 August 1976 and 15 August 1976.

14. BP, especially "Rocket Notes I"; G. Edward Pendray, *The Coming Age of Rocket Power* (Harper & Bros.: New York, 1945), p. 116.

15. BP, including untitled and undated newspaper article, "Rocket Plane May Result As Bull's Next Invention," probably from *The Post-Standard*, Summer-Autumn, 1931.

16. BP, especially "Rocket Notes III."

17. *Ibid.*

18. *Ibid.*

19. "Rocket Plane," *op. cit.*,; BP, especially, "Rocket Notes II."

20. "Rocket Notes II," *op. cit.*; Harry W. Bull, "Increasing the Range of the Rocket," *Astronautics*, No. 21, July 1932, pp. 1-4; G. Edward Pendray, "The Conquest of Space by Rocket," *Bulletin of the American Interplanetary Society*, No. 17, March 1932, pp. 2-3.

21. Bull, "Increasing the Range," *loc. cit.*, p. 2.

22. *Ibid.*; Eugen Sänger, "Der Verbrennungs Raketenmotor," *Schweizer Bauzeitung*, Bnd. 107, 11 January 1936; Peter von Dresser, "The Rocket Motor," *Astronautics*, No. 33, March 1936, p. 10; Eugen Sänger, "A Rocket Combustion Motor," *Astronautics*, No. 35, October 1936, pp. 2-12; James H. Wyld, "The Liquid-Propellant Rocket Motor -- Past, Present, and Future," *Journal of the American Rocket Society*, No. 70, June 1947, p. 8; James H. Wyld, "The Liquid-Propellant Rocket Motor," *Mechanical Engineering*, Vol. 69, No. 6, June 1947, p. 461; James H. Wyld, "History of the Rocket Engine," in *The Complete Book of Outer Space* (Mac Magazine Corp.: New York, 1953), pp. 60, 65; Irene Sänger-Bredt and Rolf Engel, "The Development of Regeneratively Cooled Liquid Rocket Engines in Austria and Germany, 1926-42," in Frederick C. Durant, III, and George S. James, eds., *Smithsonian Annals of Flight Number 10 -- First Steps Toward Space* (Smithsonian Institution Press: Washington, D.C., 1974), pp. 217-246, now available in Vol. 6, *AAS History Series*, Univelt, Inc., San Diego, California.

23. Esther C. Goddard and G. Edward Pendray, eds., *The Papers of Robert H. Goddard* (McGraw-Hill Book Co.: New York, 1970), Vol. II, p. 667, Vol. III, p. 1652; Letter, James H. Wyld to G. Edward Pendray, 27 April 1935 and continued 5 June 1935 (p. 16), Astronautical Department Archives, National Air and Space Museum, Smithsonian Institution, Washington, D.C.

24. Cedric Giles, "Thrust Augmentors for Rockets," *Astronautics*, No. 58, June 1944, pp. 10-11.

25. BP, especially "Rocket Notes III"; Harry W. Bull, "A Survey of Rocket Fuels," *Astronautics*, No. 29, September 1934, pp. 5-8; Letter, Charles G. Philip, Caffley, England, to Harry W. Bull, 17 December 1934, in BP; "New Groups Begin Rocket Experimentation," *Astronautics*, No. 23, October 1932, p.4.

26. Telephone Interview, John W. Herrick, *loc. cit.*

27. Pendray, *The Coming Age*, *loc. cit.*, pp. 21-22.

28. Wyld, "The Liquid-Propellant Rocket Motor," *op. cit.*; John D. Clark, *Ignition!* (Rutgers University Press: New Brunswick, N.J., 1972), p. 10.

29. Clark, *op. cit.*; "Rocket Notes III," *loc. cit.*; Luigi Crocco, "Early Italian Rocket and Propellant Research," in *Smithsonian Annals, loc. cit.*, pp. 44-48.

30. "Rocket Boat Builder Hurt By Explosion," *The Post-Standard*, Syracuse, 19 June 1933, p. 8, col. 3.

31. BP; Letter to Frederick C. Durant, Bertha K. Bull, Midland, Michigan, 22 June 1973.

32. Letter to Harry W. Bull, Dr. Robert H. Goddard, Roswell, N.M., 15 October 1934, in BP.

33. BP; Letters to the author, Bertha K. Bull, 2 August 1976 and 15 August 1976; Bull, "A Survey," *loc. cit.*, pp. 7-8; "Mysterious New Aircraft Powered by Reaction Motor," *Popular Science*, Vol. 1256, No. 1, january 1935, p. 27; Cedric Giles, "Elevators and Levitators," *Journal of the American Rocket Society*, No. 68, December 1946, p. 35; A.V. Cleaver, "Interplanetary Flight: Is the Rocket the Only Answer?", *Journal of the British Interplanetary Society*, Vol. 6, No. 5, June 1947, pp. 135-136.

34. BP; Letter from James H. Wyld to G. Edward Pendray, *loc. cit.*; Ugo Andres (pseud. for G. Edward Pendray), "Men of Space," *New Outlook*, Vol. 164, October 1934, p. 29; Esther C. Goddard and G. Edward Pendray, eds., *The Papers of Robert H. Goddard, loc. cit.*, Vol. II, pp. 903, 916-917.

35. BP; Letter to Frederick C. Durant, III Bertha K. Bull, *op. cit.*

INDEX

Available in two volumes is an INDEX TO ALL AMERICAN
ASTRONAUTICAL SOCIETY PAPERS AND ARTICLES 1954-1985/86

This index is a numerical/chronological index (which also serves
as a citation index) and an author index. (A subject index volume
will be forthcoming.)

It covers all articles that appear in the following:

Advances in the Astronautical Sciences (1957-August 1986)

Science and Technology Series (1964-September 1986)

AAS History Series (1977-1986)

AAS Microfiche Series (1968-August 1986)

Journal of the Astronautical Sciences (1954-March 1986)

Astronautical Sciences Review (1959-1962)

If you are in aerospace you will want this excellent reference
tool which covers the first 30 years of the Space Age.

Numerical/Chronological/Author Index in two volumes, Library
Binding (both volumes) $95; Soft Cover (both Volumes) $80;
Volume I (1954-1978) Library Binding $40; Soft Cover $30;
Volume II (1979-1985/86) Library Binding $60; Soft Cover $45.
Order from Univelt, Inc., P.O. Box 28130, San Diego,
California 92128.

AMERICAN *Astronautical* SOCIETY

NUMERICAL INDEX[*]

VOLUME 9

AAS HISTORY SERIES, *HISTORY OF ROCKETRY AND ASTRONAUTICS,*
(IAA History Symposia, Volume 4)

(Proceedings of the Ninth, Tenth and Eleventh History Symposia of The
International Academy of Astronautics, Lisbon, Portugal, 1975; Anaheim,
California, U.S.A., 1976; and Prague, Czechoslovakia, 1977; R. Cargill Hall,
Series Editor, Frederick I. Ordway, III, Volume Editor, 1989)

AAS 89-300   Analysis of Rocket Construction, Described in Manuscripts and Printed
Books During the 16th and 17th Centuries, M. Subotowicz

AAS 89-301   Analysis of Early 19th Century Swedish Solid Propellants, J. Hansson,
A. I. Skoog

AAS 89-302   Beginnings of Airborne Aeromedical Weightlessness Research,
H. J. von Beckh

AAS 89-303   Early Concepts of Aerospace Systems, A. N. Ponomarev, V. S. Mikhailov

AAS 89-304   Computer-Oriented Dynamic Modeling of Spacecraft: Historical Evolution
of Eulerian Multibody Formalisms Since 1750, R. E. Roberson

AAS 89-305   Organization and Results of the Work of the First Scientific Centers for
Rocket Technology in the USSR, I. A. Merkulov

AAS 89-306   Genesis of Liquid Hydrogen Propulsion Through 1945, J. L. Sloop

AAS 89-307   History of Development of First Space Rocket Engines in the USSR,
V. I. Prishchepa

AAS 89-308   Beginnings of Rocket and Missile Activities in Switzerland, N. A. Schliep

AAS 89-309   Operation Backfire: England Launches the V2, M. R. Sharpe

AAS 89-310   Early Upper Atmospheric Research with Rockets, T. Bergstralh, E. Krause

AAS 89-311   Early History of the Skylark Rocket, E. B. Dorling

AAS 89-312   First Rocket Experiments for Research on Solar Shortwave Radiation,
G. S. Ivanov-Kholodnyy, L. A. Vedeshin

AAS 89-313   Structure of Neutral Upper Atmosphere Air Samples and Falling Spheres,
L. M. Jones

AAS 89-314   Upper Atmosphere Research and the First Rocket Experiments in the
USSR, B. A. Mirtov, L. A. Vedeshin

---

[*]   IAA history papers presented in 1975-1977. AAS numbers have been assigned for identification purposes.

AAS 89-315	Early Scientific History of the Rocket Grenade Experiment, W. G. Stroud
AAS 89-316	Early French Upper Atmosphere Research Using Rockets, A. Vassy
AAS 89-317	Development of the First Automatic Stations for Lunar Flight in the USSR, G. Y. Maximov, Y. A. Matusevich
AAS 89-318	Kepler's "The Dream, or Lunar Astronomy" as a Predecessor of Space Research, Z. Horsky
AAS 89-319	Albert Fonó: A Pioneer of Jet Propulsion, I. G. Nagy
AAS 89-320	S.P. Korolev and Soviet Rocket Technology, B. V. Rauschenbach
AAS 89-321	Harry Bull, American Rocket Pioneer, F. H. Winter

AUTHOR INDEX[*]

---

[*] For each author the paper number is given. AAS numbers for these IAA history papers presented in 1975-1977 have been assigned for identification purposes. The page numbers refer to Volume 9, **AAS History Series.**

AAS HISTORY SERIES

Volume 1   *Two Hundred Years of Flight in America: A Bicentennial Survey*, Edited by Eugene M. Emme, 1977, 326p, Third Printing 1981, Hard Cover $35; Soft Cover $25; special price for classroom text or bulk purchase.

Volume 2   *Twenty-Five Years of the American Astronautical Society: Historical Reflections and Projections*, 1954-1979, Edited by Eugene M. Emme, 1980, 248p, Hard Cover $25; Soft Cover $15.

Volume 3   *Between Sputnik and the Shuttle: New Perspectives on American Astronautics*, 1957-1980, Edited by Frederick C. Durant, III, 1981, 350p, Hard Cover $40; Soft Cover $30.

Volume 4   *The Endless Space Frontier: A History of the House Committee on Science and Astronautics*, By Ken Hechler, Abridged and edited by Albert E. Eastman, 1982, 460p, Hard Cover $45; Soft Cover $35.

Volume 5   *Science Fiction and Space Futures: Past and Present*, Edited by Eugene M. Emme, 1982, 278p, Hard Cover $35; Soft Cover $25.

Volume 6   *First Steps Toward Space*, Edited by Frederick C. Durant, III and George S. James, 1986, 318p, Hard Cover $45; Soft Cover $35.

Volume 7   *History of Rocketry and Astronautics*, Edited by R. Cargill Hall, 1986, Part I, 250p, Part II, 502p, sold as a set, Hard Cover $100; Soft Cover $80.

Volume 8   *History of Rocketry and Astronautics*, Edited by Kristan R. Lattu, 1989, 368p, Hard Cover $50; Soft Cover $35.

Volume 9   *History of Rocketry and Astronautics*, Edited by Frederick I. Ordway, III, 1989, 330p, Hard Cover $50; Soft Cover $35.

These volumes are available to individual members of space and astronautical societies and students at half the list price.

Order from Univelt, Incorporated, P.O. Box 28130, San Diego, California 92128